SYNTHESIS AND PROPERTIES OF LOW- AND HIGH MOLECULAR COMPOUNDS. QUANTITATIVE LEVEL

Synthesis and Properties of Low- and High Molecular Compounds. Quantitative Level

Gennady E. Zaikov
Irina V. Savenkova
and
Klara Gumargalieva
Editors

Nova Science Publishers, Inc.
New York

For permission to use material from this book please contact us:
Telephone 631-231-7269; Fax 631-231-8175
Web Site: http://www.novapublishers.com

Library of Congress Cataloging-in-Publication Data

Synthesis and properties of low- and high-molecular compounds : quantitative level / Gennady E. Zaikov, Irina V. Savenkova, and Klara Gumargalieva (editors).

p. cm.

Includes bibliographical references and index.

ISBN 1-59454-716-5

1. Polymers. I. Zaikov, Gennadii Efremovich. II. Savenkova, Irina V. III. Gumargalieva, K. Z. (Klara Z.)

TA455.P58S97 2006

668.9--dc22 2005037875

Published by Nova Science Publishers, Inc. ✣ New York

CONTENTS

Preface

«Dare be wise»
Horatio, Ancient Rome

« History teaches us the only thing
that it teaches us nothing»
A joke

"Laboremus" – Latin
«Let us labour» – the English translation

«Ora et labora" – Latin
«Pray and work» – the English translation

Pythagoras (Ancient Greece) taught us that the World is based on number and numerical dependencies. This statement is valid still. Quantitative description of chemical processes is the proper (key) way to the control of chemical reactions, prediction of properties of chemical compounds, forecasting of the lifetime (reliable operation) of articles from polymers. The present collection is mostly devoted to these problems.

Diogenes (before he became the famous philosopher of Ancient Greece) was the false coiner. Then, when he had changed this sort of activity, he stated that "you better forge money than the truth. Putting aside the problem of forging money we can agree with Diogenes truth is of extreme importance.

The current collection includes articles, devoted to production of polymers, polymeric mixtures, composite and filled polymers, questions of expanding lifetime of polymeric articles, biologically active substances, modification of polymers and polymer-analogous transformations, fractal physical chemistry of polymer solutions, the study of structural transformations in polymers and some other questions.

Of special attention is also the production of pure substances and protection of the environment. Remember that in the fourteenth and fifteenth centuries in Venice any polluter of the Venetian Lagoon was prosecuted by striking off the right hand for the first time; the repeated defiance caused gouging of the left eye (we do not know the prosecution for the third crime, but we are sure that it was nothing good).

The editors and the authors of this Collection will be grateful for any constructive notes on the articles published.

The Collection editors:

Prof. Gennady E. Zaikov
N.M. Emanuel Institute of Biochemical Physics

Dr. Irina V. Savenkova
Kursk State Technological University

Prof. Klara Z. Gumargalieva
N.N. Semenov Institute of Chemical Physics

In: Synthesis and Properties of Low- and High-Molecular Compounds ISBN 1-59454-716-5
Editor: Gennady E. Zaikov et al., pp. 1-26

Chapter 1

COMPOSITION MATERIALS BASED ON POLYMERS AND DISPERSED WOOD

Yu. A. Sangalov[1] and A. I. Ilyasova[2]
[1]Institute of Petrochemistry and Catalysis, Bashkortostan Academy of Sciences and USciC RAS; 141, Prospekt Oktyabrya, 450075, Ufa, Russia;
[2]Ufa State Institute of Service, 145, ul. Chernyshevskogo, 450014, Ufa, Russia

ABSTRACT

The discussion covers today's position of dispersed wood problem related to creation of composition materials. This involves a general description of the product, methods of its modification, guidelines for application in compositions with inorganic binding agents, thermoreactive resins and, mainly, with thermoplastic polymers.

1. INTRODUCTION

Wood and its basic component cellulose reproduced in nature by virtue of solar energy are of ever-growing importance to mankind with the view to crude oil and coal resources going depleted. The world wood resources (360 billion m^3) are huge, and ¼ of them is located in Russia.

Man has been utilizing wood as energy carrier, raw and construction (manufacturing) material since time immemorial [1-3]. The share of wood as solid fuel is gradually going down, but in some countries it stands at 30%, though. The ways undergoing development for liquefying and gasifying wood to obtain liquid fuel and fuel gas prove promising. In this respect, microbiological processes are worth special attention. The amount of chemical wood processing, I. e. the production involving paper and pulp, hydrolysis and wood chemical industries, is steadily increasing. Modern techniques employed to activate raw materials (plosive autohydrolysis, mechanical chemistry, electrohydraulic, plasmochemical, radiative treatment, etc.) boost the reaction ability and solubility of cellulose-legnitic materials and ease their processing [4, 5]. This goes along with the general trend of passing over from the intensive treatment of wood to its heavy processing. As far as materials technology is concerned, round timber and precut lumber keep significant in the balance of wood application, though the advent of alternative polymeric and other materials having high-quality physical and mechanical as well as artistic and decorative along with architectural and building features limits the range of wood application [6]. The modification of wood to make it of higher strength, incombustibility, chemical and bacteriological resistance, thus specifically, enabling us to replace scarce hard sorts of wood by more easily available soft ones, upgrades its technological and operational properties [7]. Another clue, that is the utilization of combined composite materials based on wood and various binding agents, also provides greater opportunities for wood application and makes it competitive on the market of modern building materials.

The reduction of material quantity required and the utilization of secondary wood resources comprise a considerable reserve to boost the efficiency of construction work. These resources include the waste products of industries involved in sawmill operation, as well as the manufacture of paper and pulp, cardboard, plywood, etc. Here are some figures of illustrative value. According to various assessments, the wastes yielded by the woodworking industry alone in Russia annually amount to 120 – 150 million m^3, and the third part of that is actually dispersed wood (sawdust, flour) [8, 9]. The wastes in plywood manufacture stand at about 5% of the raw material volume involved and include 100 thousand m^3 of sawdust, 70 thousand m^3 of shavings and 55 thousand m^3 of wood dust [10]. An essential part of the stuff remains unutilized. The involvement of wood wastes into practice leads to the solution of several problems: utilization, environment protection and creation of new cheap materials of useful properties.

This review deals with systematizing the data referred to modern trends of dispersed wood application in polymer materials technology and those concerning construction, above all. The description of dispersed wood is followed by the discussion of compositions based on dispersed wood with binders of inorganic and organic (thermoreactive and thermoplastic polymers) nature employed. And the attention is basically drawn to the analysis of compositions with large-tonnage thermoplastic polymers – a comparatively young area in polymeric materials technology. The discussion of the compositions has involved the use of the data as to impregnation of wood with polymers as an efficient technique for modification of wood properties.

2. Dispersed Wood

2.1. General Description

Dispersed wood suggests a broad concept since it embraces a range of various substances obtained from the logging, working and reprocessing of timber. Taking into consideration general requirements to be met by fillers of polymers, the range of dispersed specimens under discussion for wood-polymer composites ought to be confined, if we exclude roughly dispersed wood (chunks, ends and the like). Among the basic ones, those are shavings, sawdust, bark, grinding work dust normally used without preliminary preparation. The other group of dispersed materials consists of wood (liginic) flour, powder and microcrystalline cellulose, cellulose-liginic powders, thermomechanical fibre and others subject to physical and chemical treatment. They are distinguished for their more controllable dispersity, narrow-range chemical composition, lower content of impurities, but, naturally, they are more expensive and have a narrowly-specified range of application.

Compared to traditional mineral fillers, dispersed wood in lots of features proves sophisticated reflecting inborn nature of wood. Although the elemental chemical composition for all sorts of wood is practically identical, the content of the basic organic components, i. e. cellulose, lignin, hemicellulose, vary within rather a wide range (5 – 20%) related to a single species sort as well as to different (coniferous and leafy) species [1-3]. The availability of relatively small amounts of extractives (tannin, resins), essential oils, water-soluble and water-insoluble salts – carbonates, silicates, calcium, magnesium, iron phosphates - must not be neglected. They cause a higher ash content compared to organic polymers.

Various elements of the microstructure of wood, i. e. annual coats, vessels, tracheaides, pores, and the like, exposed to mechanical action, transform into particles of highly heterogeneous shapes and sizes. Obviously, this is encouraged by the anisotropy of wood. For example, the size of crushed bark particles features in terms of a few millimeters and tens of millimeters. Depending on the source of formation, sawdust particles vary in size from 2mm to 5mm, in thickness from 1mm to 3mm and differ in the flexibility factor (ratio of length to thickness), in porosity and elasticity [10]. Wood flour contains particles of sizes ranging from 10 to 700 microns, and of various and irregular shape. The optimal filler dispersity is considered to be 1 – 40 microns for normal and up to 200 – 300 microns for high-filled composites [2]. As far as the shape and the size of particles are concerned, non-availability of standard size and shape requirements is noteworthy because the nature of a binder and the character of a composite may make fibre-like, rough-surface and low-porosity, etc. particles more preferable.

Moisture content is a principally important feature of wood. As the original wood contains 60 – 100% of moisture against dry material condition and the equilibrium moisture content (8-15%) is far lower, the samples, when drying out, will shrink, warp, develop cracks and the like. It is especially characteristic of different size wood samples. Moisture content affects plenty of physical properties of wood along with that of dispersity, and they are important with regard to creating wood-polymer compositions. For instance, the density of wood substance for different species amounts to ~1.55 kg/m^3, whereas its realistic values vary within 0.4 – 0.7 kg/m^3 (at normal humidity). A number of features (heat capacity, size stability, electric, dielectric and thermal properties) show that wood rates equal to those of known synthetic polymers, and with regard to some other features (specific rigidity, tensile strength, modulus of elasticity), surpasses them [1-3]. This is connected with one of the highest values polymers possess, i. e. energy density of cohesion so much characteristic of wood [2]. Moisture deteriorates a lot of wood features as it is a polar plasticizing additive. Some parameters of wood, for example, electric resistance, are not high enough; but soaking with mineral oils and hydrocarbon polymers considerably increases its resistance to breakthrough.

It is noteworthy that certain conditions for the storage of dispersed wood have to be maintained, i.e. to exert thermostatic control over big unpackaged batches (filled heaps) [11]. This conditional character, however, can be eliminated by means of surface modification of material, the point to be discussed below.

On the whole, once dispersed wood as a potential filler for composite materials has been chosen, it is necessary that, along with the above-mentioned properties, the balance of a few positive and negative points should be kept in view. The positive points are low density and cost, availability of raw materials, feasibility of huge amounts incorporated in compositions. The unfavourable points are, actually, a polar nature of surface constraining compatibility with thermoplastic hydrocarbon polymers, lower resistance to water, chemical, thermal and biological effects. They affect inorganic and organic binders in compositions in different ways. As a rule, the properties of wood-polymer compositions are optimized by using special additives and by means of varying composition; this is going to be discussed in Section 3 of this Review. It is to be pointed out that the key-parameter, i.e. water resistance, for the composition of wood with organic polymers, controls many other properties and should be preferably corrected for dispersed wood right at its initial stage. Therefore, the next Section is dealing with the discussion of its water-proofing techniques known and employed.

2.2. Hydrophobization Techniques

Like in the case of water-sensitive mineral fillers, hydrophobization of dispersed wood can be implemented by means of various techniques. The organic nature and the availability of functional groups (hydroxyl, aldehyde, and others) possessed by wood components extend the possibilities of hydrophobic protection through joining (grafting) respective fragments. Besides dispersed powders, hydrophobization is implemented on products made of them, individual components and massive (dimensional) samples. These methods should also be kept in mind because, in all the cases, hydrophobization (modification) goes on at the places of the accessible elements of the material surface. Now let us discuss them in the above-mentioned order.

The simplest method for upgrading moisture resistance (and at the same time for increasing filled density and bringing ash content down) of wood flour consists in actually steam-curing the raw mass followed by sulfuric acid treatment before drying [12]. The effect of the treatment is obviously connected with the removal of amorphous (soluble) part from the wood.

Hydrophobization of wood powder as per a physical scheme (screening) is carried out by dint of treatment of vapour-phase heavy organic substances (bitumen, tar, paraffins comprising 0.2-1.5% of powder) at 160-350°C in a vortex dryer [13]. Water resistance and strength of the powder, as observed, go up simultaneously.

Methods connected with the application of silicon compounds frequently used in practice prove efficient [14]. For example, there has been offered a combined method of initially thermal followed by two-stage chemical treatment of wood particles with 2-10%-calcium chloride solution at 20 – 30°C and a further treatment with 2-15%-sodium silicate solution at 30 – 60°C combined with preliminary machining (cutting, flattening with a hammer crusher) and sorting. In this case, insoluble calcium silicates perform a proofing function. Water absorption is considerably (twice or thrice as much) brought down by means of consecutive treatment of the wood sample at first with 30%-solution of hydrophilic organophosphorus compound – trichloroethyl phosphate in CCl_4, and then with 10%-toluene solution of hydrophobizator – methylpropoxy(tributoxy)lane [16 - 17], the process finishes with drying out at a high temperature. The pre-treatment of wood with phosphorus compound assists fixation of silcone compounds (due to the coordination type P:→Si≡) which does not occur without a primary treatment.

The technique, close to the above-mentioned method, consists in using the mixture of chloroparaffin and oxydiphenyl in the ratio 1/1 to provide wood powder with high resistance to fire and biological damage besides water resistance after the primary treatment with trichloroethylphosphate [18].

Hydrophobization techniques, which exclude the application of toxic compounds and upgrade the ecological aspect of the process, are worth attention. Specifically, the utilization of the traditional inorganic binder, i.e. oligoethoxysiloxanes (ethylsilicates) and the products of their ester interchange performed by higher and aromatic alcohols, is undoubtedly interesting [19 - 25]. Wood flour soaked with them and subsequently heat-treated in fluidized bed at 100 – 180°C allows to bring down the water absorption of the samples by a factor of 10 and to raise their resistance to biodegradation under the influence of cellulose ferment extracted from the fungus "Trichodrma viride". The latter may positively tell on the period of product preservation – a problem faced by huge batches of wood flour. The effect of hydrophobization by ethylcilicate is connected with the course of ester interchange reaction of oligoethoxylosiloxanes with the hydroxyl groups of wood components, with the screening influence volumetric bound water repellant and with the structuring of silicone fragments in the surface layers of wood to form spatial net of polysiloxanes. In the aggregate, they form a reliable proofing effect.

Another method of hydrophobization associated with the utilization of natural resins, for example, pine galipot, mostly consisting of higher resin acids – $C_{19}H_{29}COOH$ – is still more attractive. Wood flour water absorption is brought down with a considerable effect (down to 15 – 30% compared to 500% with the original sample) at a small amount of water repellant (2 – 5% of a theoretically rated value) to indicate a high screening ability of the organic groups fixed on the surface [26 - 27]. This method proves quite original due to the fact that it demonstrates the possibility of water proofing the parent cellulose-lignitic material with its filial one – pine tar. Besides, it complies with the modern trend of a complex way of utilizing natural raw materials.

The high sorption power of modified samples compared to that of oils and petroleum many times exceeding the features rated by initial wood and standing at the same level with the popular sorbent puffed up perlite is an interesting and practical result (and at the same time the proof) of hydrophobization of wood flour by means of ethylsilicate and pine galipot [28]. Therefore they are of practical interest for collecting various oil products.

In the case of items produced by means of compacting compositions based on dispersed wood (crushed wastes, sawdust, fibres), along with a binder, additionally, a water repellant or a binder-water repellant is used, e.g. bone glue – water glass [29], bitumen – water glass [30], lignosulfonate – ethylhydrosiloxane [31]. Besides upgrading water resistance, other problems are sorted out, i.e. increasing strength, reducing thermal conductivity and others.

Although the most common wood items like wood fibre slabs and splint-slabs contain water-proofing binding agents, specifically, phenol-formaldehyde resins, their effect is enhanced by the addition of petroleum water repellant at a ratio of 4/1 with tall oil [32], paraffin or petrolatum with petroleum bitumen added [33], vat residues after the vacuum refining of paraffin-containing petroleum products [34] as well as sodium silicate. As a rule, water repellants are added in an amount of 1 – 10% against the bulk of the basic substance. The treatment of wood material with sulfur melt at 140 – 150°C holds promising because it provides for a comprehensive improvement of the properties: water-, bio- and acid resistance, static bend strength [36].

The modification of cellulose material is interesting with the view to hydrophobization of dispersed wood. Among a number of those known methods there are two fundamental ones worth noting: the formation of siliceous esters of cellulose on the surface due to the reaction among haloidmethyltrialkylsinanes and mixed alcoxyacetoxymoxysilanes with a substrate [37, 38] and the graft of various polymer fragments (polyisoprene, a fluorine-containing polymer, polysiloxane and others) with the aid of known polycondensation reactions, ionic and free radical polymerization, reaction of ready polymers and others [39 - 41]. It may be assumed that the availability of "a polymer coat of its own" on wood particles affects its compatibility with the basic polymer binder.

As to non-dispersed but dimensional wood samples, hydrophobization is part and parcel of filling (impregnation of material pores with polymer) aimed at sorting out a wide-range problem of wood refining. It is only relevant to present instances of impregnation directly aimed at wood hydrophobization. Primarily, it is the incorporation of low-molecular polythene [42 - 43], elemental sulfur [44 - 47] and organosilicon monomers – alkoxy- and acetoxysilanes [38, 48]. Their efficiency varies depending on the character of the reaction to the surface. The water proofing function of polythene is of a temporary character since, while in the sample, it is vulnerable to the action of the water in the lignocarbon complex and, as a result of gradual cellulose fibre liberation and wood swelling, it is expelled. The sulfur uniformly filling the vessels and intracellular space in wood can react to the components of the material. All this results in a durable water resistance and shape stability of wood. A similar behavior of organosilicon compounds active towards cellulose and other components of wood is observed. Thermochemical surface modification known in the chemistry of polymers as "siloxane cross-linking" takes place [49].

Thus a set of chemical substances and hydrophobization techniques being realized on dispersed wood as well as arousing a potential interest in this respect is rather great and may be used to create wood-polymer composites.

3. The Features of Wood-Polymer Composites

3.1. Some Principles for the Creation of Dispersed Wood-Polymer Composites

Taking into account the availability and cheapness of dispersed wood, it is natural that all these factors should be employed to create composites with polymers, keeping in mind, that additional operations to modify the filler will inevitably lead to making it more expensive and potentially confined as to its application. Besides, the choice of a polymer binder to achieve a complex of properties required determines a complex of requirements (operations) imposed on the preparation of dispersed wood.

Section 2. 1. mentioned a sophisticated nature of dispersed wood akin to the initial material regarding only the approximate elemental composition. The basic components of wood change, when exposed to mechanical action, and thus alter their properties [4, 5]. And the supramolecular structure of native wood, regarded as a natural composition material, has to undergo still deeper transformations [50]. Unfortunately, even the most dispersed form (flour) has been only discussed in print so far with regard to production and application [51, 52]. Therefore, tentative knowledge regarding the behavior of dispersed wood-polymer systems can be obtained from bulky information about the impregnation of various wood samples leading to the creation of wood-polymer composites having the initial anatomical wood structure. Since these problems are elaborately discussed in a number of reviews and materials of conferences [43, 53-56], we will concentrate on a few consequences of a predicting force for compositions with dispersed wood.

In the first place, it is imperative to observe the principle of chemical similarity, i.e. to use impregnants of close chemical nature for the utilization of modifying properties. Those are hydrous inorganic binders. Furthermore, those are reactive oligomers or low-molecular polar polymers akin to wood and those reacting to its components (phenol-, urea-, melamine-, aqcetone- and its other furanformaldehyde resins, polyethethyleneglycoles, alkyd resins, polyvinilacetate and others). The same refers to water-soluble hydrophilic polymers – polyacrylic acids, polyhydroxyalkylates, their co-polymers which are incorporated in wood matrix by way of polymerizing respective monomeric systems. In this case, the effect of modification is traced clear-cut, and it is due to the interlocking of hydrophilic centres of wood and polymer to ensure the formation of hydrogenous bonds.

In the case of chemically incompatible modifiers (elemental sulfur, polyoxanes and others), a chemical reaction to form a respective spatial structure is required. A technique of employing combining agents is possible, i.e. before high-molecular compound of low polarity is incorporated in wood, it is treated with a low-molecular compound [57]. By the way, it should be noted that not every chemical modification, whatsoever, of wood can be acceptable since the realization of a reaction to a great depth, e.g. acetylation, is accompanied by a considerable alteration of the material properties is not always admissible. Another aspect of forming wood-polymer compositions by means of the impregnation method, i.e. binding with a capillary-porous structure and anisotropy of wood, is also obviously applicable for compositions with dispersed wood. It can be assumed that cellulose microfibrils and the concentration of the polymer in the cavities impermeable for the polymer or cell walls soaked with the polymer remain invariable for the compositions [58]. The cell wall acts as transient adhesive layer providing for the compatibility of the polymer with the frame structure of wood.

As for the technique of wood-polymer composition preparation, it is naturally different from those of impregnation, but the common condition remains that pores and voids in wood should be filled with the polymer to maximum.

Thus, the creation of wood-polymer composites on the basis of dispersed wood is possible for water-containing mineral polymeric binders (the simplest case), for polymers with functional groups reacting to the wood filler and for thermoplastic, including hydrocarbon, polymers (the most problematic case which requires observing a few conditions). The characteristics of each type of wood-polymer composite are provided hereafter.

3.2. Dispersed Wood – Inorganic Polymers (Binders)

Mineral binders capable of forming spatial polymeric structures, when hardening, belong to the most frequently used ones in compositions with dispersed wood. The widely spread application of mineral binders in building practice and easy adaptation of wood to them as natural hydrophilic material are the top prerequisites for the creation of wood-polymer composites. The main trends of utilizing wood as secondary raw material has been given enough light to, e.g. in [10, 59-62]. That is why it is expedient to emphasize the systematization of the data published and the analysis of the potentials of systems of this type.

The properties of wood-cement composites are determined to a great extent by the nature of the wood component, by its morphological structure, physicomechanical and other properties. The principal significance belongs to water-soluble agent content determining the suitability of wood to hit the above-mentioned targets (see the table below).

Table.

Wood nature	Water-soluble substances content, %	Degree of suitability downwards
S	1.	1
P	1.	2
Birch	2.67	3
Pine	3.16-6.2	4
Oak	2.55-7.33	5
Ash tree	2.24-5.81	6
Larch	10.6	7

Therefore, the history of the material, starting with logging along with seasoning, mode of delivery (dry or floating) and finishing with storage conditions, is of great importance. The utilization of mineralizers ($CaCl_2$ solution and others) reducing the negative influence of succhars and other extractive substances upon cement strength properties is a matter of general advice.

Depending on the nature of an inorganic binder employed, its amount in a composition varies within ½ - $^2/_1$ related to a wood component, but there can be other proportions as to the wood components. The general picture looks like this: mixing, laying into patterns, compacting (pressing), exposure or heat treatment, hardening (getting ripe), pressing out, sorting, storing, i.e. no special technique is required. The fundamental properties of the compositions suggest that they should be strong, refractory, bio-resistant, less dense and thermostable, easy-to-treat, enjoying physical, technical and hygienic properties, i.e. combining the merits of inorganic and organic components.

The principal group of wood-polymer composites with mineral binders consists of arbolites or lightweight concretes in the simplest case prepared out of wood, Portland cement, calcium chloride and water. The process of preparation (the efficiency of cement hydration, cut-back on hardening period, etc.) and the physicochemical properties (decreasing the density, thermal conductivity, increasing the strength, etc.) of arbolite are improved through maximum removal of water-soluble substances from the wood component in mixtures of sawdust and splinters [64], the modification of wood particles to elongate them ($l/d=20\div40$)

when rolling [65], the incorporation of additives (still waste obtained from soda production) to bring down the corrosion of machine parts [66], the addition of TPP ash [67] and the utilization of binding mixtures (cement and lime) [68]. The problem of compacting the compositions in the process of making arbolite still remains quite acute because vibration normally practised proves low efficient due to low gravitational and elastic properties of the mixture, and the compaction leads to pressing out and breaking down the structural integrity after relieving [10].

An attractive variety of arbolite is elstar – electrostabilized arbolite. The exposure of a composition under preparation to direct current makes the liquid phase composition level off at a cost of the destruction of hydrate shells around cement grains. This results in reducing the structure formation period, enhancing the strength of cement stone and, thus, enabling to bring down the thickness (weight) of building structures, to increase their dimensions and decrease labour required for assembly operations. Other advantages suggest a wider choice of wood particles (not only coniferous, but also foliate) and binders (low-grade Portland cement with lower rates of consumption, water glass, etc.).

Sawdust concrete is an economically beneficial material in which sawdust (in small amounts, though, up to 10%) goes mixed with sand, and cement does with lime. In later formulas there have been used slag-alkali binders, i.e. ground blast furnace slag closed by calcined soda solution, soda-alkali melt, etc. [69, 70].

The "strong" features of the basic components, i.e. cement and gypsum binder, sawdust and other wood wastes, are most effectively combined in fast-hardening sawdust concrete. So, gypsum imparts quick-setting property and good formability to a composition, but its negative qualities (solubility in water, creep) in the composition are considerably weakened. Despite its relatively low consumption, Portland cement imparts the properties of hydraulic hardening, water resistance, strengthening in time to the concrete, and its characteristic shrinkage in the composition is entirely eliminated. Eventually, whereas wood has disposition to inflammability and decay, sawdust concrete has none, and the merits, i.e. enhanced impact strength, volumetric stability, high hygienic properties and ease of working, brought in are displayed by sawdust concrete clear-cut. The distinctive complex of the material properties, namely, quick hardening, considerable tensile and impact strength, high pliability, adhesion to other building materials, foster using them for making large-sized items of a multilayer structure.

Among other inorganic binders utilized in wood-polymer composites the following ones should be noted: magnesian binder (caustic magnesite combined with magnesium chloride and sulfate) ensuring high water resistance of the basic products, i.e. xylolith and compression-molded building beams [10]; nepheline sludge (frame aluminosilicate) [70]; ethylsilicate [31]; clay [71]; pure gypsum [10, 72] and liquid glass [29, 30, 73]. In the case of liquid glass, various targets can be met: to obtain highly-filled (up to 90-92%) wood compositions, to obtain artificial stones, to briquet charcoal dust, etc. Although none of the above-mentioned binders challenge to create compositions enjoying an all-purpose complex of properties, they allow adjusting individual important properties (incombustibility, resistance to cold, water resistance, etc.) in a direction required.

As to the wood component of compositions, due attention should be paid to wood chips used in cement splint-slabs and to crushed bark (after being processed for the production of tan extracts). The latter is used to create a series of materials, i.e. arbolite, bark-concrete, cement corolyith, and suggests utilizing the same binding and auxiliary additives (antiseptics, etc.) as in the production of materials based on sawdust [10].

3.3. Dispersed Wood – Thermoreactive Resins

Combinations of dispersed wood with thermoreactive resins represent a type of composites in which components are combined according to a physical scheme as well as through chemical reactions. This is assisted by the application of phenol-, resorcin- and ureaformaldehyde resins and the like containing the same functional groups or those naturally close to the filler. As a number of combinations of wood with these resins (phenoplasts, aminoplasts, etc.) have won their places on the market and given publicity to in printed monographs and handbooks [1-3, 9, 10, 74], we are pulling up at a few peculiarities and trends of up-grading with regard to wood and a polymer binder.

The preparation of compositions involves a wide range of dispersed wood, specifically, bark, chips, sawdust, fibre-likes and other particles. In the case of bark, spruce wastes of wood are more preferable since they contain more elastic bast fibre, which is the basis for wood cortical slabs. For the preparation of another product, i.e. coroplast, involving lower-grade raw materials, i.e. the bark of pine, larch, it is possible to add sawdust. In both cases the preferable binder is quick-setting carbamidoformaldehyde resin (KC-68, KФ-MT) used in an amount of 8-12% against the filler in combination with a hardener and special additives. Filler water content is regulated strictly as it is important to provide for transport, mass exchange and other processes when pressing. The density, strength and other properties of material and its designation, I.e. the manufacture of heat-insulating and soundproofing, structural heat-insulating, lining materials, are adjusted with the size of wood particles and the pressure of compaction.

Specially fabricated wood cuttings, machine-tool waste cuttings, crushed wood wastes undergo hot pressing to make splint-slabs which have a wide range of application. Along with phenol-formaldehyde and ureamelaminoformaldehyde resins, the prescription of splint-slabs includes water repellant. To prepare splint-slabs, a progressive extrusion method is used alongside with pressing. Among the varieties of splint-slabs there are to be noted one-, three- and multilayer slabs distinct in the size of particles and binder content in each layer and film-coated with coloured polymer.

Another wide-spread wood-polymer material is wood fibre slabs obtained by means of utilizing raw materials which consist of wood splinters and other wastes of woodworking, including low-grade foliate wood ground down to fine fibre condition after resinous and sugary substances have been neutralized. The prescription contains phenol-formaldehyde binder, water repellant (paraffin emulsion), antiseptic and fireproofing additives. Like splint-slabs, items made of wood fibre slabs vary in density, strength and technical application.

Wood in other dispersed forms combined with the above-mentioned binders is used to prepare tyrsolith (mixture of sawdust and wood flour) and parquelith (mixture of machine-tool waste chips and sawdust).

Wood flour soaked with urea- and phenol-formaldehyde resins subsequently heat-hardened and pressed proves to be one of the most aged polymeric products, i.e. amino- and phenoplasts. They are produced in various forms, mainly in the form of molding powders. It is noteworthy that with regard to numerous properties, molding materials made from powders with wood flour surpass similar materials containing mineral fillers.

A complex mixture of dispersity-wise different wood samples (crushed chunky chips, sawdust, wood flour, hydrolytic lignin) combined with non-spinnable wastes of weaving is used for manufacturing lignowood plastics (slabs).

Based on various crushed wastes from logging and woodworking, lignocarboplastics demonstrate an interesting variety of wood-polymer composites [75]. Their formation is not based on adding a polymer binder, but on the generation of an in-situ binder when plasticizing wood due to the transformation of its lignin-component and polysaccharides [75]. The slab-material obtained outdoes even materials with a thermoreacrive binder as to physicomechanical properties. The wood-polymer composites of the type under discussion go upgrading along the path of modifying the properties of wood component and varying the set of components in a composition. For example, it is suggested utilizing wood filler preliminarily matched with the very resin further applied to prepare molded material [76]. Another option suggests soaking wood flour with various polymers (epoxy, etc.) and, before compounding, with phenol-formaldehyde resin [77]. Wood filler is activated when treating it with wastewater containing phenol [78] or by means of grafting polyacrolein [79].

The adjustment of composition properties involves a wide range of problems to be solved. The economy of difficultly available wood flour and, at the same time, the improvement of composition physcochemical properties can only be ensured by incorporating hydrolytic lignin and lignitic flour [80, 81], and in the case of the latter, its amount is commensurate with the amount of base wood filler. The consumption of the binding agent (urea-formaldehyde resin) goes down with a simultaneous rise in bend strength as soon as traditional acidic hardeners are replaced by a polymeric one (polyacrylic acid) [82]. The utilization of a hybrid binding agent (liquid glass and urea-formaldehyde resin) has resulted in compositions with porous structure [83]. The properties of phenoplasts are upgraded by incorporating polyacrylonitrile fibres (increasing resistance to water and chemicals) [84], a set of additives, i.e. organic ones, pyrenes, pigments, dyes (increasing thermal stability) [85, 86] and elemental sulfur (increasing strength) [87]. The effect of sulfur is evidently connected with its participation in the structurizing of the composition due to the formation of mono- and polysulfide bridges among aromatic fragments. Besides the customary including of fireproofing additives in the prescription to make wood plastics fire-proof, a combination of carbamide, ammonium phosphate and phosphogypsum are incorporated into the outside layer of slabs [88].

Amongst compositions of non-traditional contents there should be noted press-molded material made from wood and a protein additive [89] as well as wood and fluoropolyurithane obtained from toluene diisocyanate and polyalcilenpolyols (containing up to 5% of free isocyanate groups) [90]. The latter composition asks for changing fluoropolymer into polyurethane and reactive joining wood flour. The content-close composition (wood flour pre-treated with polyethylenedlycol in combination with isocyanates) after heat treatment changes into a material similar to foam polystyrol [91]. The possibility of extending the range of resources in this manner is sated, thus.

To conclude the section, it is to be pointed out that one more sort of the compositions under discussion is a glue-type one which is actually a combination of dispersed wood with reactive resin and solvent [92, 93]. And as regards to challenging the creation of wood composites, the fact of controlling epoxy hardening through cellulose agents is worth making note of [94].

3.4. Dispersed Wood – Thermoplastic Polymers

Large-tonnage thermoplastic polymers obtained from carbon raw materials available are attractive as objects to be filled with wood. Besides the modification of these polymers and creation of materials with new properties, the application of dispersed wood is found expedient with the view to meeting one of the fundamental requirements to be faced by fillers, i.e. economy of base product. Therefore, it is obviously a natural reason for non-fading interest in the problem of wood-polymer composites of the type rated among promising functional materials to be applied in technology and construction [95, 96]. It is noteworthy that the works in this field published are dated back to the 80s-90s, and, as per entries covering polymers in encyclopedias, dispersed wood as filler is solely applied in thermoreactive plastics, but not in thermoplasts [97].

According to the publications reviewed, dispersed wood has been a filler to be incorporated in the most common thermoplasts – polythene, polypropylene, PVC, polystyrol as well as other important polyolefins, polyvinyl and co-polymer products – polybutenes, polybutane, polyacrylates, polyvinyl alcohol, polyvinylacetate, butyl rubber, ethylene propylene co-polymer, ABS plastic, etc.

The actual list of the thermoplastics is still greater because, besides standard polymers produced industrially, the products of their oriented modification, secondary polymers and mixtures have been tested. This results from searching for polymer products which meet the requirements for the compatibility with wood fillers. And to find the ways to meet these requirements, researches into obtaining more accurate information related to the physical properties of wood powders, their modification (hydrophobization) and incorporation of composition additives are being done. Keeping in view the above-mentioned, the analysis of the compositional systems handled in this section goes down to discussing general problems of the effect of dispersed wood on the behavior of polymer systems and efforts to find (prepare) prescriptions specifying optimal properties and degree of filling related to specific thermoplastic polymers.

As mentioned in Section 2.1., dispersed wood is a complicated chemical property-wise and heterogeneous physical parameter-wise filler. The systematization of the data related to the behavior of wood fillers in compositions with thermoplastic polymers allows to particularize the range of their parameters taking into consideration the nature of wood as well as the conditions for preparing and processing the compositions. As it has turned out, a kind of wood (a species of wood) is not essential with the view to its functioning as dispersed filler, and this is an important factor taking into account different functional abilities of dimensional materials based on hard (valuable) and soft species of wood. The size and shape of wood particles are more significant. Wood flour (a dispersity of $0.01 \div 1$mm) and sawdust (1-10mm), less frequently, chips (10-20mm) and particles of compulsory shape (flaky, fibresome, etc.) are more often used. From the economical point of view, big wood particles are naturally more beneficial. But they increase the roughness of item surface, non-uniformity of item properties and possess lower density that brings down the efficiency of the processing equipment for respective compositions, thus. Plasticization of wood with water or ammonia is in a position to overcome the afore-mentioned drawback. To this end, the most rational way is to apply ammonium salts $(NH_4)_2CO_3$, NH_4HCO_3, etc. decomposing in the process of treating the compositions to release ammonia [98]. Water content is also subject to regulation. Although this feature is not specified in every work printed, water content should be under equilibrium and amount to a few per cent. In this regard, it is relevant to note the technique of incorporating calcium oxide (1-20%) into compositions consisting of various thermoplasts and dispersed wood to make extra filler dry-out redundant and to avoid the release of volatile components when processing so as to provide for good quality of item surface [99]. A similar effect is achieved when utilizing gypsum in compositions [100].

The processes of wood filler surface modification (hydrophobization) to be discussed further on also enable to receive samples of low water content and to evade the negative influence of water upon the properties of items.

It is desirable to process wood-filled thermoplasts by applying modern methods at temperatures no higher than $200^{0}C$, i.e. to take into account insufficient thermal stability of wood. As a rule, the application of rheological and fireproofing additives combined with respective temperature and timing modes ensure the implementation of this condition.

The actual behavior of dispersed wood as filler for polymers like in the case of mineral fillers is determined by the chemical and physical nature of its surface (availability of functional groups, pores, the value of density, etc.) and the nature of the polymer. The specificity of the behavior can be illustrated with nonpolar (polyethylene – PE, polypropylene - PP) and polar (polyvinyl chloride – PVC) polymers.

Owing to poor compatibility of wood with thermoplastic polymers (a great difference in cohesion energy densities), corresponding compositions are characterized by a low level of properties, i.e. low water resistance, low mechanical strength, etc. [101, 102]. As observed, the increase in wood particle size leads to monotonous decrease in the impact strength of filled PVC materials and the increase in melt fluidity. The physicomechanical properties considerably go down especially in the case of using large-size wood particles (5mm and over) as the signs of instability show when flowing – uniformity of melt flow fails. The alteration of wood component concentration has revealed three characteristic scopes of compositions resulting from structural peculiarities of the PVC – wood flour mixture [103]. At a small wood content (up to 15%), i.e. within a scope where wood can be considered as a modifying additive, the polymer matrix keeps weakly-oriented, wood particles are kept far apart by boundary layers of the polymer, and, as a result, when the share of wood goes up, tensile strength along with impact strength goes down. Within a scope of higher concentration of wood flour (15-50%), the behavior of compositions is determined by an effective thickness of the polymer layer among the filler particles in which oriented polymer structures closer to the surface gradually grow into weakly-oriented and further into non-oriented structures. Within this scope, the property alteration of compositions related to the filler content variation is insignificant. At 50-60% of wood flour content (the third scope), the polymer is mostly in a highly oriented state, and compositions represent a stable framework formed by chains of wood particles coated with polymer layers. The properties of compositions within this scope considerably result from the structure of wood particles, e.g. there has been noted a sharp increase in water absorption. A similar story can be obviously expected from highly wood-filled polymer systems.

Rheological investigations on the properties of compositions consisting, for example, of low-density PE and wood flour (the particle size of up to 0.25mm) within a wide range of speeds (10^{-6}–$5c^{-1}$) and shear stresses ($3 \div 1 \cdot 10^4$ Pa) reveal the influence of wood filler amount and its density [104]. The effect of orientation of anisodiametric wood particles when flowing brings down the viscosity (anomaly) of compositions with small (up to 10%) filler concentrations. Within the scope of low speeds and shear stresses, compositions with wood content of 20% and over are characterized by a sharp rise in melt viscosity due to the formation of the structural framework of filler particles. In compositions with a greater wood content, the elasticity of melt rises due to the elastic properties of wood filler and its capacity of deforming at small pressures [105]. The elastic properties of wood are great enough thanks to the capillary-cell structure of wood [106]. When compacting, the capillary structure breaks down, the elastic properties go down and, accordingly, the elasticity of wood –polymer composite melt gets down as the wood flour content goes up [107]. The effect received in the latter reference work for PP composition is connected with high viscosity of wood particles (1.32 kg/m^3) close to the saturated (genuine) density of wood substance.

Thus the parameters of wood particles (size, density), their quantity and the nature of polymer determine the behavior and properties of specific wood-polymer compositions.

The greatest number of works on wood-filled thermoplasts cover polyolefins, especially, PE. Besides conventional polymer of low density, there have been tested compositions with recycled PE (wastes) and PE of high density. As to the former, attention is basically paid to raising the compatibility of components with the aid of physicochemical treatment of wood. To this end, waxes combined with mineral additives [108], glyoxal [109], co-polymers of ethylene with propylene, of propylene with acrylic and metaacrylic monomers and others [110] were used. As a rule, modifying additives are taken in small amounts (not exceeding 10%) and incorporated individually at higher temperatures or through solutions (in the case of polymers) eventually followed by the removal of the solvent. Otherwise, the combining additives are incorporated directly into PE compositions (other polyolefins) and dispersed wood. Among the additives there can be found solid saturated hydrocarbons [111], atactic PP [112], pyrolytic resin of propane-butane fraction of petroleum [113], copolymers of ethylene with vinyl acetate, butyl rubber, chlorinated butyl rubber and others [114]. The incorporation of combining additives generally results in lowering melt viscosity and improving the conditions for processing the compositions and raising the strength, hardness and other deformation features of materials.

The range of opportunities for obtaining wood-polymer compositions grows wider if recycled PE is applied [115] and, especially, when preparing mixtures with it while imposing shear deformations [116, 117]. The pre-treatment of wood filler with urea formaldehyde resin КФ-МТ has led to the improvement of the strength features of the material and to the rise in water resistance [118]. A similar effect is brought about by a rise in the pressure of compaction and, accordingly, by a rise in the density of wood-polymer material [117]. It should be noted that the degree of wood filling in PE is high resulting, besides other reasons, from the availability of functional groups in the polymer due to partial oxidation.

With regard to PE of high density outstanding for its considerable molecular weight (2 x 10^6), the amount of the polymer in the composite can be brought down to 10-30% [119]. In this case the physicomechanical properties change in a sophisticated manner; specific elongation at tensile strength test goes up with up to 60% of filler (flour) content whereas breaking point at tensile strength test changes in an extreme way; the impact strength of compositions goes down while the filler content rises up to 29% in normal conditions and goes down if the test temperatures get down to minus 40^0C [120]. The conditions for processing deteriorate, i.e. the pressure for extruding PE compositions of high density at 40% of wood filler content increases 3-5 fold compared to a sample without filling [121]. Nevertheless, it is stated that, taking into account ecological safety, comparatively low cost and simplicity of item manufacture, the wood-polymer composites of the type must be competitive compared to the traditional materials, i.e. wood fibre slabs and splint-slabs.

In the case of molding material made from micropowders of PE (20%) and wood, a more optimistic forecast is pointed out still that they are more beneficial than wood fibre slabs and splint-slabs [122, 123].

The work [124] on obtaining a biodegrading composition made from PE of low density and 10-30%-powder cellulose with photosensitizer (0.1%-ferrocene) added is worth attention. The predicted period of natural photodegradation of film material comes to 2 – 3 years depending on its thickness.

Due to a high crystallinity of PP, the problem of its compatibility with wood fillers goes more acute than that of the one in the case of PE. Even for the most dispersed form, i.e. flour, the influence on the physicomechanical properties of PP-compositions is negative throughout the entire range of concentrations [125]. As a rule, radical steps are taken to create operational compositions, i.e. either one or both polymeric and wood components at a time are modified. One of the techniques suggests the application of wood in the form of fibres [126]. Those can be lignocellulose as well as hemicellulose fibres (with lower lignin content) chemically treated [127]. Good compatibility of fibroid filler with polymer and the creation of composites having a high module of elasticity, strength and hardness are noted. Another example is the utilization of thermomechanical fibres obtained by means of fibrillating woodworking wastes at high temperatures and pressure [125]. Low concentration of fibres in compositions with PP (no higher than 9%) is notable, and it is optimal as to the properties obtained, i.e. the upgrading of the module of elasticity, strength and impact strength. The application of powder cellulose preparations (25-35%) as filler increases steam and gas resistance of polymer films twice as much and ensures maintaining the level of heat resistance, hardness and specific elongation high enough [128].

Chemical treatment of wood filler proves to be effective. For example, wood flour to reinforce PP is treated with γ-metacryloxipropyltrimetoxicylane (1%), and the addition of cumyl peroxide to the composition allegedly enhances the influence of wood [129]. With the upgraded level of mechanical properties attained, the addition of 40% of flour stands at the level of addition of 40% of traditional fillers, i.e. talcum and chalk.

Otherwise, the polymer component is modified by means of incorporating organic peroxide and organosilane prior to mixing it with the filler, eventually to cause a 15-25% increase in breaking point value at tensile and bend tests [130].

The greatest effect, specifically for obtaining compositions highly filled with wood (up to 60%), is achieved by means of simultaneous modification of PP and wood. The combinations of agents used for the treatment of the components (for the above-mentioned sequence) are described as follows: unsaturated dicarboxylic acid anhydride and meta-phenylenebysmaleinimide [126], maleinic anhydride and acetic anhydride (acetylation) [131], unsaturated dicarboxylic acid anhydride and silane dressing [132], ethylene-propylene copolymer and lamellar inorganic fillers (talcum or mica) [133]. Additive-initiated reaction between PP-matrix and wood filler brings down the melting point temperature and the crystallinity of PP, i.e. improves the reaction across the phase boundary. Among the upgraded composition properties there is strength, hardness, impact strength, adhesion and thermal stability.

The additives considerably affecting properties are also a mixture of $CaCO_3$ and SiO_2 (5 ÷ 6/1) amounting to 3-6% reducing the pyrolysis of wood quite well while preparing and processing wood-PP compositions [134].

Although there is little information at the moment as to practical perspectives for the above-discussed type of compositions, their application is undoubtedly expedient for producing non-critical items made from large-tonnage polymers when the consumption of polymer is a prevailing factor.

In the case of polystyrene (PST), a stiff-chained polymer, wood filling is aimed at increasing the level of mechanical properties. The set of techniques is similar to the above-discussed ones applied to PP-compositions. We are pointing out the most characteristic ways enabling the achievement of a noticeably positive result. In the first place, it is the filling of PST with wood fibres under chemo- and thermomechanical treatment of compositions providing for the formation of grafted copolymers in the system [135]. For wood powders, it is expedient to use oblong particles, to treat them with dressings (isocyanates, alkoxysilanes) or to graft copolymer products [136]. After the incorporation of phenol-formaldehyde resin, furfural (1-5%), wood sawdust in a composition with secondary PST is distinguished for its strength and high water resistance, i.e. it retains that basic feature of the original polymer [137]. Unfortunately, not a single investigation on PST-compositions has ever rated collision protection property that is actually a weak point of the polymer.

With regard to another stiff-chained polymer, PVC, as it is pointed out at the beginning of the 1section, the incorporation of dispersed wood brings down the rates of the basic properties. Although wood is an active filler in relation to PVC (a reaction to the polymer matrix is possible through the formation of hydrogenous bonds), all attempts to find a favourable optimum of properties fail, and the negative effect from the incorporation of wood comes out even within the scope of its small portion addition ranging up to 15% (a drop in strength and impact strength) and within the scope of its big portion addition ranging at 50-60% (risc in water adsorption).

Wood and polymeric component modification techniques make it possible to improve the situation when creating wood-PVC composites. The works published may be divided in to two groups: those related to hard PVC items (vinylplast) and those related to soft plasticized ones (plastic compound). The treatment of wood (wood flour basically) with polymers and resins, i.e. with chlorinated PE, styrene-butadiene copolymer [138], polyvinylbutyral with additives [139], phenolo- and ureaformaldehyde resins, unsaturated polyesters [140], favourably affect the processing of PVC compositions increasing the viscosity, uniform flow accompanied by obtaining extrudates free of surface defects and easily yielding to extra operations on foaming or stretching. Although the amount of modifying additives varies within a wide range (from fractions to tens of per cent), their influence obviously comes down to the control over the wood-PVC reaction and eventually upgrades the compatibility which enables processing high-filled (up to 70%) compositions.

For emulsifying PVC, it is manageable to get viable (up to 6 months) compositions with wood flour (ratio 1/1) only in case of pre-treatment of the wood component with the solutions of oligooxyethelene glycols with oleic acid added [141]. The effect of the additives manifests itself also in final products – increase in tensile strength and hardness.

A convenient technique has been offered in [142]. Emulsifying PVC is mixed with wood sawdust and then heated up to the temperature exceeding the temperature of the polymer softening point. The formation of polymer film on the surface of the filler provides for its uniform dispersion within the same polymer to accompanied by the ease of processing and entails the production of items of high mechanical strength.

The incorporation of 2-5% plasticizers – dibutylphthalate or di-2- ethylhexylphthalate – improves the processing (power economy) of 1:1 compositions of crushed wood-PVC at simultaneous reduction of water absorption displayed by the compositions down by 30% [143].

There are only two publications discussing the behavior of plasticized PVC, but they demonstrate the capabilities of these compositions convincingly enough. In the publication [102] resorting to the behavior of the non-plasticized PVC – wood sawdust system there is formulated and solved the problem of creating highly filled (up to 150 m.p. per 100 m.p. of PVC) plasticized compositions designated for building industry. It is shown that the filler content 'capacity' of the composition goes up parallel to the increase in the plasticizer content (up to 50%); and acceptable thermotemporal modes for the processing of PVC compositions are maintained well. For better soaking wood with polymer melt, reactive heterocyclic oligomers amounting to 1-5% are employed. They noticeably push up the values of fluidity and impact strength of the compositions. High fluidity of the melt is very important for the processing of compositions through the application of highly effective techniques (extrusion, injection molding); and low molecular copolymer of butadiene with styrene is added to ensure this fluidity. Even its small amounts (0.75 m.p. per 100 m.p. of PVC) increase the melt fluidity 4 times as much. At the same time the speed of relaxation processes goes up to enable the formation of highly filled wood-vinyl plastics of a more equilibrium structure and to encourage long-term endurance of items made from such materials.

The comparison of the influence of the wood filler type was implemented when investigating PVC-dioctyl phthalate – wood compositions (100/50/10 m.p. ÷100 m.p.) [144]. The increase in the filler content entails the decrease in specific elongation, which, in its turn, drops in the line cellulose > wood flour > lignin. And friability temperature goes down in a similar way. The cause is reported to be the increase in the stiffness of chains in boundary layers resulting from the formation of PVC-filler bonds and the orientation of chains in the plane of the division boundary. The water absorption of the compositions rises along with the increase in wood filler content, besides, for lignin, due to its water repellency, the effect is lower. There has been revealed a PVC-related thermostabilizing effect of wood flour preparations and lignin added in small amounts, the effect related to the acceptance reaction of HCl released by the filler. These data testify for extra possibilities opened up by the choice of a specific wood filler when creating compositions.

Among other wood – polymer compositions there should be discussed those related to the application of thermoplastic systems of a narrower scope of application. Wood flour hydrophobized by means of treatment with ethyl silicate, oligoalkoxisiloxanes mixed with pine galipot (see Section 2.2) is used to obtain compositions with hydrocarbon polymers based on isobutylene [25, 145-148]. Hydrophobic reactions of the polymer to the filler have to ensure the viability of such systems. The properties of the compositions made from polyisobutylene (octol 200) and butyl rubber (Grade 2045) with wood have been evaluated by means of applying direct and indirect compatibility features of components (viscosity, water resistance, surface stickiness). It is found that, with the coorelation wood/polymer = 40/60 and 50/50, the compositions possess homogeneous consistence, they are moldable, have yield stress at room temperature and are outstanding for low water absorption, satisfactory stickiness, i.e. meet a complex of requirements for nondrying hermetics. The above-mentioned coorelation of the components is essential since at a 30% flour content undesirable cold flow of the polymer matrix remains and at a 60% flour content stickiness gets lost, and the system goes stratified. The chemical stability displayed by compositions kept in diluted solutions of sulfuric and nitric acids (pH = 1÷5) for 10-15 days is especially noteworthy. Under these conditions compositions made from butyl rubber and chalk – an analog of nondrying polyisobutylene hermetic [149] – undergoes complete destruction. There has been offered the formula of a nondrying plastic sealing compound consisting of ПИБ П –118, of wood flour hydrophobized by ethyl silicate-40 and of pine galipot; this compound is, actually, analogous to the commercial УМС-50 type seal, but of a greater chemical stability [150].

In order to increase thermal resistance of bituminous compositions, wood sawdust (50%) combined with liquid glass and asbestos are used [151]. The functions of the additives are obviously aimed at the modification of the wood component.

The formula of lignobituminous compounds, in which fine-ground hydrolytic lignin (it should be borne in mind that, on the whole, it is more water-repellant than wood) performs the function of a filler as well as a modifier of the composition properties, should be recognized as a more efficient one [152].

Those of interest are molded materials containing polar polymers and additives: cellulose acetate – glyceryltriacetate [153] and cellulose acetate – polyvinyl acetate dispersion [154], as partners related to wood sawdust. The components obviously enjoy good compatibility, therefore the compositions containing up to 50-60% of wood are highly strong at low density and when swelling in water. In this respect, the sealing composition including ~80% of wood flour, 12-16% of polyvinyl alcohol and 4-5% of PVC is also illustrative [155]. Although the polyalcohol is considered to be a binding agent, it is, no doubt, a combining agent for wood and PVC. The latter provides for the water resistance of the composition.

Now it is worth discussing some aspects of the technology for obtaining wood-polymer composites with the view to their properties. Up to 5% of high water-absorption resin, like grafted copolymer of starch and acrylonitrile in the form of fine-dispersed powder, is incorporated in compositions made of thermoplastic polymers and wood fillers (sawdust, small-size chips) [156]. The items made from these compositions possess the surface imitating the surface of natural wood. Such materials enter practice termed as 'artificial wood' [96].

The application of small amounts of pigments (hydrocarbon soot, titanium dioxide, chrome green, etc.) in compositions made of thermoplasts and wood flour, after being extrusion-processed and then cold-molded, ensure the formation of decorative sheet materials with uniform surface and volumetric colouring to make additional frequent practice of surface painting redundant [157].

Highly dispersed magnesium oxide substantially reducing the corrosion of press molds and oxide spotting is a high-technology additive for processing wood-polymer compositions [158].

The term 'high-technology' is also relevant with regard to the secondary wood filler, i.e. plywood grinding wastes, which, due to high dispersity, hardness and the ability to retain shape once exposed to mechanical deformation, ensures the best rheological properties of the compositions with thermoplasts even at a higher degree of filling compared to the compositions with sawdust and are processed by means of highly intensive methods [159]. Obviously, it is a fact of no small importance that the said filler is not native, but wood modified with organic additives.

In conclusion, it should be pointed out that, besides the traditional method for creating wood-polymer compositions based on mixing with subsequent utilization of molding technology, there is also known a method of reactive creation, i.e. the application of monomers instead of ready-made polymeric binding agents. In particular, there has been descried a method consisting in soaking crushed evacuated wood with olefin, vinyl and vinylidene monomers and with an initiator taken over by heating under hydrogen pressure causing the rapid polymerization and formation of wood-polymer plastics [160]. Another publication describes a reactive filling for wood flour pre-treated with polybutadiene or with copolymer of styrene and butadiene to impart olefin properties [161]. The combination of the polymer formed thus with the wood filler by means of a 'polymeric coat' applied upon it imparts high endurance, elasticity module and wide technical applicability to a composition material.

4. Conclusion

The above-mentioned discussion related to wood-polymer composites testifies for the fact that dispersed wood as a huge by-product of the industries dealing with wood and wood materials is within the scope of materials technology. Research and, mostly, practical work covers a wide range of problems, regarding first the application of various forms of wood, polymeric binders and compounding technology. The availability of the raw materials with a special accent on the necessity of the utilization keeping in view the ecological aspect serves as an extra stimulus for the development of this trend.

Out of the three fundamental types of wood-polymer composites, the compositions involving dispersed wood with thermoreactive resins very likely only belong to the category of those having undergone sufficient critical analysis, and the fact of the wide application of wood fibre slabs and splint-slabs, amino-and phenoplasts, etc. in practice testifies in favour of that. However, as to this type of materials, new original solutions related to property modification through formula upgrading come into being.

As far as the compositions with inorganic binding agents are concerned, we should recognize a wide range of opportunities to apply practically every binding agent dealt with in building practice for the compounding of wood. In essence, they are one of the first hybrid composition materials suitably combining components of organic and inorganic nature. The range of these materials is great – from lightweight concrete to artificial stone. However, the utilization of 'organic stuffing' in an inorganic by nature product requires the application of a complex of protective additives, like those intended to withstand wood decay. In this case like in the case of thermoreactive resins, it is obviously expedient to incorporate hybrid binding agents 'tuned' to wood as well.

The composites with thermoplastic binding agents belong to later objects of materials technology. The ideology of these compositions is built on the experience of practice with thermoplasts, with filled thermoplasts, to be more precise. And this is, actually, the main trend in modern materials technology. Although the filling of large-tonnage polyolefins and vinyl polymers with wood causes a series of problems (insufficient refractoriness, bio- and chemostability of materials, peculiarities of processing related to the physics of powder, etc.), on the whole, the materials, as to the complex of their properties, are not inferior to those based on inorganic fillers. The possibility of using dispersed wood fillers regardless of an initial wood species is a positive feature. The requirements for the physicomechanical properties of wood powders (size, shape, surface nature and others) are decisive like in the case of other wood-polymer composites. Although the application of dispersed wood in the form of industrial wastes requiring no special treatment looks attractive a lot, it has to be found expedient to take certain steps. Above all, it is the restricting of moisture content. Then, those are the processes of plasticizing, fibrellizing and others to enable obtaining wood particles of an oblong, fibrous and other shape preferred with the view to the improvement of final item properties. Wood hydrophobization processes are investigated quite well, and it is expedient to utilize them for dispersed materials more comprehensively.

It is also imperative to prepare wood by treating it with polymers – by preliminarily soaking it with the same polymer or with a polymer of other type than that of the product functioning as the base of the composition. A method should be recognized efficient once it suggests combining dispersed wood with the basic non-polar or low-polar polymer of high molecular mass by means of soaking with low-molecular polar polymer. The effective filling of pores in wood particles of a designed shape and the formation of a layer ('coat') 'active' towards the basic polymer on their surface provide for obtaining wood-polymer composites of good quality.

Therefore special wood wastes, like ground plywood dust and the like, meet filler requirements to a greater extent because they are distinguished for high dispersity, uniformity and the content of modifying additives incorporated in items.

It is viewed that the problem of obtaining cheap non-critical items made of wood and large-tonnage polymers (PE and others) aimed, above all, at economizing polymer material has been sorted out. Full-value substitution of wood polymer composites with thermoplasts applied for wood fibre slab and splint-slab materials is a realistic and important task to cope with. However, in this case, the strength features of the thermoplasts have to be raised. The compositions made of PE (PP) and cellulose fibres in the form of pulp preliminarily esterified with carbon acids [162] can serve as a guide. At a 40% content of the reinforcing agent, the bending strength of items reaches ~70 Mpa (for wood fibre slabs – 30-40 MPa) at a high value of compression strength, resistance to impact and a low rate of water absorption. This review has covered numerous instances of specific compositions showing the expedience of utilizing dispersed wood to sort out various problems.

It is expedient to consider the problem of creating wood-polymer composites in the context of a more comprehensive utilization of wood raw materials as well. Well, for example, provided an optimal variant of obtaining composites ensures ecological cleanliness of a material [163], the utilization of powder cellulose and a photosensitizer as fillers lends PE-composites the property of biodegradation [124]. The possibilities of obtaining wood-polymer composites on the bases of thermoreactive resins are extended due to the substitution of synthetic phenol formaldehyde oligomers for mixed-type binding agents involving phenol and hydrolyzed lignin, technical lignic sulfate, wood technology and pyrogenic resins and others [164]. Lignin, hydrolyzed, in particular, is an effective structure-plasticizing (rheological) additive when processing PVC and secondary PE to improve the parameters of the processing and the quality of items [165-167]. It should be noted that the problem of utilizing lignin as well as dispersed wood is pending quite acutely.

The above-mentioned examples along with the materials published earlier [169-172] and the data available as to the impregnation of wood with polymers as a way of obtaining composition materials with an anatomical wood structure testify for the formation of a wide-range trend related to a comprehensive application of secondary and low-value wood raw materials and polymers, including even predominantly those secondary ones subject to utilization. Wood-polymer composites based on wood dispersion proves to be part and parcel of this promising trend to develop in the time to come.

REFERENCES

[1] Chemical Encyclopedia. Moscow; *Sovetskaya Entsyklopedia,* 1990. V. 2, p.116.

[2] Encyclopedia of Polymers. Moscow; *Sovetskaya Entsyklopedia*, 1972. V.1, p.764.

[3] Lesnaya Entsyklopedia, Moscow.; *Sovetskaya Entsyklopedia*, 1985. V.1, p. 563; 1986. V. 2. 639 pages.

[4] Babkin B. A. *J. of Appl. Chemistry,* 1994. V. 67. No. 12, p. 2047.

[5] Alexandrov I. V.,. Vasilyev M. N, Gavrilov Yu. V. *J. of Appl. Chemistry*. 1996. V. 69. No.12, p. 2042.

[6] Sangalov Yu. A., Khalilova N. A. *Vestnik ASci.RB* (Ufa). 2002. V. 7. No. 3, p. 68.

[7] Shamayev V. A. Modification of Wood. Moscow.: *Ekologia,* 1991.128 pages.

[8] The Utilization of Woodworking Wastes and Protection of Wood with Antiseptics. Collection of Articles / edited by Permikin I.M., Sverdlovsk: Sredne-Uralsk Publishing House, 1984. 280 pages.

[9] Dodenkov S.V., Zaitsev V.A. Pekelis G.L The Utilization of Industrial Wastes. Proc. Sci. and Techn. Ser.: *Ecology and the Renewal of Natural Resources.* Moscow; VINITI, 1983, V. 13. 132 pages.

[10] Krylov V.N.. How To Make Money of Wood Wastes (the Utilization of Woodworking Industrial Wastes in the National Economy). Handbook. St.Petersburg, 1993. 200 pages.

[11] Melekhov I.V., Kuntysh V.B., Abramov N.B. // Proc. all-Union Conf. 'The Protection for Wood and Cellulose-Containing Materials against Bio-Damage'. Riga, 1989, p, 123.

[12] USSR Inventor's Certificate No.1518123 // *Bull. Izobr.* No.40 1989.

[13] USSR Inventor's Certificate No.1723072 // *Bull. Izobr.* No.12 1992.

[14] Pashchenko A.A., Voronkov V.G., Mikhailenko L.A. Hydrophobization. Kiev: *Naukova Dumka,* 1978, 238 pages.

[15] USSR Inventor's Certificate No. 1433400 // *Bull. Izobr.* No. 39 1988.

[16] Pokrovskaya Y.N., Sidorov V.I, Melnikova N.N. *Chemistry of Wood.* 1990, No.1, p.90.

[17] Sidorov V.I, Pokrovskaya Y.N., Melnikova N.N. *Chem.technol.,* Properties and Application of Plastics. Leningrad. 1989, p. 140.

[18] USSR Inventor's Certificate No.1109309 // *Bull. Izobr.* No. 31 1984.

[19] Sangalov Yu.A., Ilyasova A.I., Antonova N.E., *Journal of App.. Chemistry.* 1994. V. 67. No.11, p. 1867.

[20] Sangalov Yu.A., Ilyasova A.I., Antonova N.E. *Bash. Khim. Zh.* 1995. V. 1. No.4, p.54

[21] Sangalov Yu.A., Ilyasova A.I., Antonova N.E. Proc. VI All-Russian Conf. on Metalurg. *Chemistry*. N-Novgorod. 1995. V. 2, p. 434.

[22] Sangalov Yu.A., Antonova N.E. Proc. at Meeting II 'Wood Chemistry and Organic Synthesis' Syktyvkar. 1996, p.65.

[23] Russ. Patent No. 2126774 // *Bull. Izobr.* No. 6 1999.

[24] Sangalov Yu.A., Krasulina N.A., Ilyasova A.I. // Izvestia Vuzov. *Chemistry and Chem. Technology*. 1999. V.42. No.4, p.66.

[25] Sangalov Yu.A., Ilyasova A.I., Krasulina N.A..// Collection of Sci. Articles 'Building Materials Based on Raw Material Resources of the RB'. Ufa. *Bashniistroi*. 1998, p.120.

[26] Russ. Patent No. 2158193 // *Bull. Izobr.* No. 30 2000.

[27] Sangalov Yu.A., Krasulina N.A., Turyanov R.A. // Proc. All-Russian Conf. 'Chemistry and the Technology of Vegetable Substances'. Syktyvkar. 2000, p.133.

[28] Sangalov Yu.A., Ilyasova A.I., Krasulina N.A. // *J. of Appl. Chemistry*. 1999. V. 72. No. 7, p.1209.

[29] Russ. Patent No. 2001064 // *Bull.Izobr.* No. 8 1994.

[30] USSR Inventor's Certificate No.1579910 // *Bull. Izobr.* No. 27 1990.

[31] Russ. Patent No. 2001064 // *Bull. Izobr.* No. 37-38 1993.

[32] USSR Inventor's Certificate No.1133098 // *Bull.Izobr.* No. 1 1985.

[33] USSR Inventor's Certificate No.1219622 // *Bull.Izobr.* No. 11 1986.

[34] USSR Inventor's Certificate No.1465328 // *Bull.Izobr.* No. 10 1989.

[35] USSR Inventor's Certificate No.1104124 // *Bull.Izobr.* No. 27 1984.

[36] Panov V.V., Mikhailishin I.O., Torokhova I.V. // Proc. All-Russia Sci. and Techn. Conference 'The Modifying and Protective Treating of Wood'. Krasnoyarsk, 1989. Vol.1, p,40.

[37] Ivanova N.V., Rogovin Z.A., Nguen Vin-chi // Izvestia Vuzov. *Chenistry and Chemical Technology*. 1965. V. 8. No. 1, p. 124.

[38] Tseitlin A.G.. Kononov G.N. // Nauchn. Tr of Moscow Wood Tech. Institute. 1990. No. 230, p. 112.

[39] Rogovin Z.A.. The Chemistry of Cellulose. Moscow: *Khimiya,* 1972. 520 pages.

[40] Sletkina A.S., Rogovin Z.A. // *Tekstil. Prom.* 1967. No.8, p. 62.

[41] Grigoryan R., Rogovin Z.A. // *Izvestia Vuzov. Techn. of Textile Industry*. 1967. No. 4, p. 110.

[42] Olekhanovich F.M., Kazanskaya S.Yu., Vikhrov Yu.V. // The Talk at All-Union Conf. 'Modification of Wood'. Minsk, 1990, p. 98.

[43] Sangalov Yu.A., Ilyasova A.I., Antonova N.E. // *Bashk. Khim. Zhur.* 1994. Vol. 1. No. 3, p.22.

[44] Khrulyov V.M., Gorety V.V., Galtsova E.A.. // *Izvestia Vuzov. Construction and Architecture*. 1988. No. 12, p. 63.

[45] Sangalov Yu.V.. // *Vestnik ASci.RB* (Ufa). 2001. V. 6. No. 1, p. 26.

[46] Sangalov Yu.A., Dmitriev Yu.K., Lakeyev S.N., Maidanova I.O., Karchevsky S.G. // *Vestnik of Bashk.* State University (Ufa). 2004. No.2, p. 31.

[47] USSR Inventor's Certificate No.1782737 // *Bull.Izobr.* No. 47. 1992.

[48] Potekha V.L., Nevzorova A.v. Investigation of Tribotech. Charact. Of Compos. Mat. Based on Wood and Oligoorganosil. Liquids. Depos. In *ONIITECH*. Cherkassy. No. 944-XII 80.1989.

[49] Sangalov Yu.A., Ilyasova A.I.. *Alloying of Polymers Preprint BSC UrO RAS.*Ufa, 1992. 55 pages.

[50] Bezruk L.I., Khoreva G.B. // *Compos. Polym. Materials.* 1982. Issue 12, p. 39.

[51] Tsyvin M.M., Kotsev S.G., Shmakov I.V. The Poduction of Wood Flour. Moscow: *VNIPIEIlesprom,* 1977. 38 pages.

[52] I.M. Fridman, A.Ya. Dirks. The Production of Wood Flour. Moscow: *VNIPIEIlesprom,* 1972. 42 pages.

[53] Sangalov Yu.A., Yakovlev V.V. // *Plast. Massy.* 1997. No. 4, p.35.

[54] Sangalov Yu.A., Ilyasova A.I., Yakovlev V.V. // Collection of Sci. Articles 'Building Materials Based on Raw Material Resources of the RB'. Ufa. *Bashniistroy.* 1998, p 105.

[55] Modification of Wood // *Proc. All-Union Conf.* Minsk. 1990. 125 pages.

[56] The Modifying and Protective Treating of Wood. // *Proc. All-Union Sci. and Techn. Conference.* Krasnoyarsk. 1989. V. 1. 166 pages; Vl. 2. 77 pages.

[57] USSR Inventor's Certificate No.9394978 // *Bull.Izobr.* No. 24 1982.

[58] Tanner Yu.A., Nikitchenko L.A.. // *Tr. Tallin Polytech.* Institute, 1988. No. 677, p.60.

[59] Korotayev E.M., Simonov V.I.. The Production of Building Materials from Wood Wastes. Moscow: *Lesnaya Prom.,* 1972. 144 pages.

[60] The Secondary Material Resources of Forest and Woodworking Industries. Handbook. Moscow: *Ekonomika,* 1983. 224 pages.

[61] Mikhailov G.M., Serov I.A., The Ways to Improve the Utilization of Secondary Wood Raw Materials. Moscow: *Lesnaya Prom,* , 1988. 224 pages

[62] Nanazashvili I.Kh. Building Materials, Items and Structures. Handbook. Moscow: *Vysshaya Shkola,* 1990. 495 pages.

[63] USSR Inventor's Certificate No.1534031 // *Bull.Izobr.* No.1 1990.

[64] USSR Inventor's Certificate No.1574572 // *Bull.Izobr.* No.24 1990.

[65] USSR Inventor's Certificate No.1560518 // *Bull.Izobr.* No.16 1990.

[66] USSR Inventor's Certificate No.1675268 // *Bull.Izobr.* No.33 1991.

[67] USSR Inventor's Certificate No.1682341 // *Bull.Izobr.* No.37 1991.

[68] USSR Inventor's Certificate No.1204598 // *Bull.Izobr.* No.2 1986.

[69] USSR Inventor's Certificate No.1386606 // *Bull.Izobr.* No.13 1988.

[70] Russ. Patent No. 2001030 // *Bull.Izobr.* No. 37-38 1993.

[71] USSR Inventor's Certificate No.1813757 // *Bull.Izobr.* No.17 1993.

[72] . Russ. Patent No. 2017699 // *Bull.Izobr.* No. 15 1994.

[73] Sychyov M.M.. *Inorganic Glues.* Leningrad: Khimiya, 1986. 152 pages.

[74] Nikolayev A.F.. *The Technology of Plastics.* Leningrad:Khimiya, 1977. 368 pages.

[75] Slab Materials and Items Made of Wood and Vegetable Remains Lignified without Adding Binding Agents / Edited by Prof. I.V. Petri. Moscow: Lesnaya Prom., 1976. 360 pages.

[76] Japanese Requisition No. 56-92715 // *R.Zh.Ch.* 1984 7T 1147 П.

[77] FRG Requisition No. 2849808 // *R.Zh.Ch.* 1981 6T 130 П.

[78] Babina M.D., Vilshansky A.I., Kuzmin V.G. // *Collection of Works by All-Union Research and Design Institute for Polymeric Building Materials.* 1981. No. 55, p. 65.

[79] Hirabayashi // *J. Appl. Polym. Sci.* 1989. Vol. 37. No. 8, p.2283.

[80] USSR Inventor's Certificate No.787435 // *Bull.Izobr.* No.46 1980.

[81] USSR Inventor's Certificate No.1131856 // *Bull.Izobr.* No.48 1984.

[82] USSR Inventor's Certificate No.1638137 // *Bull.Izobr.* No.12 1991.

[83] Khozin V.G., Abdrakhmanova L.A. // *Proc. 7th International Conf. on the Chemitsry and Phys.Chem. of Oligomers 'Oligomers 2000'.* Moscow – Perm – Chernogolovka, 2000, p. 14.

[84] Pavlova S.I., Belotskaya L.M., Yekimenko N.A. // Proc. All-Union Conf. '*The Ecology of the Production and Appl. of Plastics'.* Leningrad, 1989,p. 84.

[85] Russ. Patent No. 2098438 // *Bull.Izobr.* No. 34 1997.

[86] Russ. Patent No. 2078104 // *Bull.Izobr.* No. 12 1997.

[87] Zhyrnov A.R., Lukasik V.N., Subbotin V.Ye. // *Proc. Conf. On Neutr. and Util. of Solid Wastes'.* Penza, 1991, p. 47.

[88] USSR Inventor's Certificate No.1618659 // *Bull.Izobr.* No.1 1991.

[89] USSR Inventor's Certificate No.2017770 // *Bull.Izobr.* No.15 1994..

[90] French Requisition No. 2608961 // *R.Zh.Ch.* 19891 76T 252130 П.

[91] *Chem. Eng.* 1994. V.101. No. 9, p. 21.

[92] Mori M., Saltoh M. // *Wood Ind.* 1981. V.36. No. 6, p. 278.

[93] *Phenol Resins. Catalogue.* Cherkassy, 1985. 34 p.

[94] Menters G.Ya., Vatulev V.P., Magdints V.V. // *Compos. Polym. Mater.* 1991. No. 50, p.82.

[95] Yokoyama M. // *Gyps and Lime.* 1993. No. 246, p. 272.

[96] Volfson S.A. // *Plast. Massy.* 1999. No. 4, p.6.

[97] Encyclopedia of Polymers. Moscow: *Sovetskaya Entsyklopedia,* 1974. V. 2, p. 344.

[98] Vigdorovich A.I., Yefremov V.N.. // *Plast. Massy.* 1997. No. 3, p. 30.

[99] Japanese Requisition No. 58-14393 // *R.Zh.Ch.* 1984 19T 1115 П.

[100] Lukasik V.A., Zhyrnov A.G., Antsupov Yu.A. // *Plast. Massy.* 2000. No. 7, p. 39.

[101] Mamunya Ye.P., Mishak V.D., Lebedev Ye.V. // *Plast. Massy.* 1989. No. 8, p. 39.

[102] Tikhonov N.N. // *Plast, Massy.* 2000. No. 9, p. 41.

[103] Athanasova N. // *Plaste und Kautsch.* 1982. V. 29. No. 9, p. 537.

[104] Mamunya Ye.A., Mishak V.D., Shumsky V.F. // *Vysokomol. Soed.* 1991. B. 33. No. 11, p. 839.

[105] Vigdorovich A.I. // *Plast. Massy.* 1985. No. 11, p. 44.

[106] Borovikov A.M. Handbook on Wood. Moscow. 1989. 296 p.

[107] Maiti S.N., Hassan M.R. // *J. Appl. Polym. Sci.* 1989. V. 37. No. 7, 2019.

[108] French Requisition No. 2471274 // *R.Zh.Ch.* 1988 24T 29 П.

[109] US Patent No. 4687799 // *R.Zh.Ch.* 1988 10T 30 П.

[110] French Requisition No. 2602513 // *R.Zh.Ch.* 1988 24T 29 П.

[111] USSR Inventor's Certificate No. 1694598 // *Bull. Izobr.* No. 44 1991.

[112] US Patent No. 4165302 // *R.Zh.Ch.* 1980 2T 87 П.

[113] USSR Inventor's Certificate No. 1574566 // *Bull. Izobr.* No. 24 1990.

[114] Armer S.S.,Silochenko M.A., Mironov N.A. // *Proc. 5 all-USSR Conf. on Cem. and Phys. of Cellulose.* Tashkent, 1982, p. 61.

[115] Mamunya Ye.P., Mishak V.D., Semenovich G.D. // *vysokomol Soed.* 1994. V. A36. No. 8, p. 1359.

[116] Kaplan A.M., Koritsky A.T., Nikolsry V.G. // *Ross. Khim. Zhur.* 1993. V. 37. No. 4, p. 115.

[117] Melnik I.P., Lebedev Ye.V., Anenkov V.F. // *Plast. Massy.* 1987. No. 6, p. 54.

[118] Anenkov V.F., Lebedev Ye.V., Mamunya Ye.P. // *Mat.Sci.Tech.Sem.* 'Processing of polimer wastes and protection of environment'. Leningrad, 1988, p. 62.
[119] USSR Inventor's Certificate No. 2016022 // *Bull. Izobr.* No. 13 1994.
[120] Dechev A.G., Atanasova I.D. *Plast. Massy.* 1979. No. 11, p. 7.
[121] Vigdorovich A.A., Vigdorovich A.I. // *Plast. Massy.* 1991. No. 2, p. 29.
[122] Bagayev S.I., Abramochkin E.S., Kotenina Ye.N. // *Proc. VI International Conf. on Sci. Chem.Technol.* Moscow, 1999, p. 286.
[123] USSR Inventor's Certificate No. 1818233 // *Bull. Izobr.* No. 20 1993.
[124] Salakhova G.L., Sopin V.F., Budarina L.A. // *Proc. Interrepubl. USSR Stud. Conf. 'Synth., Investing. Of Prop.,Modif. and Process. of High-Mol. Compounds'.* Kazan, 1991, p. 128.
[125] Lightsey G.R. Polym. *Appl. Renewable – Resour. Mater. Proc. Sump. Use Renewable Resour. Mater. Coat and Plast.* New-York, London. 1983, p. 193.
[126] Sain M.M., Kokta B.V., Imbart C. // *Polym. Plast. Technol. and Eng.* 1994, V. 33. No. 1, p. 89.
[127] Amer. Inst. Chem. Eng.Spring Naf. Meet. Extend Abstrm New-York. 1992, p. 33.
[128] Stalnova I.O., Teleshov A.V., Shnyrev V.A. // *Proc. all-Union Conf. 'Chem., Technol. and Appl. of Cellul. and its Derivat.'* Vladimir, 1985, p. 21.
[129] Xantos M. // *Plast. and Rubber Process and Appl.* 1983. V. 3, p.223.
[130] USSR Inventor's Certificate No. 979427 // *Bull. Izobr.* No. 45 1982.
[131] Kishi H., Yoshioko M., Yamanoi A. et al // *J. Jap, Wood, Res Soc.* 1988. V.34. no. 2, p. 268.
[132] Jap. Requisition No. 61-97593 // *R.Zh.Ch.* 1988 18T 32 П.
[133] Jap. Requisition No. 58-92101 // *R.Zh.Ch.* 1986 3T 136 П.
[134] USSR Inventor's Certificate No. 1100288 // *Bull. Izobr.* No. 24 1984.
[135] *Polym. News.* 1988.V, 13. No. 11, p. 331.
[136] Maldas D., Kokta B.V., Rai R.G. // *Polymer* 1988. V. 29. No.7, p. 1255.
[137] Gamova I. A., Vikhrova V.N., Kashchenko I.A. // *Chem. and Mechan. Process. of Wood and Wood Wastes.* Leningrad. 1981. V. 7, p. 65.
[138] P.R. Bulgar. Inventor's Certificate No. 41567 // *R.Zh.Ch,* 1990 1T 63 П.
[139] USSR Inventor's Certificate No. 1224319 // *Bull. Izobr.* No. 14 1986.
[140] Natow.M., Waddileva S., Georgijew W. // *Plaste und Kautsch.* 1982. V. 29. No. 5, p. 277.
[141] USSR Inventor's Certificate No. 1052519 // *Bull. Izobr.* No. 41 1983.
[142] Jap. Requisition No. 54-65748 // *R.Zh.Ch.* 1980 4T 237 П.
[143] USSR Inventor's Certificate No. 1705317 // *Bull. Izobr.* No. 11 1992.
[144] Yezhov V.S,, Morzhukhin V.B., Kozlov I.I. *Plast. Massy.* 1988. No.7, p. 12.
[145] Sangalov Yu.A., Krasulina N.A., Ilyasova A.I. // *Proc. Internat. Sci. Tech.Conf. 'Polymer Composites'.* Gomel. 1998, p. 115.
[146] Sangalov Yu.A., Krasulina N.A., Ilyasova A.I. // *Russian Polymer News.* 2001. V. 6. No. 2, p. 38.
[147] Sangalov Yu.A., Krasulina N.A., Turyanov R. A. // *Proc. XVI Mendeleev Congr. on Gener. and Appl. Chem.* Moscow. 1998, p. 224.
[148] Sangalov Yu.A., Ilyasova A.I., Ismagilov F.R., Krasulina N.A. // *Proc. Internat. Sci.Pract. Conf. 425th Annivers. of Ufa. Ufa.* 1999, p. 57.

[149] Labutin A.P. Anti-corr. and Seal. Mater. Based on Synth. Rubbers. Leningrad. Khimiya. 1982. 213 pages.
[150] Russ. Patent No. 2144554 // Bull.Izobr. No. 2 2000.
[151] USSR Inventor's Certificate No. 1579910 // Bull. Izobr. No. 27 1990.
[152] Plotnikova T.N., Magdalin A.A., Khrulyov V.M. // *Ivestiya Vuzov. Construction.* 1994. No. 5-6, p. 56.
[153] USSR Inventor's Certificate No. 1509475 // *Bull. Izobr.* No. 35 1989.
[154] USSR Inventor's Certificate No. 1509476 // *Bull. Izobr.* No. 35 1989.
[155] USSR Inventor's Certificate No. 2005760 // *Bull. Izobr.* No. 1 1994.
[156] Jap. Requisition No. 61-233061 // *R.Zh.Ch.* 1987 1T 19 П.
[157] Jap. Requisition No. 54-29367 // *R.Zh.Ch.* 1980 9T 280 П.
[158] FRG. Requisition No. 2757258 // *R.Zh.Ch.* 1980 11T 107 П.
[159] Gubkin V.I., Kovalyova Z.G., Melnikov S.F. // *Plast. Massy.* 1991. No. 2, p. 47.
[160] Jap. Requisition No. 54-12524 // *R.Zh.Ch.* 1980 12T 12 П.
[161] Jap. Requisition No. 55-94916 // *R.Zh.Ch.* 1981 17T 123 П.
[162] Thomas G., Rogers D.K., Woodhams R.T. 'Antec 84 Plast. World Econ. 42nd Techn. Conf. and Exhib., New Orleans 1984; *Proc. 'Brookfild Conn.* 1984. p, 687.
[163] Korilup O.A., Romanov N.M., Manazashvilli Ch. Kh. // *Building Materials.* 1997. No. 5, p.8.
[164] Balakin V.M., Korshunova N.I., Zhurko G.O. // *Proc. II Meeting 'Wood Chem. And Organic Synth.' Syktyvkar,* 1996, p. 84.
[165] Lubeshkina Ye.G., GulV.Ye. // *Plast. Massy.* 1991. No. 2, p. 3.
[166] Galimov E.R., Nizamov R.K., Yevdokimov I.V. // *Plast. Massy.* 1989. No. 4, p.58.
[167] Galimov E.R., Nizamov R.K., Yevdokimov I.V. // *Plast. Massy.* 1989. No. 6, p.91.
[168] Chudinov S.V., Trofimov A,N., Uzlov G.A. *Handbook of Wood Chemist.* Moscow. Lesnaya Prom. 1987. 272 pages.
[169] Sangalov Yu.A., Krasulina N.A., Ilyasova A.I. // *Khim. Prom.*. 2002. No. 3, p. 34.
[170] Pervushin Yu.S., Sangalov Yu.A. // *Vestnik AsciRB* (Ufa) 2003. V. 8. No. 3, p. 3.
[171] Sangalov Yu.A., Krasulina N.A., Ilyasova A.I. // *Plast Massy.* 2001. No. 7, p. 34.
[172] Sangalov Yu.A., Ilyasova A.I., Krasulina N.A., Turyanov. R.A., Miftakhov A.A. // *Khim. Prom.* 2001. No. 12, p. 46.

In: Synthesis and Properties of Low- and High-Molecular Compounds ISBN 1-59454-716-5
Editor: Gennady E. Zaikov et al., pp. 27-47

Chapter 2

MECHANISM OF HCL ELIMINATION REACTIONS VIA A FOUR-CENTER TRANSITION STATE DURING PVC THERMAL DESTRUCTION

V. M. Yanborisov*, K. S. Minsker and S. S. Borisevich
Bashkir State University; 32 Frunze STR. 450074 Ufa Russia

ABSTRACT

Reactions of initiation and propagation of polyenyl chloride sequences in PVC macromolecules, which do not contain defect groups, have been considered. Thermodynamical parameters of dehydrochlorination reaction of low-molecular substances, which model PVC macromolecular sections with various tacticities, were calculated via four-center unimolecular mechanism. Dehydrochlorination of syndiotactic and izotactic sections ~(CH_2-CHCl)~ proceeds with identical reaction rate forming mainly *trans*- and *cis*-isomers of β-chloroallylic groups, accordingly. The reaction rate of HCl elimination from β-chloroallylic groups is higher than the one of ordinary monomer units. Further dehydrochlorination of polyenyl chloride structures proceeds faster than HCl elimination from β-chloroallylic groups. Thus initiation step of PVC dehydrochlorination is combination of two consecutive reactions: 1) the HCl elimination from ordinary monomer units with β-chloroallylic groups formation; 2) the further dehydrochlorination of β-chloroallylic groups with chlorodienes formation. Tacticity of macromolecules insignificantly influences the rate of initiation and propagation reactions when PVC dehydrochlorination is taking place.

INTRODUCTION

Poly(vinyl chloride) is unique because HCl is the only volatile product of PVC destruction [1] obtained as a results of a number of parallel-sequential reactions of

* Valery M. Yanborisov; Chemical Department; Bashkir State University; 32 Frunze STR. 450074 Ufa Russia; tel. +7 (3472) 23-67-27; e-mail: YanborisovVM@mail.ru

dehydrochlorination of macromolecules [2]. The mechanism of these reactions can differ very much depending upon conditions. Ionic mechanism is most probably realized during PVC destruction in solutions; dehydrochlorination reactions take place in solid PVC degradation and run according to the concerted molecular or radical mechanism [2-5]. The following two cases must be distinguished: when heated above 200 °C the radicals are discovered experimentally [3] and dehydrochlorination reactions obviously run according to radical mechanism; when heated up to 180-190 °C they are likely to run according to concerted molecular mechanism. It has been shown earlier [6], that experimental investigation of solid PVC destruction proves to be correct up to 180 °C because in this case no other reaction mechanism but molecular one takes place, and besides one can escape HCl catalyze effect because of powder polymer sintering. So, the research of PVC dehydrochlorination reaction mechanism should logically be started with the more “clear” case i.e. powder polymer degradation at comparatively low temperatures. This process is called thermal PVC degradation.

Naturally there is a question to be asked: why does in spite of long-term studies of PVC destruction and rather successful results concerning its stabilization, one have to come back to reaction mechanisms? The point is that it is difficult enough to prove anything experimentally in this particular case. So one has to use indirect indices such as radical identification [3] or effect of solvent basicity [7, 8]. That’s why the schemes of PVC destruction mechanism were offered a priori. As for theoretical quantum chemical calculation methods, they were used long ago. We can mention a paper [9] where thermal stability of different groups in PVC macromolecules was estimated according to static index reaction ability and a series of papers [4, 10-14] where activation energies of different groups in various mechanisms were calculated with the help of semi-empirical quantum chemical method. But now when power capacity of computers has increased enormously the investigations of PVC destruction mechanism are carried out at a much higher level of quantum-mechanical theory. Nowadays computers are powerful enough to definite PVC dehydrochlorination reactions mechanism at non-empirical theory level within a reasonable computation period of time using wide enough basis sets, perturbation theory and taking into account electronic correlation, in particular.

Basic dehydrochlorination reactions proceeding at poly(vinyl chloride) heating have been known for a long time already [1, 2]. They are reaction of polyene sequences initiation and growth. Initiation can occur at dehydrochlorination of abnormal groups, which differ from ordinary monomer units and are contained in PVC macromolecules. Once there were animated and heating discussions on their chemical structure and presence in PVC [2, 6]. However there are reactions, which run in all samples without exception, irrespective of concentration of abnormal groups in PVC [15]:

- Chloride hydrogen is eliminated from ordinary PVC chain units (random-law) to form *β*-chloroallylic groups with reaction rate constant $k_r \approx 10^{-7}$ sec^{-1} (448 K):

$$\sim CH_2 - CHCl - CH_2 - CHCl \sim \xrightarrow[-HCl]{k_r} \sim CH_2 - CH = CH - CHCl \sim$$

- *β*-Chloroallylic groups dehydrochlorinate to obtain diene structure with $k_\beta \approx 10^{-4}$ sec^{-1} (448 K):

$$\sim CH_2 - CH = CH - CHCl - CH_2 - CHCl \sim \xrightarrow[-HCl]{k_\beta} \sim CH_2 - CH = CH - CH = CH - CHCl \sim$$

– HCl is eliminated from chlorodiene groups with $k_p \approx 10^{-2}c^{-1}$ (448 K) to form conjugated polyenyl chloride sequence and their further dehydrochlorination is accompanied by the growth of conjugation length:

$$\sim CH_2 - (CH = CH)_n - CHCl - CH_2 - CHCl \sim \xrightarrow[-HCl]{k_p} \sim CH_2 - (CH = CH)_{n+1} - CHCl \sim \xrightarrow[-HCl]{k_p} ...$$

The process of fast consecutive elimination of chloride hydrogen along macromolecule is called "zipper" reaction, sometimes [4, 10, 16].

In the authors' opinion [4, 10-14], dehydrochlorination reaction of ordinary monomer units 1 (scheme 1) runs via four-center molecular mechanism to form *β*-chloroallylic group 2 or 3 with activation energy equal to 210 kJ/mol. It is supposed that HCl diffuses from the next macromolecular and can catalyze this reaction. Thus the activation energy calculated by semi-empirical method is equal to 34 kJ/mol [4]. As the activation energy of initiation reaction found experimentally is equal to 140 kJ/mol [4], the authors assume, that simultaneous run of both reactions is probably possible in the real polymer.

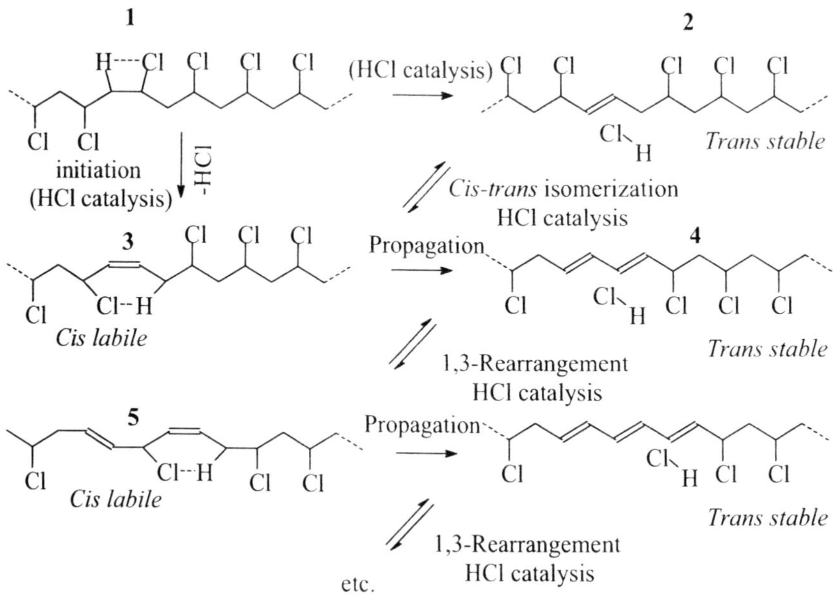

Scheme 1. Mechanism of PVC thermal destruction [4]; (HCl catalysis) - means that reaction can run both with are without chloride hydrogen catalysis.

As the authors consider [4, 10, 11] further dehydrochlorination depends upon isomer of *β*- chloroallylic group. The process of destruction stops, if the ordinary unit of macromolecular eliminates HCl to form stable *trans*- structure 2 [4]. If *cis*-structure 3 is formed, polyene sequence continues to grow. The labile *cis*-group 3 can also be formed from trans-group 4 via *cis-trans* isomerization. This process is catalyzed by HCl, which has not yet left the zone of reaction.

HCl elimination from *cis*-isomer of *β*-chloroallylic groups 3 can run via six-center transition state to form stable *trans*-diene structure 4 and activation energy of this reaction is equal to 110 kJ/mol. Further dehydrochlorination of structure 4 occurs after 1,3-chlorin shift [18]. This reaction is necessary to form labile *cis*-form 5. It is considered that reaction of 1,3-chlorin shifts can proceed only in the presence of HCl molecule. The process of dehydrochlorination of *trans*-isomer of polyenyl chloride structures practically stops if HCl molecule leaves the reactionary center [4].

Bacaloglu and Fisch [4] have estimated thermodynamical parameters of dehydrochlorination reaction of allylic chlorides in gas phase and have assumed that *cis*-allylic chlorides eliminate HCl faster than its trans-forms.

Dehydrochlorination reactions of 6-chloro-4-tetradecene and 4-chloro-5-tetradecene mixtures were investigated at 150 °C [17]. It is considered that 1,3-chlorine shift and *cis-trans* isomerization reaction of *trans*-structure proceed faster than its dehydrochlorination [17]. Thus it has been concluded that those *trans*-structures are more stable than *cis*-structures.

By scheme 1 Bacaloglu and Fisch explained formation of set of polyene sequences with different lengths of conjugation in destructed PVC and interruption HCl elimination.

However, Starnes [5, 18] subjected the above-mention conception of PVC dehydrochlorination assumed by Bacaloglu and Fisch to serious criticism.

For example, Starnes and his co-authors disagree that dehydrochlorination can proceed via six-center transition state [18]. They have considered destruction reactions of the following substances: 5-Chloro-6-decene and 4-Chloro-6-tridecene. As a result of their researches it is revealed, that the second substance is more stable than the first one. Reaction of dehydrochlorination of 5-Chloro-6-decene runs via four-center mechanism. 1,3-rearranges of hydrogen atom for 5-Chloro-6-tridecene formations are necessary to eliminate of HCl from 4-Chloro-6-tridecene. According to the authors, this process is slower than the destruction itself. If reaction of 1,3-chlorine shifts in 5-Chloro-6-decene proceeds, its rate is much faster than the rate of destruction of this substance. However further elimination also occurs within a four-center transition state. Having investigated the products of dehydrochlorination of 5-Chloro-6-decene and 4-Chloro-6-tridecene mixture under different conditions the authors of the article [17] have come to the above mentioned conclusions.

Starnes states [5] that in liquid phase negative activation entropy of dehydrochlorination reaction of chloroalkanes calculated in paper [12] shows that the process would proceed via four-center transition state. It is also claimed that in liquid phase the dehydrochlorination reaction rates of trans- and cis-chloroalkenes do not differ from each other.

Moreover, Starnes interpreted the experimental results described in paper [17] and came to quite opposite conclusion, that its authors did. He considers that dehydrochlorination occurs from *trans*- and *cis*-forms of 6-chloro-4-tetradecene and 4-chloro-5-tetradecene, i.e. structure 2 should dehydrochlorinate via four-center transition state forming diene structure faster, than convert into *cis*-form.

From our point of view the scheme 1 offered by Bacaloglu and Fisch suffers from the following shortcomings. First and foremost there are no defective labile groupings in the scheme. In the authors' opinion, they do not influence destruction process, and low thermostability of PVC is characteristic even of ideal polymer [10]. According to their point of view, all probable samples of PVC should have identical thermostability. However it is determined, that the dehydrochlorination reaction rate of different PVC samples can differ 3-4 fold [1]. Second, different thermal stabilities of chloroalkenes and chlorodienes are not taken into account. If dehydrochlorination proceeds via four-center molecular mechanism, the rate constants (normalized to 448 K) of chloroalkenes dehydrochlorination are smaller by 2-3 orders of magnitude than the reaction rate constant of HCl elimination from chlorodienes (table 1, # 29-33, 41, 42). If six-center molecular mechanism prevails, the values of reaction rate constant of HCl elimination from chloroalkenes are higher by 6-7 orders of magnitude (table 1, # 34-40), than in the cases when chloroalkenes are dehydrochlorinated via four-center transition state. *Cis*-isomers of chloroalkenes are much labile than *trans*-isomers, and dehydrochlorination of cis-chloroalkenes runs much faster via six-center transition state [4]. It is also necessary to note that in the liquid phase chlorodienes are dehydrochlorinated faster than chloroalkenes [28]. Third, comparison of the calculated activation energy with experimentally determined data is not correct because of the presence of compensatory effect, which consists in coordinated change of activation energy and preexponential multiplier. In paper [6] this effect has been found when studying experimental data on dehydrochlorination of low-molecular chlorine-containing compounds and groups in macromolecules of polymers that is in a liquid (condensate) phase. In the given paper selection of experimental data on destruction reaction in a gas phase also confirms the presence of compensatory effect (fig. 1). Therefore it is more logical to be guided directly by values of elimination reaction rate constant of chloride hydrogen at 448 K.

The purpose of the present paper is to calculate thermodynamic parameters and to estimate the rate of elimination reaction of chloride hydrogen from low-molecular analogues of groups participating in reactions (1-3): chloroalkanes, which model from one to three ordinary monomer units; various chloroalkenes, and also groups with conjugate double bonds.

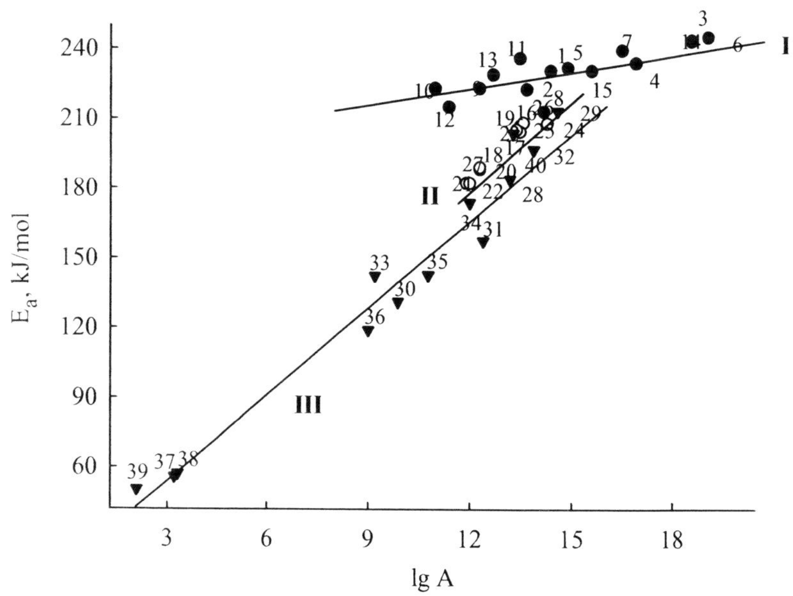

Figure 1. Compensatory effect of dehydrochlorination reaction. I – primary chloroalkanes (r = 0.82), II – secondary chloroalkanes (r = 0.94) and III – chloroalkenes (r= 0.98) in a gas phase. The numbers of points correspond to the numbers of the substances in table 1.

Table 1. Parameters of dehydrochlorination reaction of primary and secondary chloroalkanes and chloroalkenes in gas phase. *lg A* is logarithm exponential multiplier, E_a is activation energy, *k* is reaction rate constant

	#	Compound	*lg A*	E_a, kJ/mol	*k*, sec^{-1} (448 K)	References
Primary chloroalkanes	1	1-chloropropane	14.2	231.2	$3.2\cdot10^{-14}$	[4]
	2		14.4	230.8	$4.0\cdot10^{-14}$	[19]
	3	1-chlorobutane	18.6	243.4	$1.4\cdot10^{-14}$	[20]
	4		16.5	239.6	$1.2\cdot10^{-14}$	[4]
	5		14.9	232.0	$3.9\cdot10^{-14}$	[20]
	6	1-chloropentane	19.1	245.1	$1.1\cdot10^{-14}$	[21]
	7	1-chlorodecane	16.9	234.1	$6.5\cdot10^{-14}$	[22]
	8	1,2-dichloroetane	11.4	215.2	$5.2\cdot10^{-13}$	[4]
	9	1,2-dichloropropane	12.3	223.2	$9.8\cdot10^{-14}$	[23]
	10		11.0	223.2	$4.8\cdot10^{-14}$	[23]
	11		13.5	236.2	$5.8\cdot10^{-15}$	[23]
	12		12.7	229.1	$2.5\cdot10^{-14}$	[23]
	13		15.6	230.8	$8.0\cdot10^{-14}$	[4]
	14	1,6-Dichlorohexane	18.6	243.8	$1.2\cdot10^{-14}$	[22]
	15	1,10-Dichlorodecane	13.7	222.8	$2.4\cdot10^{-13}$	[22]
Secondary chloroalkanes	16	2-Chlorobutane	13.5	207.2	$2.1\cdot10^{-11}$	[24]
	17		13.6	208.5	$2.1\cdot10^{-11}$	[25]
	18	3-Chloropentane	12.3	188.3	$1.8\cdot10^{-10}$	[22]
	19	2-Chlorooctane	13.5	204.7	$4.7\cdot10^{-11}$	[26]
	20	3-Chlorodecane	12.3	188.3	$1.7\cdot10^{-10}$	[22]
	21	4-Chlorodecane	11.9	182.4	$4.7\cdot10^{-10}$	[22]
	22	4-Chlorododecane	12.0	182.4	$4.8\cdot10^{-10}$	[22]
	23	2,4-Dichloropentane	13.4	205.5	$2.6\cdot10^{-11}$	[24]
	24		15.3	296.3	$5.1\cdot10^{-20}$	[27]
	25	5,7-Dichlorodecane	14.3	208.1	$1.0\cdot10^{-10}$	[22]
	26	5,7-Dichlorododecane	14.3	208.1	$1.1\cdot10^{-10}$	[22]
	27	1,4,7-Trichlorodecane	12.3	189.2	$1.8\cdot10^{-10}$	[28]
Chloroalkenes	28	3-Chloro-1-butene	13.3	203.9	$3.8\cdot10^{-11}$	[29]
	29	3-Chloro-1-pentene	14.6	213.5	$5.2\cdot10^{-11}$	[24]
	30		9.2	142.5	$3.0\cdot10^{-8}$	[30]
	31	*trans*-4-Chloro-2-pentene	12.0	174.0	$5.5\cdot10^{-9}$	[24]
	32		13.9	196.8	$8.2\cdot10^{-10}$	[30]
	33	*cis*-4-Chloro-2-pentene	9.9	131.3	$3.5\cdot10^{-6}$	[30]
	34		12.4	157.6	$1.1\cdot10^{-6}$	[31]
	35	2-Chloro-4-hexen	10.8	142.9	$1.2\cdot10^{-6}$	[22]
	36		9.0	119.1	$1.3\cdot10^{-5}$	[34]
	37		3.2	55.9	$4.4\cdot10^{-4}$	[32]
	38		3.3	57.2	$4.4\cdot10^{-4}$	[28]
	39		2.1	50.4	$1.6\cdot10^{-4}$	[33]
	40	*trans*-5-Chloro-3-heptene	13.2	184.1	$5.5\cdot10^{-9}$	[30]
Chlorodiene	41	6-Chloro-2,4-heptadiene	10.4	144.3	$2.9\cdot10^{-7}$	[24]

CALCULATION METHODS

For testing various methods of quantum-chemical calculations using different basic sets of atomic orbitals it is necessary to choose a low-molecular analogue as an object, which reflects basic characteristics of the unit of PVC macromolecule ~(CH_2-CHCl)~. At the same time this model must have the least possible amount of atoms to save calculation time. 1-Chloropropane and 2-Chlorobutane have been chosen for the test as the smallest objects of PVC chain sections. Subsequent increase of the amount of carbon atoms, first, is accompanied by the increase of the number of orbitals; second (and it is the main thing) by the growth of probable conformers; third, by the opportunity to trace distinctions in stability of primary and secondary chloroalkanes, which have different thermodynamic characteristics of destruction reaction (table 1): primary chloroalkanes decay essentially more slowly. Further calculations of molecules of greater size simulating two, three or even four units of PVC macromolecule have proved that our choice of 1-Chloropropane and 2-Chlorobutane as test models is correct.

Semiempirical method (in parameterization AM1) and restricted Hartree-Fock method (RHF) with split-valence basic sets: 3-21G(d), 6-31G(d), 6-31G(d, p) and 6-31G(2d) were used to search for a transition state and to calculate thermodynamic parameters of dehydrochlorination reaction. It was expected that addition of *d*-function to heavy atom and *p*-function to hydrogen atom would result in correspondence with experimental data. Methods, allowing to take electronic correlation into account are the Moller-Plesset perturbation theory of second order (MP2) with basic sets 6-31G(d), 6-31G(d, p), 6-31G(3d, 3p) and B3LYP/6-31G(d), B3LYP/6-31G(2d) methods [35]. They were also applied also for the research of these reactions. Calculations were carried out on a computer Pentium-4 2.6 GHz, 1 Gb.

Semiempirical method (in parameterization AM1) is the fastest - typical time of search for the transition state of test models is about 4 minutes. Most calculation time (≈140 min) is required when applying Moller-Plesset perturbation theory with basic set 6-31G(3d, 3p). Other methods occupy intermediate position within this range.

In spite of important differences in the used methods of calculations, geometrical parameters of the activated complex of dehydrochlorination reaction of 1-Chloropropane are practically identical (table 2). But the structure of the transition state calculated by semiempirical method AM1 differs from others. Dispersion of atomic charges calculated by different quantum-chemical approximation differs from each other. However all calculation methods show that the transition state is strongly polarized. It corresponds to the reported data [5]. However, the values of thermodynamical parameters computed by various methods differ essentially from each other. Calculations by semiempirical method (in parameterization AM1) make the value of activation energy of dehydrochlorination reaction of 1-Chloropropane and 2-Chlorobutane approximately 20 kJ/mol higher and reaction rate constants lower by two orders of magnitude as compared with the experiment (table 2, 3). Similar results were received when calculating by RHF method with basic set 3-21G(d) and when using MP2 with basic sets 6-31G(d) and 6-31G(d, p) (table 2). The use of basic set 6-31G with various amounts of *d*- and *p*-functions gives the best result for 2-Chlorobutane, but in case of 1-Chloropropane overestimating of activation energy and, accordingly, understating of the rate constant are also observed (table 2, 3). The best values of dehydrochlorination reaction activation energy of 1-Chloropropane are received by B3LYP/6-31G(d) and B3LYP/6-31G(2d) method. The difference from the experiment is only 3-7 kJ/mol. The values of rate constants of dehydrochlorination reaction of 1-Chloropropane calculated by these methods are 10 times as high as the experimental ones (table 2, 3). However the tendency of understating activation energy and overstating the rate constant amplifies in case of 2-Chlorobutane (table 2, 3).

If basic set dilates within one approximation (RHF, MP2 or B3LYP) the values of dehydrochlorination reaction activation energy of 1-Chloropropane and 2-Chlorobutane decrease (table 3). However rate constants vary within one order. According to the facts mention above we have chosen three approximations of quantum-chemical calculation for the computation of the objects, which model more than one unit of macromolecule: AM1 semi-empirical method, non-empirical RHF method with split-valence basic sets 6-31G(d) and B3LYP/6-31G(d) method which takes into account electronic correlation. Semi-empirical method, which requires less computation time, has been applied as reconnaissance method.

RESULTS AND DISCUSSION

To analyse elimination reaction of chloride hydrogen from PVC macromolecules we have used models simulating ordinary monomer units of normal structure, β-chloroallylic groups and polyenyl chloride structures. Reactions of HCl elimination from substances, which model from one to three units of various sites of macromolecule (table 4), were considered.

All the methods applied showed that enthalpy ($\Delta_r H^{448}$) of dehydrochlorination reaction of the considered chloroalkanes calculated at 448 K insignificantly but naturally was going down with the increase of the number of atoms of carbon. Absolute values of $\Delta_r H^{448}$, which were calculated by non-empirical methods RHF/6-31G(d) and B3LYP/6-31G(d), proved to be much correct than other ones. No regularities in the change of free activation energy ($\Delta G^{\neq}$) and activation energies (E_a) were observed. Apparently it is the result of entropic factor. Moreover, calculations have shown that there is no principal difference in the destruction of substances that contain one, two or three secondary chlorine atoms. Therefore average values of thermodynamical parameters are given in table 4. Thermodynamical parameters values are approximately identical within the frame of one approximation: dispersion of the received values of activation energy, activation enthalpy and free activation energy is equal to about 2 %, of reaction enthalpy is not above 8 % and of activation entropy is about 24 %. However, we compared experimental data with reaction rate constants, which had been normalized at 448 K, due to compensational effect (fig. 1). The values of dehydrochlorination reaction rate constants of chloroalkanes are practically identical within one approximation (table 4). The reaction rate constants, calculated by AM1 method, are below experimental ones by three orders of magnitude and, calculated by B3LYP/6-31G(d) method, are higher by two orders of magnitude (table 4). The results, calculated with the help of RHF/6-31G(d) method correspond to the reported data: for example, dehydrochlorination reaction rates constant of 2,4-Dichlorohexane is twice as low as its experimental value (fig. 2, table 4).

Table 2. Transition state geometries of dehydrochlorination reaction 1-Chloropropane calculated by various methods, the lengths are expressed in Å, the valence angles – in degree (italic), atomic charges (bond)

Calculation method	AM1	RHF/3-21G(d)	RHF/6-31G(d)	RHF/6-31G(d, p)
Structure of transition state	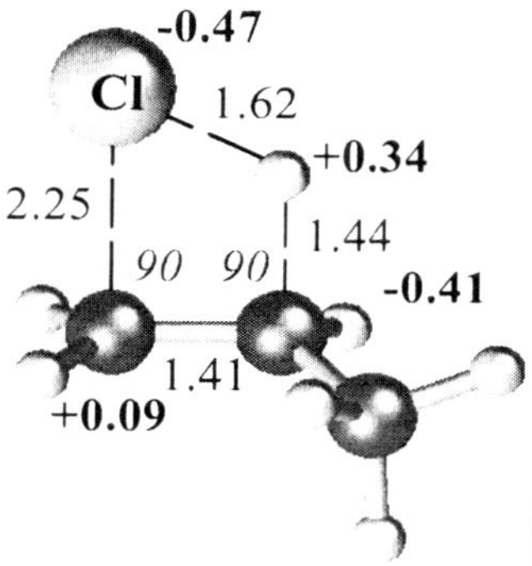	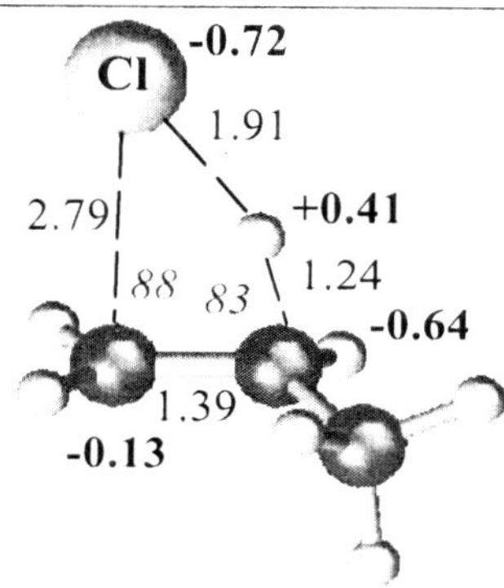	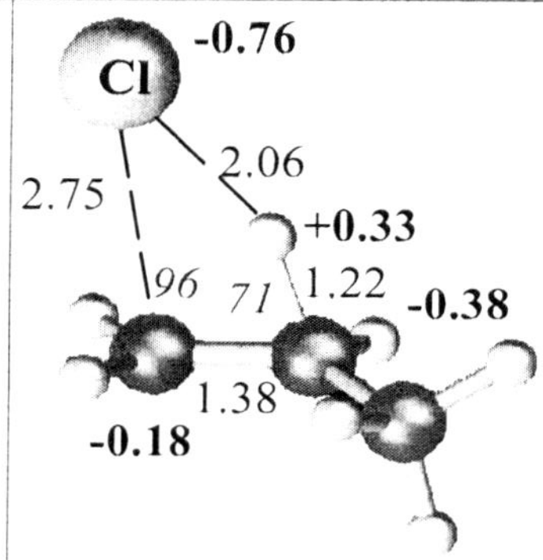	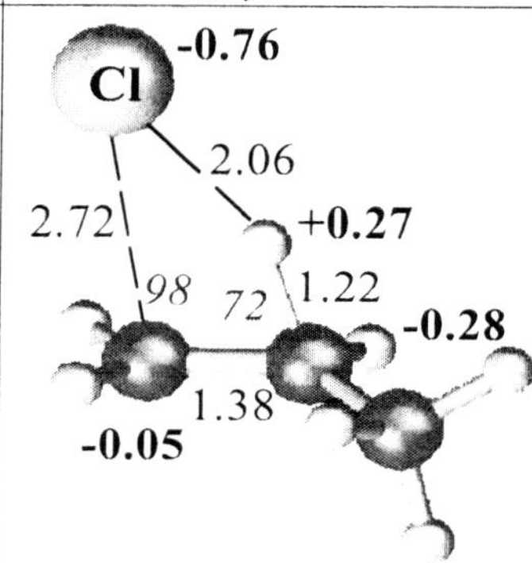
E_a, kJ/mol	251.3	269.8	264.6	257.5
$\Delta H^{\neq}$, kJ/mol	247.5	266.1	260.8	253.8
$\Delta S^{\neq}$, J K^{-1} mol	2.2	13.0	14.9	14.7
k, sec^{-1} (448 K)	$1.7 \cdot 10^{-16}$	$4.2 \cdot 10^{-18}$	$2.2 \cdot 10^{-17}$	$1.4 \cdot 10^{-16}$

Continuation of table 2

Calculation method	RHF/6-31G(2d)	RHF/6-31G(2d, p)	MP2/6-31G(d)	MP2/6-31G(d, p)
Structure of transition state	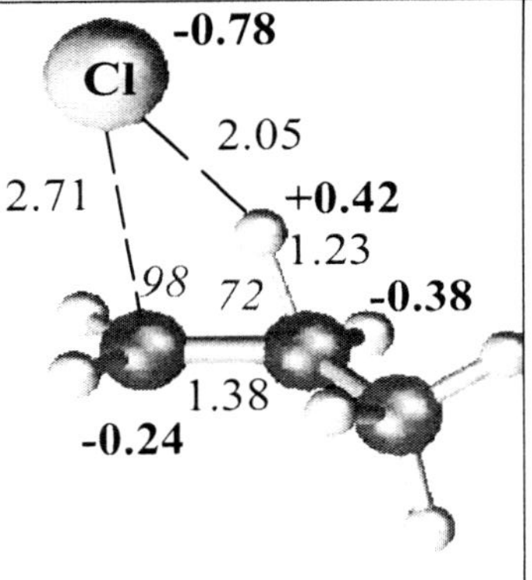	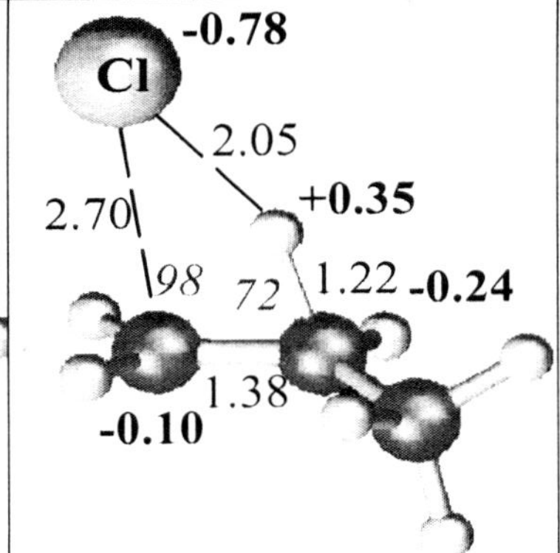	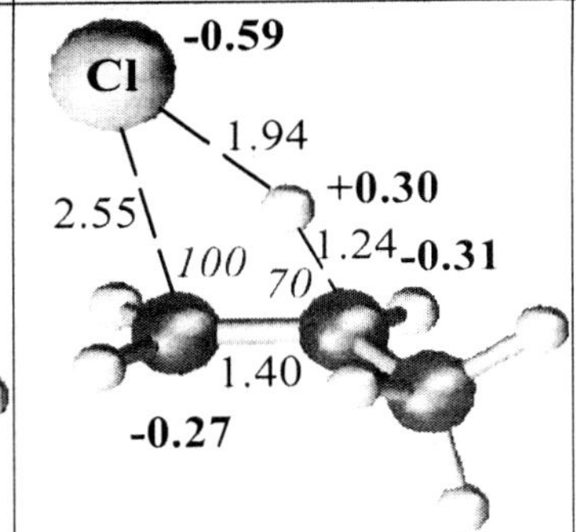	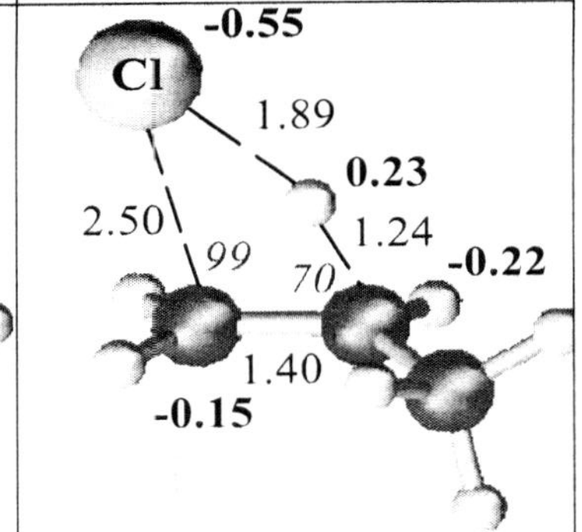
E_a, kJ/mol	256.5	251.4	279.6	274.9
$\Delta H^{\neq}$, kJ/mol	252.8	247.6	275.9	271.2
$\Delta S^{\neq}$, J K^{-1} mol	13.9	13.8	13.0	12.0
k, sec^{-1} (448 K)	$1.7 \cdot 10^{-16}$	$6.6 \cdot 10^{-16}$	$3.0 \cdot 10^{-19}$	$9.5 \cdot 10^{-19}$

Continuation of table 2

Calculation method	MP2/6-31G(3d, 3p)	B3LYP/6-31G(d)	B3LYP/6-31G(2d)	*Experimental data*	
				[4]	[19]
Structure of transition state	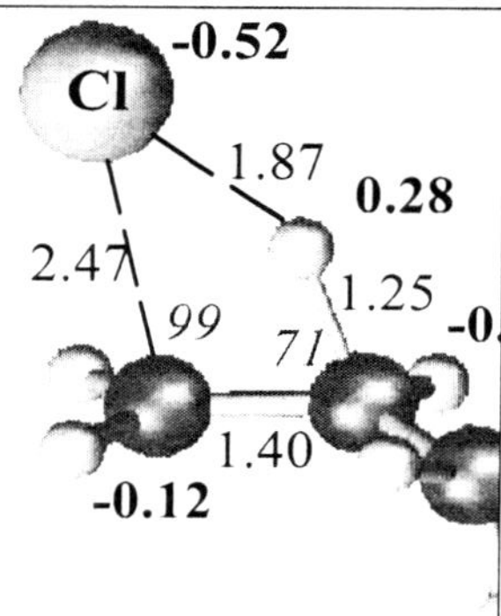	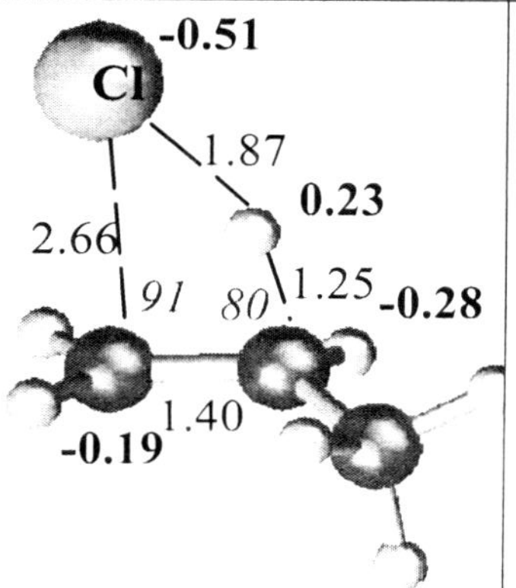	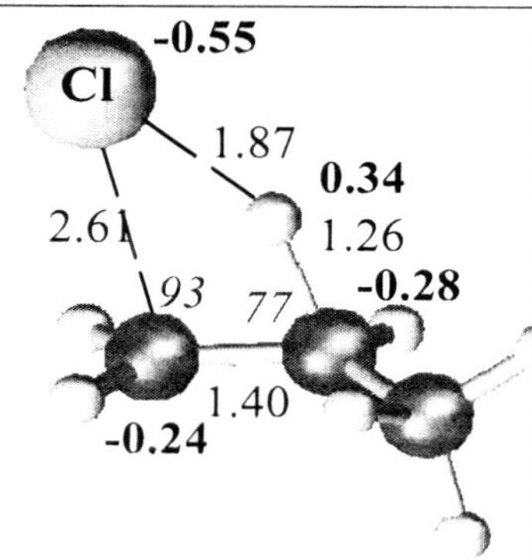		
E_a, kJ/mol	250.7	227.5	223.6	231.2	230.8
$\Delta H^{\neq}$, kJ/mol	247.0	223.7	219.9	228.7	228.2
$\Delta S^{\neq}$, J K^{-1} mol	9.6	12.5	12.6	4.2	5.2
k, sec^{-1} (448 K)	$4.7\cdot10^{-16}$	$3.4\cdot10^{-13}$	$9.8\cdot10^{-13}$	$3.4\cdot10^{-14}$	$4.2\cdot10^{-14}$

Table 3. Thermodynamic parameters of dehydrochlorination reaction of 2-Chlorobutane. E_a is activation energy, $\Delta H^{\neq}$ is activation enthalpy, $\Delta S^{\neq}$ is activation entropy, k is reaction rate constant

Calculation method		E_a, kJ/mol	$\Delta H^{\neq}$, kJ/mol	$\Delta S^{\neq}$, J K^{-1} mol	k, sec^{-1} (448 K)
AM1		234.7	231.0	5.7	$2.2 \cdot 10^{-14}$
RHF/3-21G(d)		236.1	232.4	18.5	$6.9 \cdot 10^{-14}$
RHF/6-31G(d)		227.4	223.6	24.8	$1.5 \cdot 10^{-12}$
RHF/6-31G(d, p)		219.6	215.8	20.9	$7.9 \cdot 10^{-12}$
RHF/6-31G(2d)		220.7	217.0	20.1	$5.2 \cdot 10^{-12}$
MP2/6-31(d)		257.9	254.2	16.1	$1.5 \cdot 10^{-16}$
B3LYP/6-31G(d)		199.5	195.8	18.4	$1.3 \cdot 10^{-9}$
Experimental data	[24]	207.2	204.7	4.6	$2.1 \cdot 10^{-11}$
	[25]	208.5	206.0	7.5	$2.1 \cdot 10^{-11}$

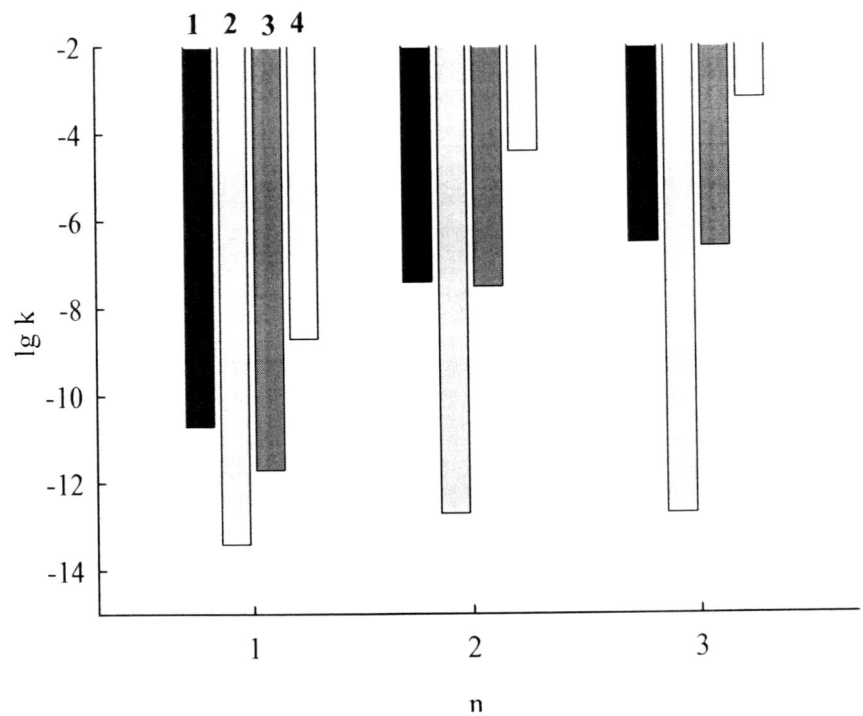

Figure 2. Averaged rate constants of dehydrochlorination reaction of chloroalkanes (n = 1), chloroalkenes (n = 2) and chlorodienes (n = 3) were determined by 1 – experimentally, 2 – method AM1, 3 – RHF/6-31G(d) and 4 – B3LYP/6-31G(d), normalized to 448 K, n – quantity of double bonds C=C which were formed at dehydrochlorination reaction.

Table 4. Thermodynamic parameters of dehydrochlorination reaction of chloroalkanes, chloroalkenes and chlorodienes

Compound		$\Delta_r H^{448}$, kJ/mol			$\Delta G^{\neq}$, kJ/mol			E_a, kJ/mol				k, sec^{-1} (448 K)			
		AM1	RHF/ 6-31G(d)	B3LYP/ 6-31G(d)	AM1	RHF/ 6-31G(d)	B3LYP/ 6-31G(d)	AM1	RHF/ 6-31G(d)	B3LYP/ 6-31G(d)	Experimental data	**AM1**	RHF/ 6-31G(d)	B3LYP/ 6-31G(d)	Experimental data
Secondary chloroalkanes	2-Chlorobutane	45.9	80.0	79.4	228.4	212.5	187.5	234.7	227.4	199.5	207.2 [24] 208.5 [25]	$2.2\cdot10^{-14}$	$1.5\cdot10^{-12}$	$1.3\cdot10^{-9}$	$2.2\cdot10^{-11}$
	2,4-Dichloropentane	42.5	70.2	74.0	223.8	211.2	187.3	230.9	230.6	201.0	205.5 [24]	$7.4\cdot10^{-14}$	$2.2\cdot10^{-12}$	$1.4\cdot10^{-9}$	$2.0\cdot10^{-11}$
	2,4-Dichlorohexane	41.9	69.3	73.5	224.0	212.5	187.5	230.5	229.4	200.4	195.0 [24]	$7.1\cdot10^{-14}$	$1.5\cdot10^{-12}$	$1.3\cdot10^{-9}$	$7.8\cdot10^{-11}$
	3,5-Dichloroheptane	40.9	67.5	73.3	223.0	207.5	180.1	228.3	222.1	192.2	-	$9.4\cdot10^{-14}$	$5.9\cdot10^{-12}$	$9.4\cdot10^{-9}$	-
	3,5,7-Trichlorodecane	39.5	64.9	71.4	230.8	213.7	186.1	236.8	225.8	194.7	-	$1.2\cdot10^{-14}$	$1.1\cdot10^{-12}$	$1.9\cdot10^{-9}$	-
	Average	42.8 ±2.2	70.4 ±5.7	74.3 ±3.0	226.0 ±3.6	211.5 ±2.4	185.7 ±3.2	232.2 ±3.4	227.1 ±3.3	197.6 ±3.9	-	$5.4\cdot10^{-14}$	$2.5\cdot10^{-12}$	$3.0\cdot10^{-9}$	$4.1\cdot10^{-11}$
Chloroalkenes	4-chloro-2-pentene	51.2	68.3	71.1	221.8	186.0	151.5	231.5	193.3	162.3	174.0 [24]	$2.7\cdot10^{-14}$	$9.7\cdot10^{-9}$	$2.0\cdot10^{-5}$	$5.5\cdot10^{-9}$
	4-chloro-2-hexene	39.3	43.3	50.2	221.0	174.8	149.2	225.7	189.5	159.8	131.0 [31]	$1.6\cdot10^{-13}$	$3.9\cdot10^{-8}$	$3.8\cdot10^{-5}$	$1.2\cdot10^{-9}$
	5-chloro-3-heptene	35.5	54.6	50.1	221.3	168.7	147.1	228.4	182.8	159.0	184.1 [30]	$1.5\cdot10^{-13}$	$2.0\cdot10^{-7}$	$6.5\cdot10^{-5}$	$5.5\cdot10^{-9}$
	5,7-dichloro-3-decene	34.4	50.9	50.0	215.6	171.3	139.5	221.5	181.1	151.8	-	$2.1\cdot10^{-13}$	$2.7\cdot10^{-7}$	$4.7\cdot10^{-4}$	-
	Average	40.1 ±7.7	54.3 ±10.4	55.3 ±10.5	219.9 ±2.9	173.7 ±4.9	146.9 ±5.1	226.8 ±4.2	186.7 ±5.7	158.2 ±4.2	-	$4.2\cdot10^{-13}$	$1.3\cdot10^{-7}$	$1.5\cdot10^{-4}$	$4.1\cdot10^{-9}$
Chlorodienes	6-Chloro-2,4-heptadiene	43.6	53.4	60.1	227.3	167.5	138.7	230.4	180.3	146.5	145.0 [24]	$3.0\cdot10^{-14}$	$2.7\cdot10^{-7}$	$6.2\cdot10^{-4}$	$2.9\cdot10^{-7}$
	7-Chloro-3,5-decadiene	34.6	47.6	42.4	212.1	162.1	132.2	217.0	172.1	142.1	-	$1.7\cdot10^{-12}$	$1.2\cdot10^{-6}$	$3.5\cdot10^{-3}$	-

Reaction enthalpy ($\Delta_r H^{448}$) of HCl elimination from chloroalkenes, which model β-chloroallylic groups, was calculated with the help of AM1 method (table 4). Its value is practically equal to the value of reaction enthalpy of dehydrochlorination of the above-mentioned chloroalkanes. However, this contradicts the results got by non-empirical methods of calculation. Reaction enthalpy of HCl elimination from chloroalkenes calculated by RHF/6-31G(d) and B3LYP/6-31G(d) methods, is on the average 16 kJ/mol lower than reaction enthalpy of HCl elimination from chloroalkanes (table 4). Free activation energy ($\Delta G^{\neq}$) of dehydrochlorination of chloroalkenes, which was computed by the semiempirical method, is on the average 5-7 kJ/mol lower than free activation energy of HCl elimination from chloroalkanes. This value is 30-35 kJ/mol lower when using non-empirical method. The values of $\Delta G^{\neq}$ calculated by AM1, RHF/6-31G(d) and B3LYP/6-31G(d) methods are equal to 219.9±2.9, 173.7±4.9 and 146.9±5.1 kJ/mol accordingly. This dispersion of values of activation energy, activation enthalpy and free activation energy is about 3 % as for reaction enthalpy and activation entropy it is about 19 % and 13 % accordingly within the frame of one method. The values of dehydrochlorination reaction rate constants of chloroalkenes calculated by RHF/6-31G(d) method closely correspond to the values of experimental data. In general, however, the values of rate constants of these reactions are higher by 3-4 orders of magnitude than the values of reaction rate constants of dehydrochlorination of chloroalkanes (depending on the method). Thus, it is possible to draw a conclusion, that dehydrochlorination of β-chloroallylic group via four-centred transition state proceeds much faster than the reaction of HCl elimination from ordinary vinyl chloride unit.

Two models for consideration of HCl elimination reaction from polyenyl chloride groups: 6-Chloro-2,4-heptadiene and 7-Chloro-3,5-decadiene, were chosen. The values of reaction enthalpy of dehydrochlorination of 6-Chloro-2,4-heptadiene, which were calculated by semiempirical and non-empirical methods (RHF/6-31G(d) and B3LYP/6-31G(d)) are equal to 43.6, 53.4 and 60.1 kJ/mol, accordingly. When HCl is eliminated from 7-Chloro-3,5-decadiene these values are equal to 34.6 (AM1), 47.6 (RHF/6-31G(d) and 42.4 kJ/mol (B3LYP/6-31G(d)). The values of activation parameters are close within one quantum chemical approximation and insufficiently depend on the magnitude of basic set when dehydrochlorination of these low-molecular substances, which model polyenyl chloride structures, is taking place. Free activation energy, calculated by various methods, is equal to 217.3 (AM1), 167.5 (RHF/6-31G(d)) and 138.7 kJ/mol (B3LYP/6-31G(d)) (table 4). The values of reaction rate constant of dehydrochlorination of chlorodienes computed by AM1 method are equal to the values of reaction rate constants of chloride hydrogen elimination from chloroalkenes. The rate constants of dehydrochlorination calculated by non-empirical method are higher by 1 - 2 orders of magnitude than the rate constants of HCl elimination from chloroalkenes. That is dehydrochlorination of chlorodienes proceeds faster than dehydrochlorination of chloroalkenes. The value of the reaction rate constant, which most closely corresponds to the reported data [24], was calculated by RHF/6-31G(d) method (fig. 2, table 4). On the basis of these results, which were received by non-empirical methods, it is possible to come to the conclusion that dehydrochlorination of polyenyl chloride groups runs faster than HCl elimination from β-chloroallylic groups.

To analyse tacticity effect on the process of PVC dehydrochlorination, reactions of sequential dehydrochlorination of 3,5-Dichloroheptane and 3,5,7-Trichlorodecane, which simulate syndiotactic and izotactic sections of macromolecule, were considered. For example, sequential dehydrochlorination reaction looks as follows:

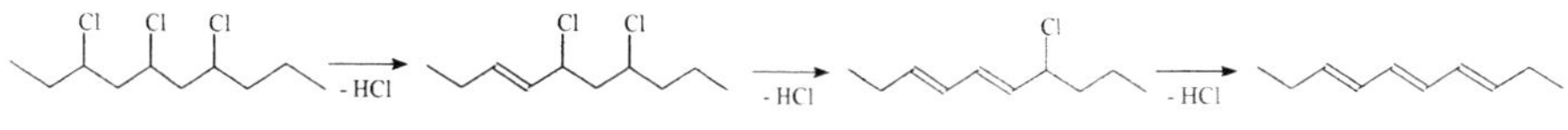

Dehydrochlorination reaction of 3,5-Dichloroheptane can proceed in four different routes, and HCl elimination from 3,5,7-Trichlorodecane can run forming eight substances, the structures of which differ (fig. 3). It is assumed here that elimination of the first molecule of chloride hydrogen from the given models results in *trans*- and *cis*-isomers formation of alkene. Further dehydrochlorination can run with *trans*- and *cis*-diene formation and HCl elimination from chlorodienes results in *trans*- and *cis*-isomer formation of triene.

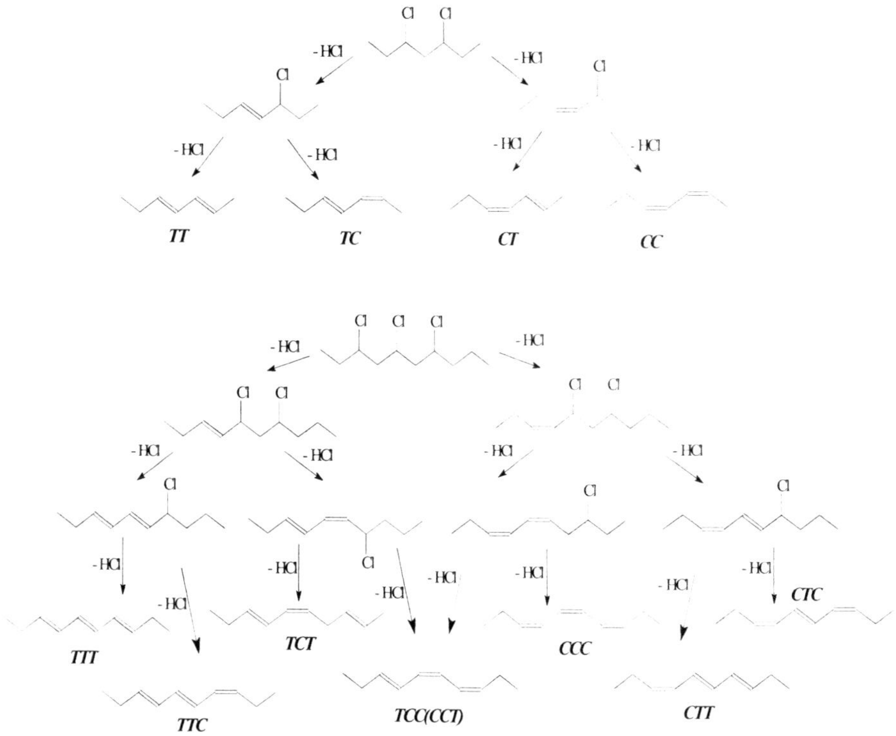

Figure 3. The route of dehydrochlorination reactions of 3,5-Dichloroheptane and 3,5,7-Trichlorodecane (T – *trans*-isomer, C – *cis*-isomer).

During dehydrochlorination of 3S,5R-Dichloroheptane, which models a syndiotactic macromolecular section, the free activation energy during *trans*-form formation is 26.5 kJ/mol less than at *cis*-form formation. Free activation energy values of HCl elimination reaction from *trans*-5-Chloro-3-heptene with *trans*- or *cis*- heptadiene formation are almost identical. It is obvious that sequential dehydrochlorination of 3S,5R-Dichloroheptane proceeds basically in two of the four possible routes: TT and TC (fig. 4a). Formation of *cis*-alkene occurs with 11.5 kJ/mol smaller free activation energy, than *trans*-isomer formation in case of HCl elimination from 3S,5S-Dichloroheptane, which is a model of an izotactic section of macromolecule. Further destruction will most likely lead to *cis-, trans*-heptadiene formation (fig. 4b).

3R,5S,7S-Trichlorodecane models syndiotactic section of PVC macromolecule. This substance dehydrochlorination proceeds forming basically *trans*-isomer of alkene because activation energy of this reaction is 25.6 kJ/mol lower than the one of *cis*-alkene formation. Obviously, in this case further HCl elimination of chloroalkene and chlorodiene will lead to *trans*-isomer products formation (fig. 4c). Thus sequential dehydrochlorination of 3R,5S,7S-Trichlorodecane proceeds in TTT route as a result *trans-, trans-, trans*-decatriene is formed.

Cis-5,7-Dichloro-2-decene or *trans*-5,7-Dichloro-2-decene are formed as a result of dehydrochlorination of 3R,5R,7S-Trichlorodecane, which simulates izotactic section of macromolecule. However, free activation energy of the first substance formation is 37.7 kJ/mol less than that of the second one. Further dehydrochlorination proceeds much faster forming *cis-, cis*-7-Chloro-3,5-decadiene. Thus sequential destruction probably proceeds in CCT route (fig. 4d).

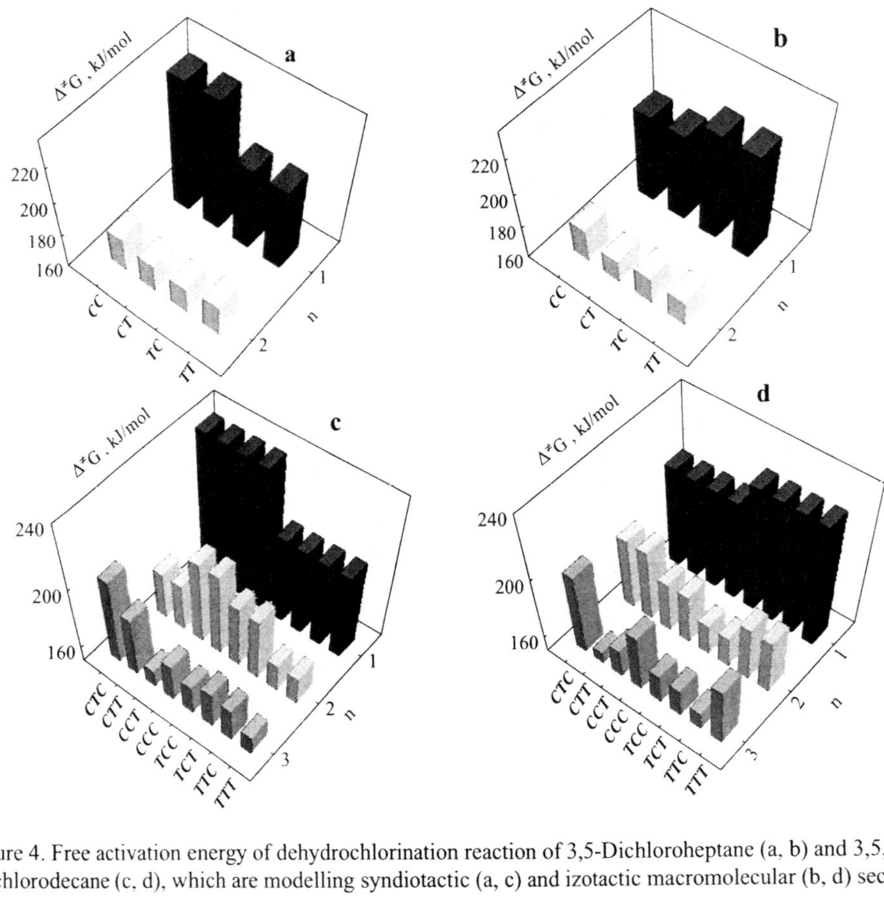

Figure 4. Free activation energy of dehydrochlorination reaction of 3,5-Dichloroheptane (a, b) and 3,5,7-Trichlorodecane (c, d), which are modelling syndiotactic (a, c) and izotactic macromolecular (b, d) sections, was calculated by HF/6-31G(d) method.

The values of rate constants of chloroalkanes dehydrochlorination reaction are practically identical within one quantum chemical approximation (AM1, RHF/6-31G(d) or B3LYP/6-31G(d)). The values of rate constants of HCl elimination from chloroalkanes that are calculated by the above-described methods exceed the values of rate constants of chloroalkenes dehydrochlorination by 3-4 orders. It corresponds to the experimental data (table 4). Thus we can assume that HCl elimination from *β*-chloroallylic groups proceeds much faster than dehydrochlorination of ordinary monomer units. The rate constants of elimination reaction of chloride hydrogen from chlorodienes calculated by RHF/6-31G(d) and B3LYP/6-31G(d) methods are higher than the reaction rate constants of dehydrochlorination of chloroalkenes, but those that are computed by AM1 method are practically identical. However, according to the experimental data (table 1) the HCl elimination from polyenyl chloride groups occurs much faster than dehydrochlorination of *β*-chloroallylic groupings. The experimental values of the rate constants of dehydrochlorination reaction of chloroalkanes, chloroalkenes and chlorodienes are higher by 3-4 orders of magnitude than those calculated by AM1 method (table 4). These differences are likely to be caused by some peculiarities of the applied semiempirical method of calculation. B3LYP/6-31G(d) method gives higher values as compared with the experimental ones and requires much more of computational time than other applied methods. Therefore restricted Hartree-Fock method with basic set 6-31G(d) is the most suitable one as for as time and results are corrected.

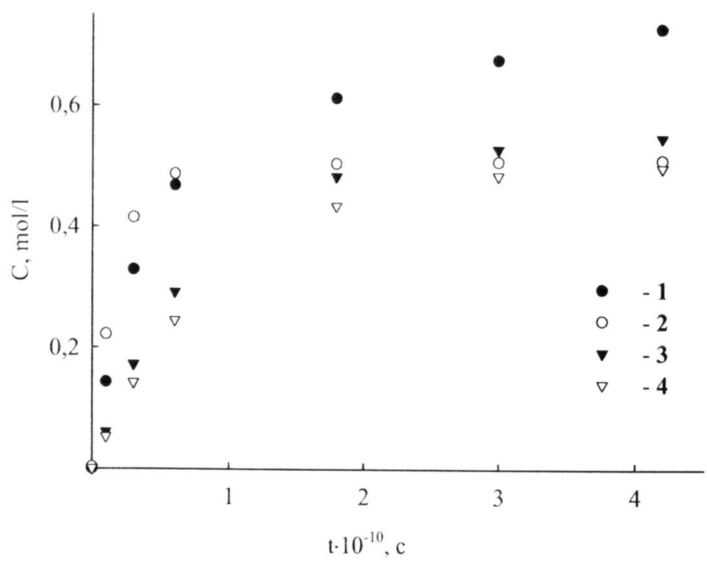

Figure 5. Concentration change of the final product of sequential dehydrochlorination reaction of 3,5-Dichloroheptane and 3,5,7-Trichlorodecane: 1,2 – concentration of heptadiene; 3,4 – concentration of decatriene; 1,3 – model simulating syndiotactic sections and 2,4 – model simulating izotactic sections of PVC macromolecule. Normalized initial concentration of 3,5-Dichloroheptane is 0.25 mol/l and 3,5,7-Trichlorodecane is 0.125 mol/l.

As we have mentioned above, sequential HCl elimination from 3,5-Dichloroheptane and 3,5,7-Trichlorodecane, which are simulating syndiotactic and izotactic sections of PVC macromolecule runs in various routes (fig. 3). However, irrespective of the route the reaction of sequential dehydrochlorination of 3S,5R-Dichloroheptane, 3S,5S-Dichloroheptane, 3R,5S,7S-Trichlorodecane and 3R,5R,7S-Trichlorodecane runs the rates of its final products accumulation are practically identical (fig. 5). Thus, macromolecule tacticity can insignificantly influence the rate of dehydrochlorination of ordinary monomer units, *β*-

chloroallylic groups and polyenyl chloride structures. However when dehydrochlorination of syndiotactic sections of PVC macromolecules takes place *trans*-isomers of β-chloroallylic groups are mainly formed, and the *cis*-isomers are formed when izotactic sections are subjected to dehydrochlorination. According to [4], the process of PVC destruction stops if during HCl elimination from the ordinary monomer unit formation of *trans*-form of chloroalkenes occurs, because dehydrochlorination of *trans*-isomers is possible only via four-center transition state. Only *cis*-isomer formation of β-chloroallylic group results in further dehydrochlorination of macromolecule via six-center mechanism. This conclusion has been drawn as a result of quantum chemical calculations of thermodynamical parameters of dehydrochlorination reaction of low-molecular models by the semiempirical AM1 method.

However, in our work we have found, that the values of rate constants of HCl elimination from chloroalkanes, chloroalkenes and chlorodienes, obtained by non-empirical restricted Hartree-Fock method with basic set 6-31G(d), are practically equal to the experimental data (in gas phase). Averaged values of these constants are summarized in table 4. First the best conformity is observed for the rate constant of HCl elimination from the ordinary monomer unit (k_c). Second, as opposed to semiempirical method (in parameterization AM1), the rate constants of dehydrochlorination of chlorodienes, calculated by non-empirical method are higher by 1 order of magnitude than those of dehydrochlorination of chloroalkenes (448 K). Therefore it is possible to assume, that the rate of dehydrochlorination of polyenyl chloride structures will be higher than the one of HCl elimination from β-chloroallylic groups in the PVC macromolecule.

The results of calculations make by non-empirical restricted Hartree-Fock method with basic set 6-31G(d) have shown, that *trans*-form formation of β-chloroallylic group during HCl eliminating doesn't cause cessation of PVC dehydrochlorination, it proceed even via four-center mechanism. As the ratio of syndiotactic and izotactic sections in the PVC macromolecules seldom exceeds 60/40, for example 54.7 %/45.3 % [10], it is possible to assume that as a result of dehydrochlorination of normal macromolecular units formation of *trans*- and *cis*-isomers of β-chloroallylic groups occurs almost in equal ratio. Further dehydrochlorination of these groups proceeds at the identical rate both for syndiotactic and izotactic sections of PVC macromolecules and results in formation of *trans*- or *cis*-forms of polyene sequences. Thus the used non-empirical method of calculation allows calculating of thermodynamical parameters of sequential dehydrochlorination reaction of the low-molecular models of PVC macromolecular groups to be more correctly, than semiempirical method of calculation in parameterization AM1, which can be used only as a reconnaissance method.

CONCLUSION

So, quantum chemical calculations of dehydrochlorination reaction of low-molecular models of PVC macromolecular groups carried out via four-center molecular mechanism have shown the following.

Thermodynamical parameters of reaction of HCl elimination from low-molecular models of various groups in PVC macromolecules calculated by restricted Hartree-Fock method with basic set 6-31G(d), correspond to experimental data on dehydrochlorination of chloroalkanes, chloroalkenes and chlorodienes in gas phase.

The study of dehydrochlorination reactions of low-molecular models of various groupings in PVC chains with the help of the quantum-mechanical theory allows making conclusions concerning the route the reactions (1-3) proceed in PVC.

The rate of dehydrochlorination reaction of ordinary monomer units is much lower than the one of chloride hydrogen elimination from β-chloroallylic groups. Dehydrochlorination of β-chloroallylic groups runs more slowly than HCl elimination from polyenyl chloride structures. Thus initiation step of PVC dehydrochlorination is combination of two consecutive reactions: 1) the HCl elimination from ordinary monomer units with β-chloroallylic groups formation; 2) the further dehydrochlorination of β-chloroallylic groups with chlorodienes formation.

Tacticity influences the rate of reaction of chloride hydrogen elimination from ordinary monomer units, β-chloroallylic groups and polyenyl chloride structures insignificantly.

The results of calculations made by RHF/6-31G(d) method allow receiving the following ratio of rate constants (normalized at 448 K) of dehydrochlorination reaction of low-molecular analogues in macromolecules: chloroalkanes ($k_r \approx 10^{-11}$ c^{-1}), chloroalkenes ($k_\beta \approx 10^{-8}$ c^{-1}) and chlorodienes ($k_p \approx 10^{-7}$ c^{-1}). This ratio differs slightly from the experimental data of dehydrochlorination of substances in gas phase.

However the rate constants ratio of dehydrochlorination of these groups, estimated by various indirect methods, which have been reported on PVC thermal destruction, is equal to $k_r < k_\beta < k_p$ (10^{-7} $c^{-1} < 10^{-4}$ $c^{-1} < 10^{-2}$ c^{-1}) [15]. These differences are likely to be connected with, first, the opportunity to run dehydrochlorination reaction of β-chloroallylic groups and polyenyl chloride sequences via six-center transition state and, second, with the effect of the neighbouring macromolecule on the reaction characteristics. Our further work will be devoted to quantum chemical research of these factors and to catalytic influence of chloride hydrogen.

REFERENCES

[1] Minsker K.S., *Chemistry of Chlorine Containing Polymers: Syntheses, Degradation, Stabilization*. New York: Nova Sci. Publ. Inc., Huntington. 164, 2000.

[2] Yassin A.A., Sabaa M.V., Degradation and Stabilization of PVC. J. *Macromol. Sci., Rev. Macromol. Chem. Phys. C*, 30(3-4): p. 491-558, 1990.

[3] Lieberman A., Reuwer J. F., Gollatz K. A., Naumann C. D., Thermal Decomposition of Poly(vinyl chloride) and Chlorinated Poly(vinyl chloride). 1. ESR and TGA Studies. *J.Polym. Sci. A*, 9(7): p. 1823-1833, 1971.

[4] Bacaloglu R., Fisch M., Degradation and Stabilization of Poly(vinyl chloride). V. Reaction Mechanism of Poly(vinyl chloride) Degradation. *Polym. Deg. Stab.*, 47: p. 33-57, 1995.

[5] Starnes W.H. Jr. Structural and Mechanistic Aspects of the Thermal Degradation of Poly (vinyl chloride) - Review. *Prog.Polym. Sci.*, 27: p. 2133-2170, 2002.

[6] Minsker K.S., Kolesov S.V., Yanborisov V.M., The Reason for the Low Stability of Poly(vinyl chloride) -A. Review. *Polym. Deg. Stab.*, 16: p. 99-133, 1986.

[7] Starnes Jr. W. H., Girois S., Degradation and Stabilization of Poly(vinyl chloride): The Current Statys. *Polym. Yearbook*, 12: p. 105, 1995.

[8] Abdullin M.I., et al., Kolichestvennaya ocenka vliyaniya plastifikatora na termookislitel'nuu destrukciu polivinilhlorida. *Vicokomolekulyzrnii coedineniya*, 30(4): p. 786-790, 1988.

[9] Minsker K.S., Kolesov C.V., Yanborisov V.M., Berlin A.A., Zaikov G.E. Effect of Macromolecular Chemical Structure and Isomerism on the Stability of Poly(Vinyl Chloride). *Polym. Deg. Stab.* 9(2): p. 103-121.10, 1984.

[10] Bacaloglu R., Fisch M., Degradation and Stabilization of Poly(vinyl chloride). I. Kinetics of the Thermal Degradation of Poly(vinyl chloride). *Polym. Deg. Stab.*, 45: p. 301-313, 1994.

[11] Bacaloglu R., Fisch M., Degradation and Stabilization of Poly(vinyl chloride). II. Simulation of the Poly(vinyl chloride) Degradation Processes Initiated in the Polymer Backbone. *Polym. Deg. Stab.*, 45: p. 315-324, 1994.

[12] Bacaloglu R., Fisch M., Degradation and Stabilization of Poly(vinyl chloride). III. Correlation of Activation Enthalpies and Entropies for Dehydrochlorination of Chloroalkanes, Chloroalkenes and Poly(vinyl chloride). *Polym. Deg. Stab.*, 45: p. 325-338, 1994.

[13] Bacaloglu R, Fisch M., The Mechanism of PVC Stabilization. *Polym. Deg. Stab.*, p. 1-9, 1994.

[14] Bacaloglu R., Fisch M., Degradation and Stabilization of Poly(vinyl chloride). IV. Molecular Orbital Calculations of Activation Enthalpies for Dehydrochlorination of Chloroalkanes and Chloroalkenes. *Polym. Deg. Stab.*, 47: p. 9-32, 1995.

[15] Yanborisov V.M., et al., Vliyanie anomal'nih grupirivok v makromolecule na kinetiku degidrohlorirovanie polivinilhlorida. *Dokl. AN USSR*, 291(4): p. 920-923, 1986.

[16] Ivan B., Szakacs T., Pollreisz F., Degradation Transformation of Poly(vinyl chloride) to New Potentially Useful Product. *Polym. Prep.*, 42(2): p. 847, 2001.

[17] Fisch M., Bacaloglu R., Degradation and Stabilization of Poly(vinyl chloride). *J. Vinyl Addit. Technol.*, 5(4): p. 205-217, 1999.

[18] Starnes W.H.J., Six-Center Concerted Mechanism for Poly(vinyl chloride) Dehydrochlorination. Requiescat in Pace?, *Macromol.*, 29: p. 7631-7633, 1996.

[19] Hartmann H., Bosche H.G., H. Heydtmann, Uber den Einflub der Kettenlange auf die Kinetik des Thermischen Zerfalls von Primaren Chloroalkanen. *Z. Phys. Chem.*,. 42(5-6): p. 329-343, 1964.

[20] Hartmann H., Heydtmann H., Rinck G., Die Kinetik des Thermischen Zerfalls von 1-Chlorbutan. *Z. Phys. Chem.* (F/M), 28(1-2): p. 85-92, 1961.

[21] Grant R.C., Swinbourne E.S., The Kinetics of the Pyrolysis of 1-Chloropentane. *J. Chem. Soc.*, Aug.: p. 4423-4426, 1965.

[22] Erbe F., Grewer T., Wehage K., Zur Kinetik des Homogenen Zerfalls von Chlorohlenwasserstoffen in der Gasphase. *Ang. Chem.*, 1962. 74(24): p. 988-993.

[23] Martens G.J., Godfroid M., Ramoisy L., Pyrolysis of 1,2-dichlorpropane. Intern. *J. Chem. Kinetics*, 2(2): p. 123-136, 1970.

[24] Chytry V., Obereigner B., Lim D., Pyrolysis of Poly(vinyl Chloride) Models in the Gaseous Phase. European Polymer Journal, 5(4): p. 379-388, 1969.

[25] Maccoll A., Stone R.H., Gas-phase Eliminations. Part II. The Pyrolysis of s-butyl Chloride, and the Direction of Eliminations from s-butyl Compounds. *J. Chem. Soc.*, July: p. 2756-2761, 1961.

[26] Harding C.J., Maccoll A., Ross R.A., The Transition State in Gas Phase Elimination from Halides. *Chem. Commun.*, (7): p. 289-290, 1967.

[27] Asahina M., Onozuka M., Thermal Decomposition of Model Compounds of Polyvinyl Chloride. I. Gaseous Thermal Decomposition of Model Compounds Having Secondary and Tertiary Chlorine. *J. Polym. Sci.*, 2(8): p. 3505-3514, 1964.

[28] Mayer Z., Thermal Decomposition of Poly(vinyl Chloride) and Its Low Molecular Weight Model Compounds. *J. Macromol. Sci.*, 10(2): p. 263-292, 1974.

[29] Thomas P.J., Kinetics of the Thermal Decomposition of 3-Chlorobut-1-ene and 3-Chloro-2-methylbut-1-ene. *J. Chem. Soc.*, B, 11: p. 1238-1241, 1967.

[30] Robinson P.J., Skelhorne G.G., Waller M.J., Kinetics and Mechanism of the Gas-phase Thermal Decomposition of Cis and Trans-4-chloropent-2-ene. *J. Chem. Soc.*, Perkin trans. II, (4): p. 349-354, 1978.

[31] Chytry V., Obereigner B., Lim.D., Study of Thermal Decomposition of Poly(vinyl Chloride) Type Polymers with the Use of Model Substances. II. Pyrolysis of Trans-1,3-Dichloro-1-pentene, Trans-5-Chloro-3-heptene, Cis-4-Chloro-2-pentene and of the Stereoisomers of 2,4-Dichloropentane in the Gas Phase. *Eur. Polym. J.*, 7(8): p. 1111-1118, 1971.

[32] Onozuka M., Asahina M., On the Dehydrochlorination and Stabilization of Polyvinyl Chloride. *J. Macromol. Sci.*, 3(2): p. 235-280, 1969.

[33] Hoang T.V., Michael A., C. Pichot, Etude de la Stabilisation du Polychlorure de Vinyle avec des Molecules - 1. Degradation ther Mique du Chloro-4-hexene-2. *Eur. Polym. J.*, 11(7): p. 469-474, 1975.

[34] Asahina M., Onozuka M., Thermal Decomposition of Model Compounds of Polyvinyl Chloride. II. Gaseous Thermal Decomposition of Unsaturated Chain End Model Compounds. *J. Polym. Sci.*, 2(8): p. 3515-3521, 1964.

[35] Becke A.D., Density-functional thermochemistry. III. The role of exact exchange. *J. Chem. Phys.*, 98: p. 5648, 1993.

In: Synthesis and Properties of Low- and High-Molecular Compounds ISBN 1-59454-716-5
Editor: Gennady E. Zaikov et al., pp. 49-54

Chapter 3

THE NANOPARTICLES, POSSESSING LOW CURIE TEMPERATURE, AS MEANS OF SELF – CONTROLLED INDUCTIVE HEATING OF TUMOURS

***F. S. Bayburtskiy*[1,3], *L. A. Goncharov*[1], *D. B. Korman*[1,2], *N. A. Brusentsov*[1,2], *O. A. Shlyakhtin*[3], *A. E. Chekanova*[3], *V. A. Naletova*[3] and *V. A. Turkov*[3]**

[1]N. M. Emanuel Institiute of Biochemical Physics, RAS, Moscow, 119991, Kosygina street. 4. E – mail: Chembio@sky.chph.ras.ru, Bayburt@mail.ru
[2]N. N. Blokhin Russian Oncology Research Center, RAMS, Moscow, 115478, Kashyrskoye shosse, 24. E – mail: Gala752@mail.ru
[3]M. V. Lomonosov Moscow State University, Moscow, 119899, Vorobyovy gory.

ABSTRACT

In the present an article investigation of nanoparticles, possessing a low Curie temperature, which can be used as self-controlled mediators in treatment of tumours by a method of magnetic hyperthermia is carried out. The authors have carried out a synthesis of nanoparticles, their physical and chemical analysis is made and is offered the device allowing qualitatively and quantitatively to estimate efficiency of a method of magnetic hyperthermia.

Key words: nanoparticles, magnetic fluids, saturation magnetization, tumour, Curie temperature, magnetic hyperthermia.

INTRODUCTION

Hyperthermia is a rapidly developing technique in cancer therapy. It takes advantage of the higher sensitivity of tumour tissue to heat and typically involves heating of the affected organ to 43 – 45°C. Magnetic fluid hyperthermia [1] attracts increasing attention, since it allows minimizing side effects by the localized heating of only desired parts of the organism, including tumours located deep inside the patient's body. The method involves introduction of ferromagnetic particles (mediators) into the desired part of the organism and heating them with an alternating electromagnetic field of radio-frequency range (RF). Magnetic fluids based on nanocrystalline Fe_3O_4, stabilized by biocompatible surfactants [2 – 6], are typically used as mediators. Unfortunately, it is impossible to control the local temperature near the mediator particles, possibly causing local overheating and necrosis of normal tissue. This problem could be solved with ferromagnetic particles of high RF absorption and a Curie temperature (T_C) 42 – 45 °C. Thus, local temperature control can be ensured even with a nonuniform distribution of mediator particles throughout the tissue, variable RF intensity and uneven dissipation of the evolving heat. If T_C of this material can be adapted to the particular medical application.

Similar approach is used in cancer thermal therapies, which utilize implantable «thermoseeds» with a particular Curie temperature [7,8]. These macroscopically sized solid units are surgically inserted in the affected organ and are heated by an external RF. The T_C of the «thermoseed» determines the temperature of the heating. Significant limitations of these methods are the necessity of a stressful surgical intervention and a relatively small volume around each «termoseed» which can be effectively heated. The reduction of size of the heat-producing elements so that they can be delivered as a suspension via catheter into the bloodstream of the tumour and spread throughout its capillaries, is the obvious solution of these problems. Sato at al. [9,10] reported using 50 μm flakes of an amorphous ferromagnetic metal alloy with T_C 45°C for intratissue hyperthermia in dogs. However, these relatively large electrically conducting particles are heated in an RF field by eddy currents even above T_C and do not penetrate into small capillaries. Numerous studies [1 – 6, 12, 13] have shown that submicron-sized non-conducting particles are most effective for hyperthermia. The goal of this work was to produce biologically compatible, electrically non-conductive nanoparticles with T_C in this range do not exist, but by combining several elements and by varying the composition of the mixture it is possible to produce alloys, amorphous structures, ferrites and other multi-component system consisting of metals and metalloids. We used several synthesis technique to produce a variety of ultradisperse particles with suitable T_C and tested their behavior in an RF field.

MATERIALS AND METHODS

In order to study their RF absorption rate, fine powders of $ZnFe_2O_4$ (T_C = 100 – 102°C), $La_{0.8}Sr_{0.2}MnO_3$ (T_C = 48°C) and $La_{0.75}Sr_{0.25}MnO_3$ (T_C = 56°C) have been prepared by the freeze-drying synthesis technique [11]. During absorption studies 0.5 g of each powder has been ultrasonically dispersed in 3 ml of water and placed in a glass test tube inside an air-cooled inductor (inner diameter 60 mm; length 200 mm) with a matching high-Q-resonator fed with RF power [12] (Figure 1). To avoid RF absorption by metal parts, the temperature of the fluid was monitored with an alcohol thermometer. A sample of magnetic fluid containing dextran-coated nanocrystalline Fe_3O_4 [4,12] was used for comparison. Previous studies have confirmed the absence of RF absorption in this frequency range by water or by components of the measuring cell [12].

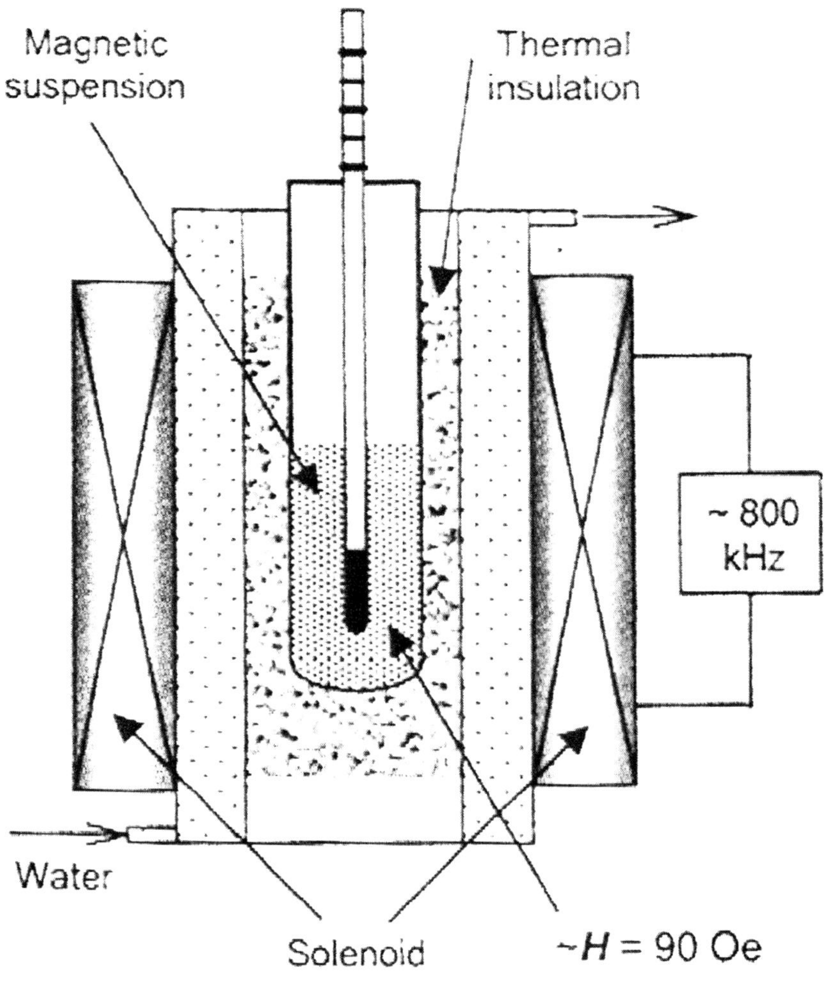

Figure 1. Scheme of the experimental setup.

Results and Discussions

Experimental heating curves are presented in Figure 2. Fe_3O_4 – based magnetic fluid demonstrates a fast, almost linear heating rate, close to that shown in [13], without any significant decrease in the tested experimental conditions. RF irradiation of the $ZnFe_2O_4$ suspension leads to significant, but less intense heating with no obvious temperature limit over the time of the experiment. This curve, taking into account the lower absorption rate of $ZnFe_2O_4$, is also similar to those of typical magnetic ferrofluids [13]. Both samples of La-Sr manganite powders demonstrate intense heating during the initial stages of the process, followed by temperature stabilization at 46.3°C and 37.8°C, respectively. These temperature correspond rather well with the T_C of the samples. The observed difference between T_C and the temperatures of RF absorption termination can be attributed to the sharp decrease of saturation magnetization M_S – usual for ferromagnetics in the vicinity of T_C and predicted by ferromagnetic exchange theory – and to the heat exchange balance. These results create many prospective applications of magnetic particles with predetermined T_C for heating of biological tissues and other objects to the optimum temperature using the demonstrated parametric feedback.

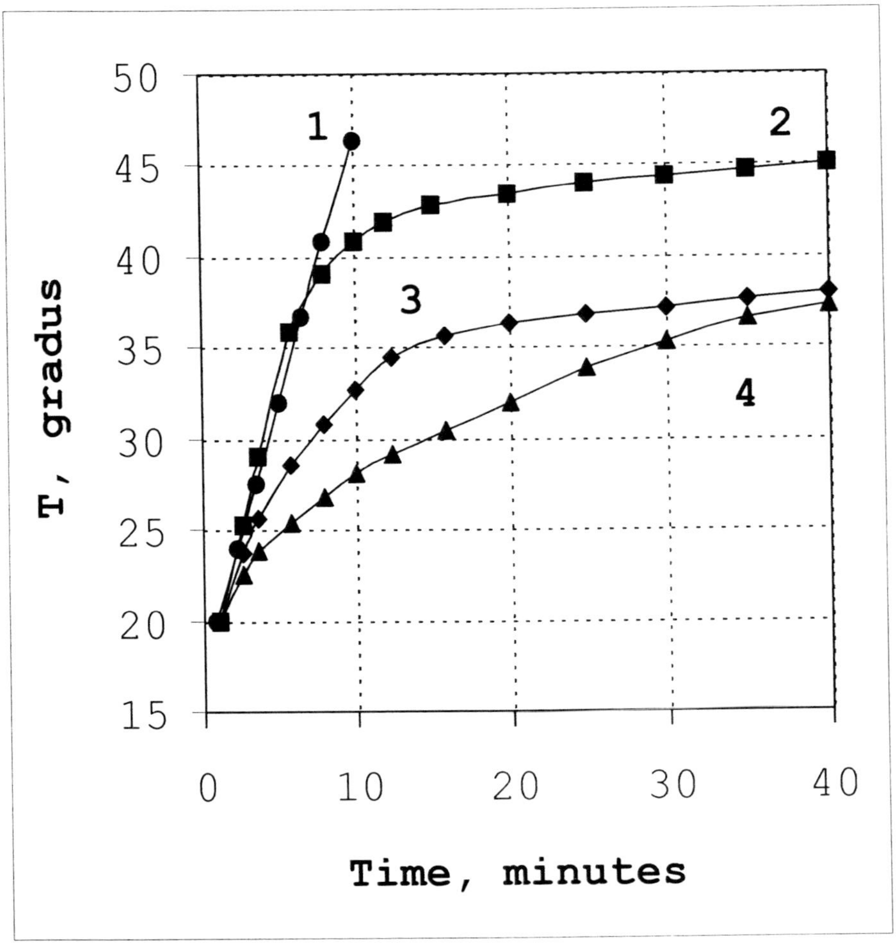

Figure 2. Time course of the temperature inside the measuring cell during RF (800 kHz) heating using the following mediators : 1 – Dextran-coated Fe_3O_4; 2 – $La_{0.75}Sr_{0.25}MnO_3$; 3 – $La_{0.8}Sr_{0.2}MnO_3$; 4 – $ZnFe_2O_4$.

Absorption of RF by ferromagnetic particles of various diameters is known to involve several physical mechanisms, including different types of remagnetization processes [5]. Usually RF absorption strongly depends on the crystallite size. Absorption rates of superparamagnetic nanoparticles are usually much higher than those of multi-domain crystallites, mostly due to Neel's losses. Powders produced by freeze-drying, are usually substantially agglomerated [14]. Intense milling of $La_{0.75}Sr_{0.25}MnO_3$ powders in a high-energy planetary ball mill resulted in a decrease of average aggregate size from 2 to 0.15 – 0.20 microns, as measured by light scattering. This is close to the average crystallite size observed by SEM (0.1 – 0.2 microns, Figure 3). Meanwhile, this treatment did not affect the RF absorption rate of this powder, with the heating curve being practically the same as that of the initial sample (data not shown). Since the observed size of crystallites even after milling is still much larger than the typical size of superparamagnetic particles, the most probable dominating absorption mechanism for these powders is scattering by displacement of magnetic domain walls. However, RF absorption rates of polycrystalline manganites are anomalously high compared to those of Fe_3O_4 polycrystals.

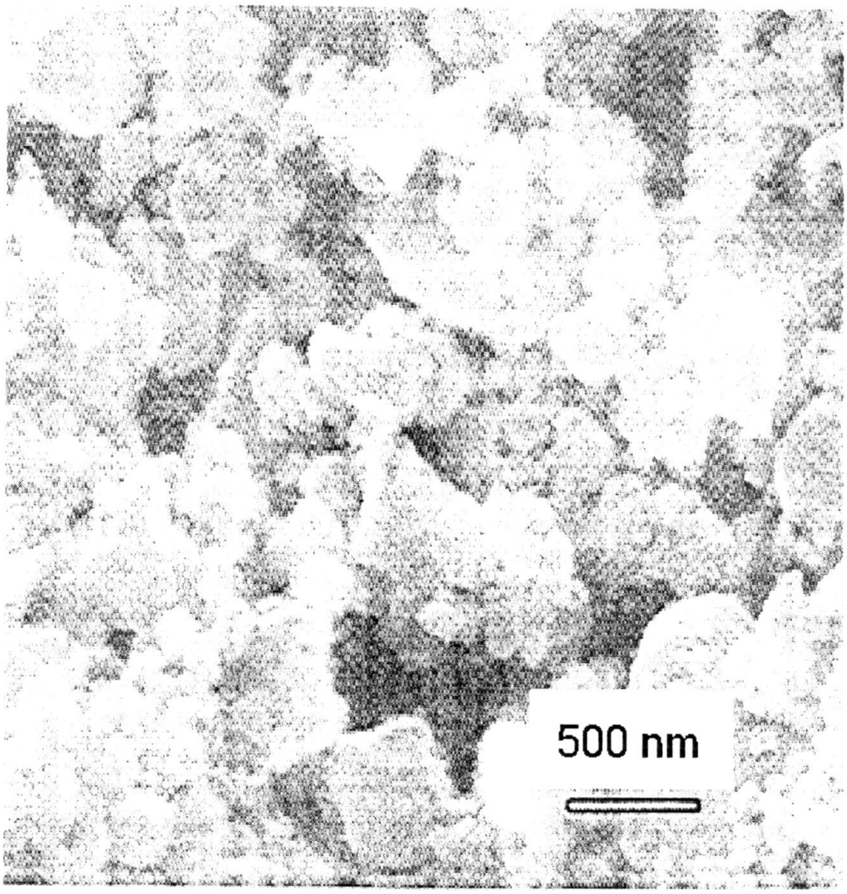

Figure 3. SEM micrograph of $La_{0.75}Sr_{0.25}MnO_3$ powder after milling.

From our results we can conclude, that powders of La-Sr manganites make it possible to heat a sample by RF to the necessary temperature without exceeding it. Further heading will be automatically swished off a T_{LIM} , which is closely related to TC. Tc of La-Sr manganites strongly depends on the content of Me in $La_{1-X}Me_XMnO_3$ (where Me = Sr, Ba, Pb, Ag, Na). By varying the composition of the manganite it is possible to create materials with T_C ranging from 20 to 90°C [15]. Thus , RF heating to any desired temperature in this range without overheating can be achieved without any external temperature control. Application of $ZnFe_2O_4$ for these purpose is less attractive due to severe dependence of T_C on the metastable, poorly reproducible cation disrtibution between sub-lattices of the spinel structure, and a lower absorption rate, while no advantages over existing Fe_3O_4-based ferrofluids were observed.

The prospects of a direct manganites application in RF hyperthermia of tumours will depend on the results of the ongoing medical compatibility studies.

CONCLUSIONS

We have proven that the freeze-drying synthesis technique permits the production of ultradisperse particles with the predetermined composition and T_C. The particles have a high absorption rate at lower temperature and abruptly stop absorbing RF energy at a particular temperature, preventing further heating of the sample. We continue searching for more biologically compatible nanoparticles for self-regulating hyperthermia.

The proposed RF heating with parametric feedback can be useful not only in medicine, but also in solving technological problems, for precise localized temperature control chemical and biochemical reactors. Coating of finely dispersed magnetic particles with a catalyst (including enzymes) combined with RF heating could ensure constant temperature at the reaction zone even in intense mass flows and strongly varying heat supply.

REFERENCES

[1] Jordan, R. Scholz, R. Felix. // *J. Magn. Magn. Mat.* 201 (1999) 413 – 419.
[2] R. K. Gilchrist. // *Ann. Surgery.* 146 (1957) 596 – 606.
[3] M. Shinkai. // *J. Magn. Magn. Mat.* 194 (1999) 176 – 184.
[4] F. S. Bayburtskiy and N. A. Brusentsov. // *J. Magn. Magn. Mat.* 194 (1999) 83 – 89.
[5] R. Hergt. // *IEEE Trans. Magnetics.* 34 (1998) 3745 – 3754.
[6] D. C. F. Chan, D. B. Kirpotin, P. A. // *Bull. in Sci. Clin. Appl. Magn. Carriers,* Proc 1st Int. Conf., Plenum, New-York, 1997, P.607 – 618.
[7] J. A. Paulus. // *J. Endourology* 11 (1997) 295 – 300.
[8] T. C. Cetas, E. J. Gross, Y. Contractor. // *IEEE Trans. Biomed. Engineering* 45 (1998) 68 – 77.
[9] T. Sato. // *IEEE Trans. Magnetics.* 29 (1993) 3325 – 3330.
[10] H. Matsuki. // *Mater. Sci. and Engineering A.* 182 (1994) 1366 – 1368.
[11] Shlyakhtin, Y. J. Oh, Yu. D. Tretyakov. // *J. Eur. Ceram. Soc.* 20 (2000) 2047 – 2054.
[12] N. A. Brusentsov and F. S. Bayburtskiy. // *J. Magn. Magn. Mat.* 225 (2001) 113 – 117.
[13] R. Hiergeist. // *J. Magn. Magn. Mat.* 201 (1999) 420 – 422.
[14] Yu. D. Tretyakov, N. N. Oleynikov, O. A. Shlyakhtin. *Cryochemical Technology of Advanced Materials,* 1997, Chapman Hall, London.
[15] N. Rao, R. Mahesh, A. K. Raychaudhuri, R. Mahendiran. // *J. Phys.Chem. Solids.* 59 (1998) 487 – 502.

In: Synthesis and Properties of Low- and High-Molecular Compounds ISBN 1-59454-716-5
Editor: Gennady E. Zaikov et al., pp. 55-66

Chapter 4

FORMATION OF CARBON NANOSTRUCTURES AND SPATIAL-ENERGY STABILIZATION CRITERION

G. A. Korablev and G. E. Zaikov
Basic Research-Educational Center of Chemical Physics and Mesoscopy, Udmurt Research Center, Ural Division, RAS, Izhevsk, E-mail: korablev@udm.net.
Institute of Biochemical Physics after N.M. Emanuel, RAS, Russia, Moscow 119991, 4 Kosygina St., E-mail: chembio@sky.chph.ras.ru.

ABSTRACT

Spatial-energy criterion of structure stabilization was obtained. The computation results for a hundred binary systems correspond to the experimental data. The basic regularity of organic cyclic compound formation is given and its application for carbon nanostructures is shown.

Key words: Spatial-energy parameter, compound stabilization, carbon nanostructures.

INTRODUCTION

The problem of a priory assessment of stable structure formation is one of the main problems of chemical physics and material science. Its solution, in turn, is directly linked with the regularities of isomorphism, solubility and phase-formation in general. Surely, such problems can be cardinally solved only based on fundamental principles defining the system of physical and chemical criteria of a substance and quantum-mechanical concepts of physics and chemistry of a solid suit it.

But many computations of phase-formation based on the application of pseudo-potential, quantum-mechanical techniques, statistic-thermodynamic theories are carried out now only for comparatively small number of systems, for instance [1-3]. A lot of papers dedicated to the phenomenon of isomorphic replacement, arrangement of an adequate model of solids, energy theories of solid solutions, for instance [4-7]. But for the majority of actual systems many problems of theoretical and prognostic assessment of phase-formation, solubility and stable phase formation are still unsolved.

This paper is developing the method where complex initial characteristics of an atom are used as a criterion of structure stabilization.

SPATIAL-ENERGY PARAMETER (P-PARAMETER)

The introduction of P-parameter as a criterion of structural interactions is based on the assumption that the resulting energy in the system: orbital-nucleus, immediately responsible for inter-atomic interactions, can be calculated based on the principle of adding reverse values of some primary atom characteristics in initial state [8]. In this model P_0-parameter is a tabulated constant spatial-energy characteristics of each orbital of an atom.

The criterion $P_E = \frac{P_0}{r_i}$ has a physical sense of some averaged energy of valence electrons in the atom at a distance r_i from the nucleus.

The reliability of initial equations and regulations was proved with numerous calculations and comparisons. In particular, it was shown [8] that P_E-parameter numerically equals the energy of valence electrons in a statistical atom model and is a direct characteristic of electron density in the atom at the given distance from the nucleus.

Spatial-energy principles of isomorphic replacement were found:

1. Complete (100%) isomorphic replacement at approximate equality of P-parameters of valence orbitals of interchangeable atoms: $P_E^{'} \approx P_E^{''}$
2. P-parameters of atom valence orbital with the least value determine the orbital that is mainly responsible for isomorphism and structural interactions.

But isomorphism is a particular case of phase-formation. Therefore, when we take its ratios as a basis and take coordination into account it can be assumed that the following condition has to be performed for atoms of a stable homogeneous crystalline structure:

$$\frac{P_E^{'}}{K_1} \approx \frac{P_E^{''}}{K_2} \qquad (1)$$

or:

$$\left(\frac{P_0 N}{Kr}\right)_1 \approx \left(\frac{P_0 N}{Kr}\right)_2; \qquad P_1 \approx P_2 \qquad (2)$$

Table 1. P–parameters of some atoms calculated via the ionization energy

Atom	Valence orbitals	E (eV)	r_i (Å)	q^2 (eVÅ)	P_0 (eVÅ)	ΣP_0 (eVÅ)	$P_i = \frac{\Sigma P_0}{r_i}$ (eV)	r_i (Å)	$P_i = \frac{\Sigma P_0}{r_i}$ (eV)	Note
H	$1s^1$	13.595	0.5295	14.394	4.7985	4.7985	9.0624	1.36	3.528	for H^-
C	$2p^1$	11.260	0.596	35.395	5.641					
	$2p^1$	24.383	0.596	35.395	10.302					
	$2s^1$	47.860	0.620	37.243	16.515					
	$2s^1$	64.480	0.620	37.243	19.281	51.739	86.810	2.60	19.900	for C^{4-}
								0.20	258.7	for C^{4+}
N	$2p^1$	14.54	0.488	52.912	6.257	6.257	12.822			
	$2p^1$	29.60	0.487	52.912	11.329	17.586	36.111			
	$2p^1$	47.426	0.487	52.912	16.078	33.664	68.984	1.48	22.746	for N^{3-}
	$2s^1$	77.472	0.521	53.283	22.966	56.63	108.69			
	$2s^1$	97.89	0.521	53.283	26.012	82.642	158.62	0.15	550.9	for N^{5+}
O	$2p^1$	13.618	0.414	71.380	5.225	5.225	12.621	1.36	3.8419	for O^-
	$2p^1$	35.118	0.414	71.380	12.079	17.304	41.797	1.36	12.724	for O^{2-}
F	$2p^1$	17.423	0.360	94.641	5.882	5.882	16.389	1.345	4.3774	
Cl	$3p^1$	12.268	0.728	59.842	8.125	8.125	11.161	1.81	4.4890	
BR	$4p^1$	11.84	0.851	73.346	8.859	8.859	10.410	1.96	4.5199	
I	$5p^1$	10.451	1.044	77.65	9.567	9.567	9.1638	2.20	4.3486	
Na	$3s^1$	5.138	1.713	10.058	4.694	4.694	2.7402	0.98	4.7898	
Al	$3p^1$	5.986	1.311	26.44	6.055	31.624	23.939			
	$3s^1$	18.829	1.044	27.119	11.396					
	$3s^1$	28.440	1.044	27.119	14.173					
Fe (II)	$4s^1$	7.893	1.227	26.57	7.098	18.462	15.046			
	$4s^1$	16.183	1.227	26.57	11.369					
Fe (III)	$3d^1$	30.64	0.365	199.95	10.564	29.026	23.656			

where: $P_E = \frac{P_0 N}{r}$, K – coordination number of atoms, r – dimensional bond characteristic of the given atom, N – number of homogeneous atoms in the compound formula.

Based on the physical sense of P_E-parameter the given condition (2) is the condition of equality of effective values of structure atom orbitals (in the assumption of paired inter-atom interaction). In a more complicated case when the central atom (A_1) has heterogeneous surroundings consisting of atoms (A_2, B, C) at different inter-nuclear distances, the condition of stable structure formation looks as follows:

$$\frac{P_0 N}{Kr} = \frac{P_0' N_1}{K_1 r_1} + \frac{P_0'' N_2}{K_2 r_2} + \frac{P_0''' N_3}{K_3 r_3} + \ldots \tag{3}$$

Here, the left-hand part of equation refers to the central atom, and the right-hand part of the equation refers to the atoms surrounding it.

Let us apply the correlations (2, 3) to some types of crystalline structures using tabulated values of P_0-parameters calculated and given in [8]. At the same time, for structures with basic ionic and metallic bond the values of P_0-parameters calculated via the atom ionization energy (E) were used – Table 1.

Crystals with Basic Ionic Bond

Equation (2) contains the value of actual dimensional bond characteristic of the given atom in the structure. In crystals with basic ionic bond, the ion radius can be applied as such dimensional bond characteristic (with a certain approximation), i.e. the stabilization condition for such structures is as follows:

$$\frac{N_1 P_0'}{K_1 r_K} \approx \frac{N_2 P_0''}{K_2 r_a}; \left(\frac{P_E}{K}\right)_1 \approx \left(\frac{P_E}{K}\right)_2; \; P_1 \approx P_2 \tag{4}$$

where r_k – cation radius, r_a – anion radius.

Table 2 contains the results of some calculations following the equation (4) for several structures, such as NaCl. In all calculations mainly the ion radii by Belov-Bokiy (first line) and partly – Goldschmidt and Poling (second line) were used. Comparisons of such calculative parameters (P_E/K) of structure atoms (7th and 8th columns) prove the equality of these values with the precision of up to 25%.

To determine the structure type from equation (4) it is necessary to calculate the ratio of coordination number of cation and anion (K_1/K_2) and taking into consideration the ratio of cation and anion radii values (in the model of rigid spheres), the structure itself can be determined.

Table 2. Spatial-energy criterion of stable phase formation in the structures of Na-Cl type

Atom	Structure	Orbital	Po (eVÅ)	K	ri (Å)	P'e/κ_1	P"e/κ_2
F	M'F	$2p^1$ $2s^1$	5.882 6.432	6 6	1.33 1.33 1.36	0.737 0.806 0.786	
Cl	M'Cl	$3p^1$	8.125	6	1.81	0.748	0.798-0.617
Br	M'Br	$4p^1$	8.859	6	1.96	0.753	
J	M'J	$5p^1$	9.567	6	2.20 2.16	0.725 0.740	
Li	LiΓ	$2s^1$	3.487	6	0.68 0.78	0.855 0.740	
Na	NaΓ	$3s^1$	4.694	6	0.98	0.798	0.806-0.725
K	KΓ	$4s^1$	5.06	6	1.65	0.634	
Rb	RbΓ	$5s^1$	5.728	6	1.49	0.641	
Cs	CsF	$6s^1$	6.106	6	1.05	0.617	0.788
H	M'H	$1s^1$	4.794	6	1.36	0.588	0.798-0.617
O	Sr0,BaO	$2P^2$	17.304	6	1.36 1.32	2.121 2.185	2.195 2.412
	MgO,CaO	$2p^2$+$2p^2$	22.653	6	1.36 1.32	2.776 2.860	2.533 3.298
Ba	BaO,BaS	$6s^2$	16.172	6	1.38	2.190	2.120 1.894
Sr	SrO	$5s^2$	17.367	6	1.20	2.412	2.185
Ca	CaO	$4s^2$	15.803	6	1.04	2.033	2.776
	CaS				1.06	2.485	2.664
Mg	MgO	$3s^2$	15.436	6	0.74	3.477	2.860
	MgS				0.78	3.298	2.78
S	BaS	$3p^2$	20.682	6	1.82	1.894	2.195
					1.74	1.981	2.195
	MgS	$3p^2$ +$3p^2$	29.092	6	1.82	2.664	3.298
	CaS				1.74	2.78	2.485
	SrS				1.82	2.664	2.412
Eu	EuO	$6s^2$	18.978	6	1.24	2.551	2.776
Ti	TiO	$3d^2$	9.483	6	0.78	2.026	2.121

Nomenclature: M' – metal of 1st group (Li, Na, K, Rb, Cs);
Γ – halogen;
M" – metal of 2nd group (Mg, Ca, Sr, Ba).

CRYSTALS WITH IONIC-COVALENT AND METALLIC BONDS. INTERMETALLIDES

Numerous and various structures belong to these classes of compounds, moreover, a lot of them are practicable.

Compounds of metals with each other belong to intermetallic compounds in the narrow sense. However, the distinct border between them cannot be made as there is no such border between metals and non-metals, and their properties frequently change considerably depending upon the composition and temperature. I.e. rational theory of phrase stability has to be the same for different types of structures.

When we apply the initial model to double compounds with ionic-covalent and metallic bonds, the calculations were made based on the equation (2) for 45 binary structures in the assumption of paired inter-atomic interaction. The results of some of them are given in Table 3.

Analogous calculations were made for dozens of crystalline structures of penetration – metal carbides and hydrocarbides (only some of them are given in Table 4). In all these cases the relative difference of values of P-parameters of interacting systems can be considered the stability criterion – (coefficient α) based on the following equation:

$$\alpha_E = \frac{P_2 - P_1}{(P_2 + P_1)/2} \cdot 100\% \qquad (5)$$

On the results of all these calculations it can be concluded: stable structures are formed if α_{ST}<(25-30)%.

Formation of Carbon Nanostructures

After different allotropic modifications of carbon nanostructures (fullerenes, tubules) have been discovered, a lot of papers dedicated to the investigations of such materials, for instance [9-15] were published, determined by the perspectives of their vast application in different fields of material science.

However, a strictly defined model of such system formation does not currently exist. To further study the problem of nanostructure phase-formation the methodology of P-parameter is applied in this paper.

The main conditions of stability of these structures formulated based on modeling the compositions of over thirty carbon clusters are given [9]:

1. Stable carbon clusters look like polyhedrons where each carbon atom is three-coordinated.
2. More stable carbopolyhedrons containing only 5- and 6-term cycles.
3. 5-term cycles in polyhedrons – isolated.
4. Carbopolyhedron shape is similar to spherical.
5. In polyhedrons – even number of apexes, 12 pentagons and any number of hexagons.

Let us show some possible explanations of such experimental data based on the application of spatial-energy concepts. As before we will consider the approximate equality of effective energies of interacting subsystems as the main condition for the formation of stable structure based on the following equation:

Table 3. Spatial-energy criterion of stabilization of crystalline structures

Atom	Structures	Structure type	Orbitals	$\sum P_0^{'}$ (eVÅ)	K	$R_И^{'}$ (Å)	$R^{'}$ (Å)	$P^{'}$ (eV)	$P^{''}$ (eV)
1	2	3	4	5	6	7	8	9	10
As	As_2Fe	FeS_2	$4S^2$	8.210	3		1.48	3.698	3.846
Fe	As_2Fe	FeS_2		18.462	6	0.8		3.846	3.698
	AgSb					1.13		0.529	0.452
Ag (I)	AgAs	Mg	$5S^1$	7.108	12				0.462
	AgCd						1.44	0.411	0.446
As (I)	AgAs	Mg	$4P^1$	8.210	12		1.48	0.462	0.524
									0.411
Ag	Ag_2S			7.108	2		1.44	4.936	3.996
	Ag_2O	Cu_2O	$5S^1$						4.164
Ag (I)	Ag_3Pt	Cu	$5S^1$	7.108	12	1.13		1.572	1.452
Pt (II)	Ag_3Pt	Cu	$6S^2$	24.043	12		1.38	1.452	1.572
Sb (I)	AuSb								0.516
	AgSb	Mg	$5P^1$	8.742	12		1.61	0.452	0.411
As (III)	AlAs	ZnS	$4P^3$	37.448	4	0.69		14.282	13.87
Al (III)	$AlAu_4$	W	$3S^2+3P^1$	31.624	8		1.49	2.764	3.092
Au (I)	$AlAu_4$	W	$6S^1$	8.909	8		1.44	3.092	2.764
Al (I)	Al_2Pt	CaF_2	$3P^1$	6.055	4		1.43	2.180	2.178
Pt (II)	Al_2Pt	CaF_2	$6S^2$	24.043	8		1.38	2.178	2.180
Al (III)	Al_2Se_3	ZnS	$3S^2+3P^1$	31.624	4		1.43	11.057	10.608
Se (II)	Al_2Se_3	ZnS	$4P^2$	22.614	4		1.6	10.609	11.057
As (III)	AsJn	ZnS	$4P^3$	39.448	4		1.48	6.663	6.137
	AsGa								6.776
Zn (III)	AsSn	NaCl	$4P^3$	40.749	4		1.66	6.137	6.617
									6.663
Au	AuCd	Mg	$6S^1$	8.909	12		1.44	0.516	0.446
	AuSb	Cu							0.452
Au	Au_2Pb	Mg	$6S^1$	8.909	12		1.44	1.032	1.045

Table 3. Spatial-energy criterion of stabilization of crystalline structures (Continued)

Atom	Structures	Structure type	Orbitals	$\sum P'_0$ (eVÅ)	K	$R'_И$ (Å)	R' (Å)	P' (eV)	P'' (eV)
1	2	3	4	5	6	7	8	9	10
K	Bi2K	Cu2Mg	4S1	5.060	12	1.33		0.634	0.594
Bi	Bi2K	Cu2Mg	6P1	12.971	12		1.28	0.594	0.634
Cd (I)	CuCd3	Mg	5S1	8.349	12		1.56	1.338	1.221
	AgCd3	Mg							1.266
Ag (II)	AgZn3	Mg	5S2+4d9	36.965	12		1.44	2.139	2.302
Ni (II)	NiMo	Mg	4S2	18.838	12		1.24	1.266	1.252
Mo (II)	NiMo		5S2	20.872	12		1.39	1.252	1.266
Li	LiAg	W	2S1	3.487	8	0.68		0.641	0.617
Ag (I)	LiAg	W	5S1	7.108	8		1.44	0.617	0.641
Cd (II)	CdSe	ZnS	5S1+4d1	16.671	4		1.56	2.672	2.929
	CdS								2.840
	CdTe								2.915
Pt (VI)	PtGa2	CaF2	6S2+5d4	136.65	8		1.38	12.377	13.554
Ni (II)	SnNi3	SnNi3	4S2	18.838	12		1.24	3.798	3.666
Sn (IV)	SnNi3	SnNi3	5P2+5S2	69.505	12		1.58	3.666	3.798
Ti (IV)	TiCu3		4S2+3d1	46.839	12		1.46	2.673	2.571
Cu (I)	TiCu3		4S1	13.165	12		1.28	2.571	2.673
Pt (V)	PtMg7		6S2+5d3	96.496	12		1.38	5.827	5.628
Mg	PtMg7		3S2	15.436	12		1.60	5.628	5.827
Sb (III)	Sb3Cu10		5P3	41.870	12		1.61	6.502	6.02
Cu (I)	Sb3Cu10		4S1	7.081	12			6.02	6.502
Ga (III)	Ga2S3		4S2+4P1	37.678	4		1.39	13.456	12.783
S (II)	Ga2S3		3P2	20.682	2.667	1.82		12.783	13.456
Ge (IV)	GeS2		4P2+4S2	61.176	4		1.39	11.003	11.364
S (II)	GeS2		3P2	20.682	2	1.82		11.364	11.003
Ni (II)	Ni2Al3		4S2+3d2	28.765	8		1.24	5.799	5.529
Al	Ni2Al3		3S2+3P1	31.624	12		1.43	5.529	5.799
Se (II)	Cu3Se2		4P2	22.614	6	1.93		3.906	3.857
Cu (I)	Cu3Se2		4S1	13.165	8		1.28	3.857	3.906

Table 4. Spatial-energy criterion of carbide and hydride formation

Atom	Structure	Orbitals	P_0 (eVÅ)	K	R_i(Å)	$[(N/P_0)/(KR_i)]_1$	$[(N/P_0)/(KR_i)]_2$
C	carbides	$2P^2 + 2P^2$	51.739	6	2.6	3.317	
α-Fe	FeC cementite	$4S^2$	18.462	6	0.6	3.846	3.317
α-Fe	FeC	$4S^2$	18.462	6	0.6	2.885	3.317
Ti (II)	TiC	$4S^2$	17.026	6	0.76	3.639	3.317
V(II)	VC	$4S^2$	17.162	6	0.72	3.973	3.317
Cr(II)	CrC	$4S^2$	18.869	6	0.83	3.769	3.317
Zr(II)	ZrC	$5S^2$	18.547	6	0.925	3.342	3.317
Hf(II)	HfO	$6S^2$	19.826	6	0.963	3.432	3.317
W(II)	WC	$6S^2$	23.344	8	0.956	3.052	3.317
Ce(II)	CeC	$6S^2$	23.4778	6	1.125	3.478	3.317
Nb(II)	NbC	$5S^1 + 4d^1$	16.669	6	0.62	3.429	3.317
SC(II)	ScC	$4S^2$	16.599	6	0.912	3.033	3.317
Mn(II)	MnC	$4S^2$	18.025	6	0.91	3.301	3.317
Ti(I)	TiH	$4S^1$	6.795	14	0.841	0.578	0.588
Ti (II)	TiH_2	$4S^2$	17.026	12	0.76	1.819	1.613
H	TiH_2	$1S^1$	4.794	4	1.36	1.763	1.619
Li	LiH	$2S^1$	3.487	6	0.66	0.655	0.882
H	LiH	$1S^1$	4.794	6	1.36	0.682	0.655

$$\left(\frac{P_0}{KR}\right)_1 \approx \left(\frac{P_0}{KR}\right)_2; \qquad P_1 \approx P_2 \tag{2a}$$

where K – coordination number, R – bond dimensional characteristic, N – number of homogeneous atoms in the structure.

At the same time, the phase-formation stability criterion (coefficient α) is the relative difference of parameters P_1 and P_2 that is calculated following the equation (5) and is α_{ST}<(20-25)%.

During the interactions of similar orbitals of homogeneous atoms $P_0' = P_0''$. When $N_1=N_2$ –

$$K_1 R_1 \approx K_2 R_2 \tag{6}$$

Let us consider these initial notions as applicable to certain allotropic carbon modifications using dimensional characteristics and values of P-parameters that are given in [8] and Table 1.

1. Diamond. Modification of structure where $K_1=4$, $K_2=4$; $P_0' = P_0''$, $R_1=R_2$, $P_1=P_2$ and α=0. This is absolute bond stability.
2. Non-diamond carbon modification for which $P_0' = P_0''$, $K_1=1$; R_1=0,77Å; $K_2=4$; $R_2^{4+} = 0.2$Å, α=3.82%. Absolute stability due to ionic-covalent bond.

3. Graphite. $P_0^{'} = P_0^{''}$, $K_1=K_2=3$, $R_1=R_2$, $\alpha=0$ – absolute bond stability.
4. Chains of hydrocarbon atoms consisting of the series of homogeneous fragments with similar values of P-parameters.
5. Cyclic organic compounds as a basic variant of carbon nanostructures. Apparently, not only inner-atom hybridization of valence orbitals of carbon atom takes place in cyclic structures, but also total hybridization of all cycle atoms.

And not only the distance between the nearest similar atoms by bond length (d) is the basic dimensional characteristic, but also the distance to geometric center of cycle interacting atoms (Д) as the geometric center of total electron density of all hybridized cycle atoms.

Then the basic stabilization equation for each cycle atom will take into account the average energy of hybridized cycle atoms:

$$\left(\frac{\Sigma P_0}{Kd}\right)_i^{'} \approx \left(\frac{\Sigma P_0}{KД}\right)_i^{''}; \quad P^{'} \approx P^{''} \tag{7}$$

where $\Sigma P_0 = P_0 N$; N – number of homogeneous atoms, P_0 – parameter of one cycle atom, K – coordination number relatively to geometric center of cycle atoms. Since in these cases K=N, the following simple correlation appears:

$$\frac{P_0^{'}}{d} \approx \frac{P_0^{''}}{Д}; \qquad P_E^{'} \approx P_E^{''} \tag{8}$$

During the interactions of similar orbitals of homogeneous atoms $P_0^{'} \approx P_0^{''}$, then:

$$d \approx Д \tag{8a}$$

Equation (8) reflects a simple regularity of stabilization of cyclic structures:

In cyclic structures the main condition of their stability is an approximate equality of effective interaction energies of atoms along all bond directions.

The corresponding geometric comparison of cyclic structures consisting of 3, 4, 5 and 6 atoms results in the conclusion that only in 6-term cycle (hexagon) the bond length (d) equals the length to geometric center of atoms (Д).

d=Д

Such calculation of α following the equation analogous to (5), gives for hexagon $\alpha=0$ and absolute bond stability. And for pentagon d≈1.17Д and the value of $\alpha=16\%$, i.e. this is the relative stability of the structure being formed. For the other cases $\alpha>25\%$ - structures are not stable. Therefore hexagons play the main role in nanostructure formation and pentagons are additional substructures, spatially limited with hexagons. Based on stabilization equation hexagons can be arranged into symmetrically located conglomerates consisting only of 3 or 7 hexahedrons.

A conglomerate of three hexagons contains one central atom and 12 atoms around it. A conglomerate of seven hexahedrons comprises 12 external and 12 internal (common) atoms. In these two cases geometric centers of hybridized molecular orbitals of each hexahedron are equidistant from such nearest centers of a conglomerate. This, apparently, explains the experimental fact that polyhedrons of carbon clusters represent an icosahedron – 12-apex crystalline structure each apex of which is connected with five other apexes.

Following such a model, for instance, clusterC_{60} can be formed of two structures 3 hexagons in each and two structures 7 hexagons in each (2x3+2x7=20) plus 12 pentagons between them located separately and acting as a binding formation.

It is assumed [12] that defectless carbon nanotubes (NT) are formed as a result of rolling the bands of flat atomic graphite net. The graphite has a lamellar structure, each layer of which is composed of hexagonal cells. Under the center of hexagon of one layer there is an apex of hexagon of next layer. Such a transition from graphite plane to nanotube should be accompanied by the change of coordination numbers of carbon atoms. Coordination numbers are 3 and 12 – for some atoms, and 3 and 2 – for other atoms. All this can be found in accordance with the stabilization formula based on the given pattern.

Examples:

From equation (2a) we have: $$\frac{K_1}{K_2} \approx \frac{R_2}{R_1}$$

Then:

1) For graphite $$\frac{K_1}{K_2} = \frac{R_2}{R_1} \approx \frac{1.675\text{Å}}{0.77\text{Å}} \approx 2:1$$

2) For ionic-covalent bond $$\frac{K_И}{K_К} = \frac{R_К}{R_И} = \frac{0.77\text{Å}}{0.2\text{Å}} \approx 4:1$$

3) For ionic-ionic bond: $$\frac{K_И^{4+}}{K_И^{4-}} \approx \frac{R_И^{4-}}{R_И^{4+}} = \frac{2.60\text{Å}}{0.2\text{Å}} \approx 13:1$$

These are 13 atoms of hexagons, the central atom of which has the coordination of 12 atoms. The process of rolling flat carbon systems into NT is, apparently, determined by polarizing effects of cation-anion interactions resulting in statistic polarization of bonds in a molecule and shifting of electron density of orbitals in the direction of more electronegative atoms.

Thus, the spatial-energy notions given allow characterizing in general the directedness of the process of carbon nanosystem formation.

General Conclusions

1. The introduction of spatial-energy criterion of structure stabilization is substantiated.

2. The application of this criterion to cyclic systems on the example of carbon nanostructure formation is given.

REFERENCES

[1] W. Harrison. Electron structure and properties of solids: *Physics of chemical bond. /* vol.1, — M: *Mir, 1983,* — 381 p.
[2] A.Yu. Zakharov, V.V. Lebedev. To the theory of reconstruction processes in multi-component condensed systems. // *Electron structure and properties of refractory compounds, alloys and metals.* / Proceedings of IAM NAS of Ukraine, 2004, p. 13-21.
[3] J. Slater. *Methods of self-coordinated field for molecules and solids.* — M: 1978, 662 p.
[4] V.S. Urusov. *Energy crystal-chemistry.* M: Nauka, 1975,—335 p.
[5] Kirkova E., Djarova M., Donkova B. *Inclusion of isomorphous impurities during crystallization from solutions, Progress in Crystal Growth and Characterization of Materials,* Volume 32, Issues 1-3, 1996, Pages 111-134.
[6] S.S. Batsanov. Structural chemistry. *Facts and dependences.* M: MSU, 2000, 292 p.
[7] M.A. Shumilov. On conditions of unlimited mutual solubility of metals in solid state. // *News of HEI, Ferrous metallurgy.* – 2001, №10, p.19-21.
[8] Korablev G.A. *Spatial-Energy Principles of Complex Structures Formation,* Leiden, the Netherlands, Brill Academic Publishers and VSP, 2005, 426 pages (Monograph).
[9] V.I. Sokolov, I.V. Stankevich. Fullerenes – new allotropic forms of carbon: structure, electron structure and chemical properties. // *Success in chemistry,* 1993, v.62, №5, p.455-473.
[10] A.L. Ivanovsky. Quantum chemistry in material science. *Nanotubular forms of substance.* Ekaterinburg, UrD RAS, 199 , 176 p.
[11] A.E. Alexeensky, M.V. Baidakova, A.Ya. Vul, V.I. Siklitsky. *Structure of diamond nanocluster.* // PTT, 199 , v.41, №4, p. 740-743.
[12] Yu.E. Lozovik, A.M. Popov. Formation and growth nanostructures – fullerenes, nanoparticles, nanotubes. // *Success in physical science,* 1997, v.167, №7, p.751-774.
[13] A.V. Eletsky. Carbon nanotubes. // *Success in physical science,* 1997, v.167, №9, p. 945-972.
[14] A.L. Kolesnikov, A.E. Romanov. *On discminary approach for describing fullerene structure.* // PTT, 1998, v.40, №6, p. 1178-1180.
[15] S.M. Dunaevsky, M.N. Rozova, N.A. Klenkova. *Electron structure of graphite nanotubes.* // PTT, 1997, v.39, №6, p. 1118-1121.

In: Synthesis and Properties of Low- and High-Molecular Compounds ISBN 1-59454-716-5
Editor: Gennady E. Zaikov et al., pp. 67-73

Chapter 5

EVALUATION OF FERROFLUIDS CONTAINING PHOTOSENSITIZER

N. A. Brusentsov[1], A. Yu. Baryshnikov [1], F. S. Bayburtskiy [2] and L. A. Goncharov [2]

[1]Russian Cancer Research Center RAMS, Russian Federation, Moscow, 115478, Kashyrskoye shosse, 24, E – mail: Gala752@mail.ru

[2]Institute of Biochemical Physics RAS, Russian Federation, Moscow, 119991, Kosygina street, 4. E – mail: Bayburt@mail.ru

ABSTRACT

In present article investigation of cytotoxicity of a magnetic liquid containing photogem, in a variable magnetic field has been carried out. By mixture of photogem (PG) sols with dextran-ferrite (DF) sols PG containing ferromagnetic fluids useful for the tumor cells PG-magneto-DF-thermosensitization in a variable magnetic field were obtained. The mechanisms of the tumor cells PG-magneto-thermosensitization most likely involves free-radical processes.

Key words: nanoparticles, magnetic fluids or ferrofluids, cytotoxicity, photogem, magnetic field, dextran-ferrite, hyperthermia, thermosensitization.

INTRODUCTION

We have developed magnetic dextran-ferrite (DF) nanoparticles [1] and photogem (PG) [2] for tumor cell induction DF magnetic field hyperthermia (MFH) [3] and PG magneto- [4] and thermosensitization [5] in the dark (MTS). DF ferrofluids (DFFs), that had been prepared from DF, may be ideal magnetic carriers [1,3,6]. DF dissipates magnetic field energy and therefore causes hyperthermia in the area of their confinement [3]. PG in analogy to haematoporphyrin [4] may generate singled oxygen or superoxide radicals and cause the destruction of tumor cells in the dark.

The inevitable technical problem of photodynamic therapy is the initiation of the absorbency of visible light by a tumor that has been injected with photosensitizing agent, because incident light at wavelengths between 600 and 1000 nm reacts with the photosensitizing agent only at shallow depth (0,1 – 1 sm) of tissue.

The purposes of this work were: to evaluate PG-containing dextran-ferrite ferrofluids for the combination of an MFH with MTS; to analyze the influence of magnetic field and hyperthermia on cell death and lysis in the presence of PG; to obtain further insights into the mechanisms of these processes.

MATERIALS AND METHODS

We have tested five water-based dextran-ferrite (DF) ferrofluids (DFFs): 12.0, 0.6; 0.2; 0.02 and 0.002 %, that were prepared by a procedure modified from [6]. The sample of the initial DFF was lyophilized. DF saturation magnetization (M_S), other physical and chemical characterizations and biological properties were determined as presented in [3, 6]. The analytical fractionation of the samples of ferromagnetic particles was performed by stepwise passage of their 1 % aqueous sols through membrane filters (100 nm, 45 nm, 20 nm, XM300, XM100, XM50, UM20 – UM5u) at a nitrogen pressure of 0,1 – 0,3 atm on an Amicon TSF-10 thin-channel ultrafiltration system or in Model 12 and Model 202 cells, and using a column gel-filtration system. Gaussian/Nicomp and volume-weighted Gaussian distribution analysis of particles in the diluted DFFs and PG sols was performed by dynamic light scattering laser particle sizing system, Submicron Particles Sizer NICOMP™ 380/DLS (Particle Sizing Systems, Inc., Santa Barbara, Calif., USA).

PG was obtained treatment of haemin with a 50 % solution of hydrogen bromide in acetic acid followed by sequentially adding acetic acid, sodium acetate, and water. Haematoporphyrin diacetate, precipitated from solution, was filtered and treated with 0,1M sodium hydroxide for 1 hour. PG was precipitated by acetic followed by filtering, washing with water, and drying in air. PG prepared as a deep-violet crystal powder represents a complex half-synthetic mixture of monomeric and oligomeric porphyrins. The solution of this substance in 0,5 % sodium hydroxide and adjustment to pH 7.4 with 1 M hydrochloric acid, produced the PG sol.

For biotesting in vitro, two types of tumor cells were used: adherent human carcinoma ovary (CaOv) and murine ascitic limpholeukosis P388 cells. The latter were obtained from tumor-bering DBA_2 mice on 7th day after intraperitoneal transplantation of 10^6 P388 cells. The survival of CaOv and P388 cells, as a result of exposure to increased temperature and a concentration of DF alone, PG alone, histidine (His) alone, DF in combination with PG (DF+PG), PG in combination with His (PG+His) was investigated. Magneto- and thermosensitization of tumor cells by PG in the dark and heating DFFs achieved simultaneously by an magnetic field or by flow thermostat. For the CaOv and P388 cell survival study, the previously used experimental setup [3] was modified. An magnetic field 0.88 MHz, 9.3 kA/m, 0.15 kW WAS achieved inside a water-cooled copper induction coil of 4.5 sm radius (20 turns with turn-to-turn distance of 0.9 sm). The tumor cells (concentration

10^6 cells / ml) alone and with reagents: DF, PG, His, PG+DF, PG+His were placed in the center of the coil and exposed for 30 min to the magnetic field in the dark. To 6 test tubes (TTs) containing 2 ml of fresh peritoneal ascitic limpholeukosis P388 or CaOv cells ($2x10^6$ / ml) were added respectively: 2 ml of 12 % (w / v) DFF (net γ-Fe_2O_3 weight: 60 mg); 2 ml of 0.6 % DSFF; 2 ml of 0.2 % DFF; 2 ml of 0,02 % DFF; 2 ml of 0.002 % DFF; and 2 ml of 0.9 % saline to the sixth as a control. The TTs then were exposed to the magnetic field as described above, and the selected temperature in the range of 37 to 44°C was maintained for 30 minutes (Table 1). The cell temperature was measured during the magnetic field treatment using an alcohol thermometer. Alternatively, the cells were exposed to the magnetic field in the dark in the presence of PG alone, His alone, PG+DF, and OPG+His. For the control, the cells were incubated at 37°C in the laboratory thermostat. To 6 isolated TTs were added 0.1 ml of fresh P388 or CaOv cells ($2x10^6$ / ml) and 0.1 ml of reagents as listed above (Tables 3 – 5); in the sixth (control TT, Tables 1 – 2) 0.1 ml 0.9 % saline was added. The volume of reaction mixture in the TTs, containing tumor cells and reagents, was 4 ml (Table 1) and 0.2 ml (Tables 2 – 6); the concentration in all the TTs was 10^6 cells / ml. The temperature of the reaction mixtures from 37 to 41°C was achieved using a flow thermostat (Tables 3 and 5); from 37 to 44°C (Table 1) and from 37 to 41°C (Tables 4 and 6) was achieved by the magnetic field. The survival of P388 and CaOv cells as a result of the exposure to concentrations of DF, PG, His, PG+DF and PG+His at 37 to 41°C during tumor cell PG magneto- and thermosensitization (MTS) achieved by magnetic field in the dark was fixed. After CaOv or P388 cells exposure to magnetic field, DFFs, PG, PG+DF, PG+His at various conditions, the survival of the cells was analyzed by a haemocytometer counting and by intraperitoneal injection of 0.1 ml analyzed compositions of P388 cells to DBA_2 mice. The interaction of DF with the cells was investigated, taking account of the recommendations in [7]. The results represent the mean ±SD from the four independent experiments.

Table I. Influence of DF on CaOv cells during 30 min of magnetic field exposure

Test tubes	Survival cells, %	Dead cells, %	DF, mg / ml	T,°C
1	0.0	100±6	60.0	43 – 44
2	4±0.8	96±5.8	6.0	42 – 43
3	48±3.4	52±3.6	1.00	41 – 42
4	91±5.5	9±1.4	0.10	39 – 40
5	95±5.8	5±1.0	0.01	37 – 38
6	96±5.8	4±0.8	0.00	37

Results and Discussion

DF appeared as dark-brown leaflets and contained about 27 % of γ-Fe_2O_3, 71 % dextran and 2 % H_2O; LD_{50} 5 g / kg. 12 % DFF appeared as a dark-brown sol, pH 7,2; M_S 1,5 kA / m, SAR 240 W / g Fe. TEM data allowed evaluation of the DF particles size: the maximal of the microcrystal and microsphere diameters were 12 and 240 nm, respectively; in a good accordance with the results of analytical fractionation and dynamic light scattering analysis of the DF particle samples and Gaussian / Nicomp and volume-weighted Gaussian distribution analysis of the [particle diameter in diluted DFFs that appeared as 2 peaks at 205 and 220 nm (Figure 1).

Table 2. Influence of PG on CaOv cells during 30 min of magnetic field exposure at 37°C

Test tubes	Survival cells, %	Dead cells, %	Cells lysis, %	PG (μg / ml)
1	0.0	0.0	100±6	325.00
2	9.5±1.5	60±4.0	30.5±2.5	32.50
3	54±3.7	28±2.5	18±1.9	3.25
4	87.3±5.5	5.7±1.0	7.0±1.3	0.65
5	91±5.5	5.0±1.0	4.0±0.8	0.06
6	95±5.8	4.0±0.8	1.0±0.1	0.00

Table 3. Influence of PG on CaOv cells during 30 min exposure in the flow thermostat at 37°C (TTs 1 – 3) and at 41°C (TTs 4 – 6)

Test tubes	Survival cells, %	Dead cells, %	Cells lysis, %	PG (μg / ml)
1	3.0±0.6	6.0±1.1	91.0±5.5	325.00
2	29.0±2.5	50.0±3.5	21.0±2.0	32.50
3	66.0±4.3	16.0±1.8	18.0±2.4	3.25
4	10.0±1.5	55.0±3.8	35.0±2.8	32.5
5	38.0±2.9	39.0±3.0	23.0±2.2	3.25
6	82.0±5.1	14.0±1.7	4.0±0.8	0.32

Table 4. Influence of DF and PG on CaOv cells during 30 min of magnetic field exposure at 41 to 43°C (TTs 1 – 3) and at 37°C (TTs 4 – 6)

Test tubes	Survival cells, %	Dead cells, %	Cells lysis, %	DF, mg / ml	PG (μg / ml)
1	0.0	91.0±5.5	9.0±1.4	9.0	0.80
2	0.0	88.0±5.4	12.0±1.6	6.0	1.60
3	3.0±1.0	52.0±3.6	45.0±3.3	3.0	32.50
4	20.0±2.0	45.0±3.3	35.0±2.8	0.10	3.25
5	10.0±1.0	50.0±3.5	40.0±3.0	0.01	32.50
6	0.0	0.0	100.0±6.0	0.001	325.0

Table 5. Influence of PG on P388 cells during 30 min flow thermostat exposure at + 41°C (test tubes 1 – 3) and at + 37°C (test tubes 4 – 6)

Test tubes	Survival cells, %	Dead cells, %	Cells lysis, %	PG (μg / ml)
1	9.0±1.4	54.0±3.7	37.0±2.9	32.5
2	39.0±3.0	36.0±2.8	25.0±2.3	3.25
3	70.0±4.5	18.0±1.9	12.0±1.6	0.325
4	29.0±2.5	40.0±3.0	31.0±2.5	32.5
5	88.0±5.4	8.0±1.2	4.0±0.8	3.25
6	91.0±5.5	5.0±1.0	4.0±0.8	0.325

Table 6. Influence of PG and His on P388 cells during 30 min of magnetic field exposure at 37°C (test tubes 1 – 3) and at 41°C (test tubes 4 – 6)

Test tubes	Survival cells, %	Dead cells, %	Cells lysis, %	PG (μg / ml)	His, mg / ml
1	94.0±5.7	6.0±1.2	0.0	0.0	1.6
2	9.0±1.4	51.0±3.5	40.0±3.0	32.5	0.0
3	77.0±4.9	12.0±1.6	11.0±1.5	32.5	1.6
4	84.0±5.2	16.0±1.8	0.0	0.0	1.6
5	3.0±0.6	51.0±3.5	46.0±3.3	32.5	0.0
6	63.0±4.2	20.0±2.0	17.0±1.8	32.5	1.6

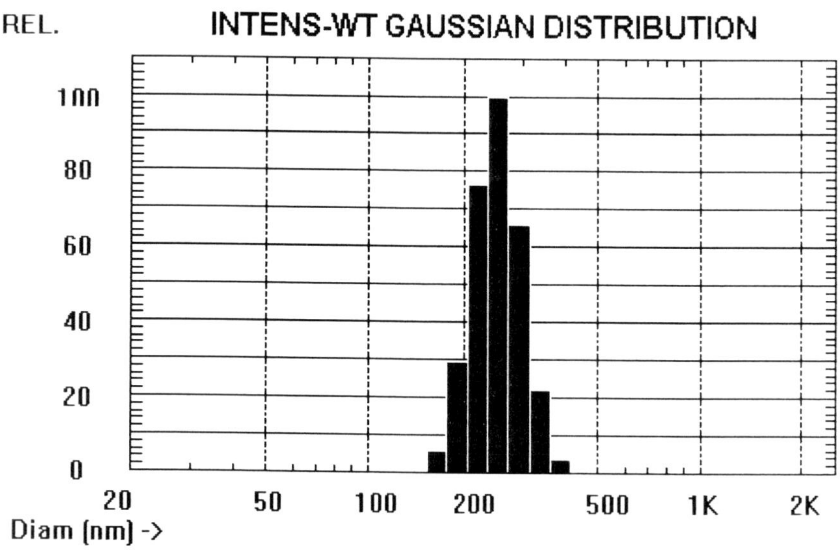

Figure 1. Particle sizing analysis of DFF

PG sol particle diameter distribution was in 3 peaks: peak 1 at 5 to 7 nm; peak 2 at 50 to 70 nm and peak 3 at 300 to 400 nm, and was in good accordance with PG gel-chromatography results. The obtained DFFs were resistant to gravitational forces, magnetic fields and liophylising. Determinations showed direct proportional decrease of M_S and heat production to decrease of DF concentration. Under the chosen conditions, the heating of a 0.9 % NaCl solution was always below the detection limit. DFFs showed satisfactory heating to 2°C / mg Fe min. The experimental results are presented in Tables 1 and 4. No long-term toxicity or acute cell death was detected when cells, were exposed to DFFs (up to 60 mg DF / ml) alone, or to magnetic field alone for periods of time up to 6 hours at + 37°C. Howerer, when P388 or CaOv cells were exposed to MFH at 41 to 44°C for 30 minutes in the presence of DFFs, the high hyperthermia effect was observed (Table 1).

In the table 1 it is shown: the temperatures in TTs 1 – 6 were proportional to DF concentration: the cell survival fractions at 37 to 41C were high, at 42 to 43°C were insignificant, and at 43 – 44°C were absent. In the table 2 it is shown: PG cytotoxicity obtained by magnetosensitization at 37°C for 30 minutes: the cell lysis and death rate fractions at the low PG concentrations were surpassingly high. In the table 3 it is shown: PG cytotoxicity obtained as a result of CaOv thermosensitization at 41°C for a 30 minutes period. The cell lysis and death fractions were proportional to PG concentration and increased with increasing temperature. The cell survival fractions at 37°C, PG concentration 32.5 μg/ml, were insignificant. In the table 4 it is shown: PG+DF cytotoxicity that were obtained at 41 to 43°C and at 37°C for a 30 minutes period; the cell lysis and death fractions were proportional to the concentrations of PG and DF. As the result of combination MFH with MTS at the moderate concentrations of PG (0.8 – 32.5 μg/ml) and the high concentrations of DF (3 – 9 μg/ml) the cell survival fraction was absent; at the moderate PG concentrations (3.25 – 32.5 μg/ml) and the low DF concentrations (0.001 – 0.1 mg/ml) the cell survival fractions ere average; at the high PG concentration (325 μg/ml) and the low DF concentration the cell survival fraction was absent. In the table 5 it is shown: PGF cytotoxicity that was obtained by the incubation of 388 cells at 41°C and 37°C for a 30 minutes period, the cell lysis and death fractions were proportional to the concentrations of PG and temperature. As a result of hyperthermia at 41°C for 30 minutes with PG thermosensitization of P388 cells at concentrations of PG (0.3256 – 32.5 μg/ml) the cell survival fractions were proportional to the concentrations of PG; at 37°C and the same PG concentrations the cell survival fractions were three times as high. In the table 6 it is shown: that substantial inhibition of cell lysis and death by PG in the presence of 1.6 mg/ml His was observed. Magnetic field cell damage enhancement by PG at 37°C (test tube 2) and simultaneous thermal- and MFH magnetic field cell damage enhancements by PG at 41°C (test tube 5) was effectively suppressed by the addition of singled oxygen scavenger, His (TTs 3,6).

We investigated the role of: DF, PG, His, PG+DF, PG+His alone; hyperthermia, Magnetic field induction, DF magnetic field hyperthermia alone; PG magneto- and thermosensitization in the dark (MTS) to increase the destruction of tumor cells. Two types of tumor cells: adherent human carcinoma ovary (CaOv) and murine ascitic limpholeucosis P388 cells were incubated in the presence or absence of the enumerated reagents and physical factors. The cells were successively heated at 41 to 44°C by magnetic field treatment with the 0.88MHz, 9.3 kA/m, 0.15 kW induction coil. The combined effects of MFH and MTS were then examined and tested for statistical significance. Significant differences between cytotoxic effects produced by MFH, MTS and the combination of MFH with MTS were found. PG at nontoxic doses at 37°C significantly enhancement by PG was effectively suppressed by the addition of His, singlet oxygen and a superoxide scavenger. In the presence of PG+His non-toxic doses, the cell survival fractions were proportional to the temperature. Significant differences between cytotoxic effects produced by PG at 37°C and 41°C at the same concentrations of PG were found. Therefore the cytotoxicity of MFH should be attributed to the effects of heat itself. Combination of PG with DF have potential as a magneto- and thermosensitizer because of the following advantages: their dose-dependent enhancement of magneto- and thermal cell damage; lack of toxicity at physiological parameters, magnetic field (frequency, induction, strength, power and temperature), and at the non-toxic doses of PG+DF required for tumor cell magneto- and thermosensitization. Combination of MFH with MTS is the summary method. These data confirm the feasibility of using induction DF magnetic field hypertermia in combination with tumor cell PG magneto- and thermosensitization. The advantage of this method is the much deeper penetration of the magnetic field into body tissues as compared to light. Further in vitro and in vivo investigations allow choosing of the PG+DF optimal doses and magnetic field range intensity and continuity.

Conclusion

Dissolution of dextran-ferrite in water results in formation of dextran-ferrite ferrofluids useful for the magnetically controlled combination of magnetic field induced hyperthermia with photogem magneto- and thermosensitization of tumor cells. The mechanism of ferrimagnetic heating most likely involves the magnetization relaxation loss process, and tumor cells photogem magneto- and thermosensitization most likely involves free-radical processes with a key role of superoxide radical.

References

[1] Autenshlyus A. I., Brusentsov N. A., Lockshin A. // *J. Magn. Mat. Mat.,* 122 (1993), 360 – 363.

[2] Mironov A. F., Nizhnik A. N., Nockel A. Yu. // *J. Photochem. Photobiol.,* 4 (1990), 297 – 306.

[3] Brusentsov N. A., Gogosov V. V., Brusentsova T. N., Sergeev A. V., Yurchenko N. Yu., Shumakov L. I. // *J. Magn. Mat. Mat.,* 225 (2001), 113 – 117.

[4] Babincova M., Babinec P., Leszchinska D., Sourivong P. // *J. Magn. Mat. Mat.,* 225 (2001), 194 – 196.

[5] Saito A., Tanaka R., Takahashi H., Kakimura K. // *Int. J. Hyperethermia,* 14 (1998), 503 – 511.

[6] Brusentsov N. A., Yurchenko N. Yu., Osipov N. E., Bayburtskiy F. S. // *J. Magn. Mat. Mat.,* 194 (1999), 83 – 89.

[7] Hafeli U. O., Pauer G. J. // *J. Magn. Mat. Mat.,*194 (1999), 76 – 82.

In: Synthesis and Properties of Low- and High-Molecular Compounds ISBN 1-59454-716-5
Editor: Gennady E. Zaikov et al., pp. 75-83

Chapter 6

DEVELOPMENT OF INFORMATION CALS-TECHNOLOGIES IN THE INDUSTRY OF CHEMICAL REAGENTS AND HIGH-PURE SUBSTANCES

A. M. Bessarabov[1], O. A. Jdanovich[1], A. M. Yaroshenko[1] and G. E. Zaikov[2]

[1]State Scientific-Research Institute of Chemical Reagents and High Purity Chemical Substances (IREA), Bogorodsky Val, 3, 107076, Moscow, Russia; E-mail: bessarabov@irea.org.ru

[2]Institute of Biochemical Physics Russian Academy of sciences, N. N. Emanuel; Kosygin St., 4, 117334, Moscow, Russia

ABSTRACT

An analysis is made of information and expert systems that are successfully used in the industry of chemical reagents and special-purity substances on the basis of IBM PC-compatible personal computers. It is considered how brand-new information technology the Continuous Acquisition and Life Cycle Support (CALS) concept can be applied to designing the production of special-purity substances.

Key words: information technologies, chemical reagents, high-pure substances, CALS, ISO-10303

Modern science can develop only if it widely uses information technologies [1]. The creation and development of information systems on the physicochemical properties of substances and materials, technologies, equipment, etc., are undoubtedly topical.

In 1989, one of the first computer systems---the REAKTIV information retrieval system---was developed [2]. The database of the information retrieval system REAKTIV (Reagent) contains information on more than 21 000 reagents and special-purity substances. The total database size is about 40 Mb. The information on reagents and special-purity substances in the database is contained in several files and has a tabular structure. Along with the master file, which includes a list of substances and their main properties, there are several directories with general (repeated in the master file) information. There are also so-called index files, which store information on the ordering of the file with information of reagents by one of the parameters. Such an organization of the file structure minimizes the information retrieval time and the size of the space occupied by the database on the hard drive.

The technology of producing components for microelectronics requires the broadening of the information base on special-purity compounds of various classes (chemical elements, organoelement compounds, hydrides, chlorides, acids, and complex etchants on their basis, and also solvents). The number of these substances is continuously increasing, and the purity requirements for them are strengthening.

One of the important problems in the technology of special-purity substances is the problem of selecting structural materials and products made from them [3]. This was the reason why the databank KONSTRUKTSIONNYE MATERIALY (Structural Materials) and the expert system KONSTRUKTSIONNYE MATERIALY V TEKHNOLOGII VYSOKOCHISTYKH VESHCHESTV (Structural Materials in Technology of Special-Purity Substances) [4] were created.

Another important problem is the selection of equipment. This problem can be solved only with the use of computer expert systems. The database OBORUDOVANIE DLYA KHIMICHESKIKH PROIZVODSTV (Chemical Process Equipment) [5] and complex rules of selection of information were nicely incorporated into the FoxBase system. This database is a complex of programs for input, storage, operative retrieval, and analysis of information on various apparatuses (vessels, filters, dryers, heat exchangers, etc.). Since the parameters describing individual types of equipment differ significantly, information on each of these types of equipment has to be treated as an individual database.

Chemical reagents, high-purity substances, drugs, etc., are produced in multifunctional small-scale process equipment [6], which is invariant to changes in process parameters, ensures the flexibility of the product range and the design, and guarantees the high purity of the reagents obtained. The reaction medium is often exposed to untraditional factors (vibration, pulsation, microwave discharge (fig. 1) etc.).

By the present time, for the main types of process equipment (reactors, filters, etc.), information databanks have been created. However, each multifunctional apparatus under consideration is a combination of original process equipment, which complicates the selection of these apparatuses. Moreover, the existing types of multifunctional equipment are continuously improving and new types of multifunctional equipment are being created. Thus, it seems expedient to create an independent databank, the databank MNOGOFUNKTSIONAL'NYE SPETSIALIZIROVANNYE APPARATY (Multifunctional Specialized Apparatuses), and the following features of these apparatuses should be taken into account. A multifunctional specialized apparatus simultaneously includes several process units, each of which is also a complex multivariant object. Therefore, the individual apparatuses are characterized by a large number of parameters, from which it is necessary to isolate a single attribute or a group of attributes common for all apparatuses. These attributes are necessary for systematization and also for operative information retrieval. Such attributes can be the type of chemical engineering processes performed in an apparatus, the material of the working chamber, the type of a stirrer, the type of energy affecting the working medium, etc. Since each multifunctional apparatus is a complex object, the databank can be efficiently used only when each apparatus and its operation are vividly represented. This is expediently performed using computer graphics.

With allowance made for these requirements, a databank was created in the FoxPro system. The program is intended to be used on an IBM PC AT or compatible. The user interface of the program is represented as a menu, which can be accessed from the keyboard of a personal computer. The work of the program begins with the opening of the main window of the program, in which all the apparatuses described in the databank are listed in a vertical menu. To the right of the apparatus menu is a control menu with the basic functions ("Input, Edit, Delete, Search, Exit"). At the bottom of the main window is a horizontal menu, whose items are the names of the reference databases, which store the values of the key parameters of apparatuses ("Processes, Materials, Actions"). Each of the menus is commented with a text line at the bottom of the screen. Graphic information is provided to be stored as a chart or video simulation of the work of an apparatus. This information is called using a menu with the items "Chart" and "Simulation", which is located in the information window of the system.

To evaluate the technological level and the raw material resources, the databank TEKHNOLOGICHESKIE PROTSESSY PROIZVODSTVA KHIMICHESKIKH REAKTIVOV I OSOBO CHISTYKH VESHCHESTV (Technological Processes of Production of Chemical Reagents and Special-Purity Substances) [7] was created. The bank contains information on products---substances obtained as a result of a technological process, raw materials---substances used in a technological process, manufacturers of products and raw materials, and flowcharts of processes. In many cases, the products of a technological process serve as raw materials for another process. Therefore, it is expedient to store information on all the substances in a single database, the database PRODUKTY (Products). Each substance in this database is assigned an individual code. Along with the principal name of a substance, the database includes its gross formula, list of synonyms, qualification, description, and storage and transport conditions. To relate a product to substances that are raw materials for this product, the database SYR'E (Raw Material) is used. This database contains links to a product substance in the database PRODUKTY, a raw material substance, and a raw material flow rate. Thus, the retrieval in the database SYR'E according to the product code provides basic information on the raw material that is necessary for the process.

For clarity, a process flowchart reflecting all the steps of manufacturing of a product is constructed. The flowchart is stored as a graphic file in the database PRODUKTY. To work with the databases, inquiries are developed which enable one to select information according to both an individual attribute and a group of attributes. For users without special training, a "Menu"-like dialog system was developed. The user can select one of the system operation modes and obtain necessary data.

The collaborative work of engineers and mathematicians for many years resulted in performing multilevel systematization of published data and expert estimates on purification methods and in creating an expert system for selecting a purification method and equipment [8]. Knowledge in the expert system is represented as objects ("Substance, Impurity, Physicochemical Properties, Purification Method, Equipment, Material, Process Mode, Control Mode") and their relating rules. The system enables one to select a method and equipment for performing thorough purification with allowance made for the physicochemical properties and concentration of trace impurities in the initial substance and the desired product. The system can give a separate reference note and also the complete description of the process and equipment for producing special-purity substances. In the operation of the system, the knowledge base can be automatically supplemented (new concepts and rules can be added).

The expert system shell is universal and can be used in other areas of science and technology. Along with individual databanks and expert systems, a powerful program complex for synthesizing optimal flexible multiproduct chemical engineering systems was developed. To analyze flexible systems, we solved the problems of multilevel systematization and decision making in a muticriterial region. Solving these problems requires intense work with the databases in combination with complex arithmetic calculations.

In recent years, as a promising information technology, methods of the Continuous Acquisition and Life Cycle Support (CALS) concept have been widely implemented. The CALS concept is based on a complex of unified information models and the standardization of methods for information access and correct interpretation of information according to the international standard ISO-10303 (STEP). Foreign experts predicted that, after 2007, it will be impossible to sell high-tech products in the foreign market if these products lack electronic documentation made according to the international CALS technology.

Examples of the implementation of information CALS technologies are standard pilot projects of the development of technologies for producing special-purity substances [1], which involve the creation of the standard computer structures "Initial Data for Design" (fig. 1) and "Project Documentation." The international CALS standard enables one to work with information from other areas and also to perform integration with any information systems. In this work, an information CALS-model of the technology of biologically active additives of a new generation is presented. The information model includes typical computer structures: marketing, design, production, service and repair, and realization and sale [9].

At present time, demands for high-pure substances have essentially increased. At the same time, analytical monitoring methods requirements of high-pure substances have increased for basic criterion of quality and operability for scientific and industrial tasks. If earlier there would be just enough to define impurity level at 10^{-3} - 10^{-4} %, then, at present time, it is necessary to determine admixtures contents with the low boundaries at 10^{-6} - 10^{-9} % level.

In last years, analysis instrumentalization of high-pure substances final production stages has been taking place simultaneously with the increase of focusing at a preparation stage of substances samples for analysis. Functions separation between classical chemical and instrumental methods has essentially allowed to improve precision of measured substances, accomplish the opportunity to automate data handling, considerably increase productivity of analytical methods and preserve high exactitude and reliability at the same time.

Information on modern and original preparation methods of chemical reagents and high-pure substances samples analysis has an essential value in creation of a competitive high-pure materials technology used in microelectronics, fibber optics and others scientific applications. For information system analysis and control, there carried out the development of a software package, including standard output documents (GOST (State Standards of Russian Federation), TU (technical standards), protocols, certificates etc.) (fig.2). Development was carried out within frameworks of the most modern and perspective computer aided system - CALS-technologies (Computer-Aided Life Cycle Support).

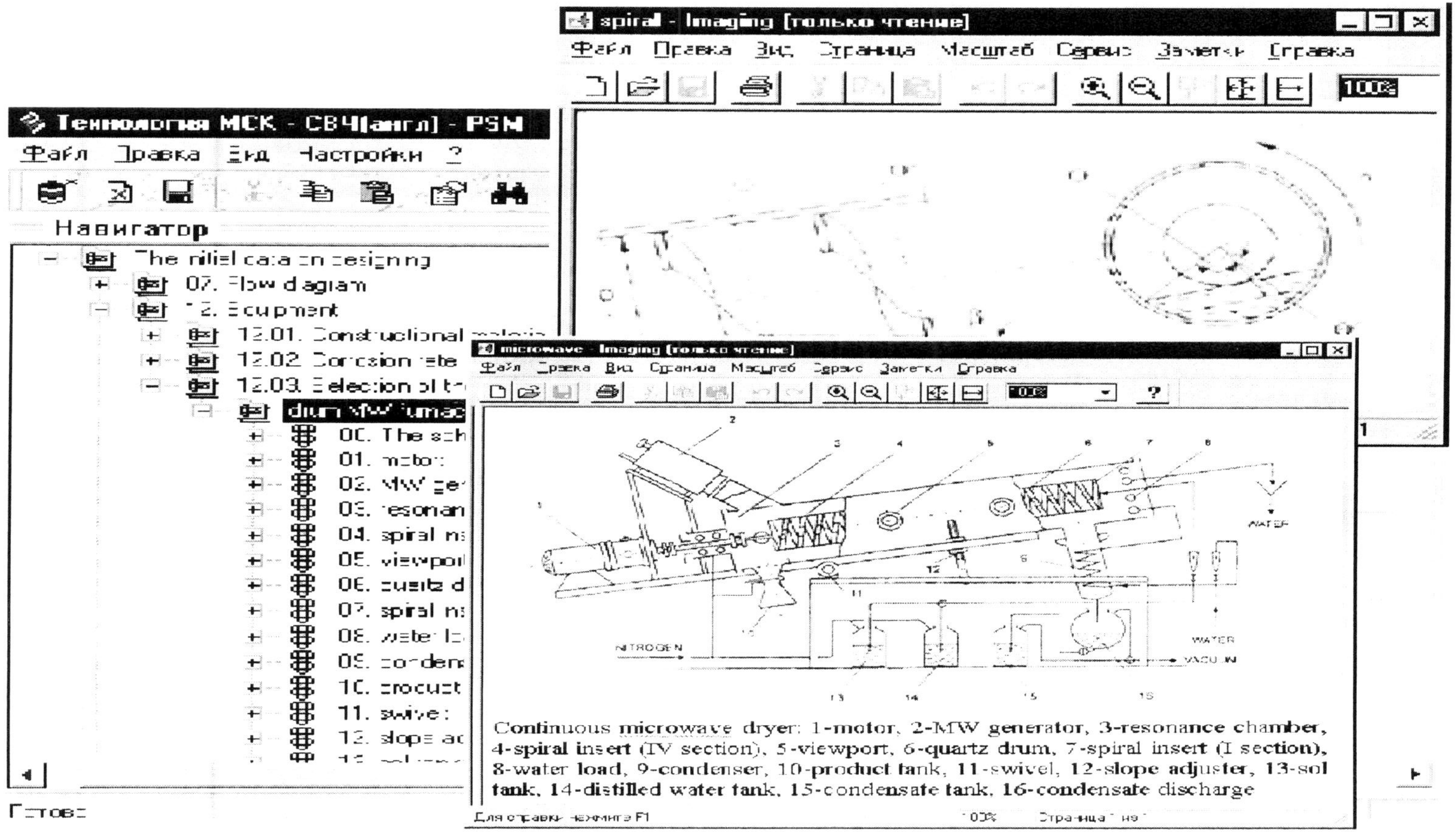

Figure 1. Pilot CALS Project "Microwave drum for drying multicomponent silicate materials for fibre optics".

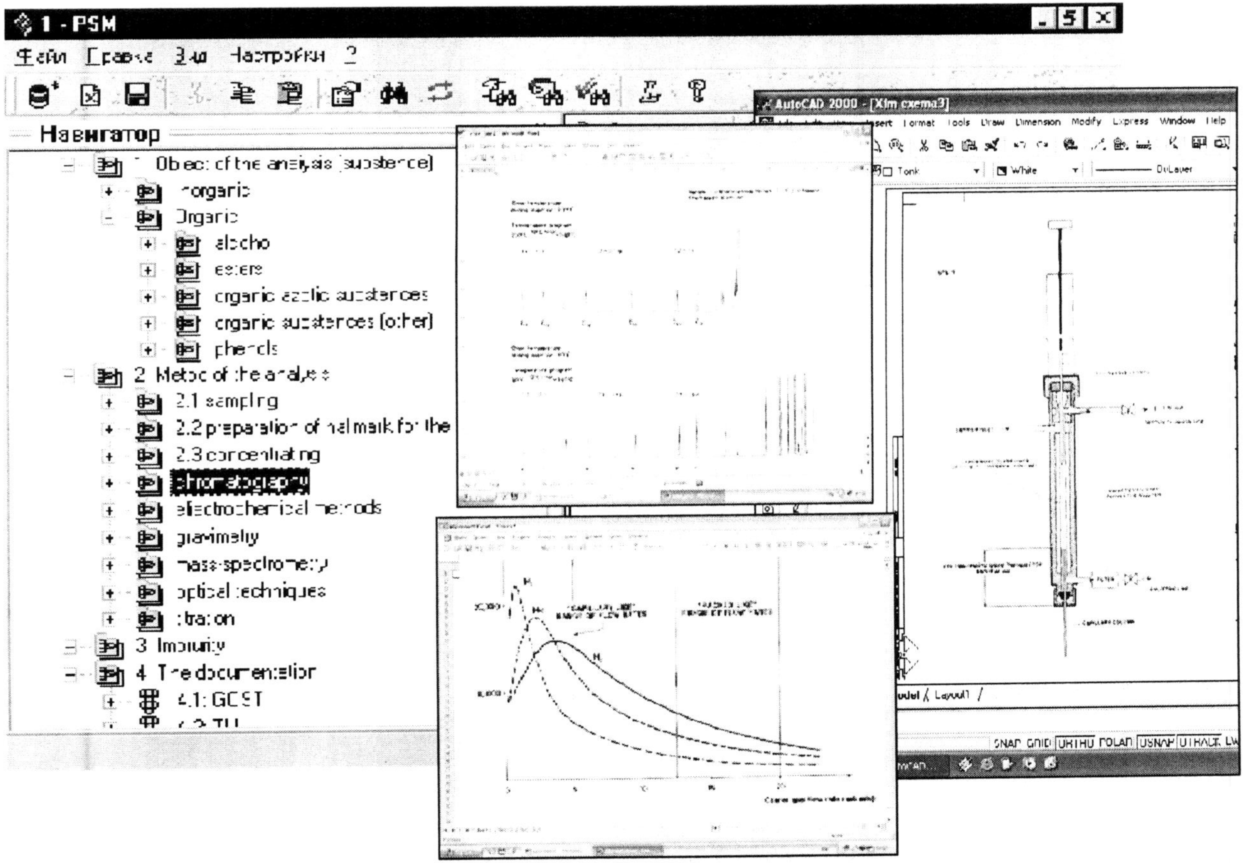

Figure 2. Pilot CALS Project “Chromatographs: optimization of process of chromatographic separation”.

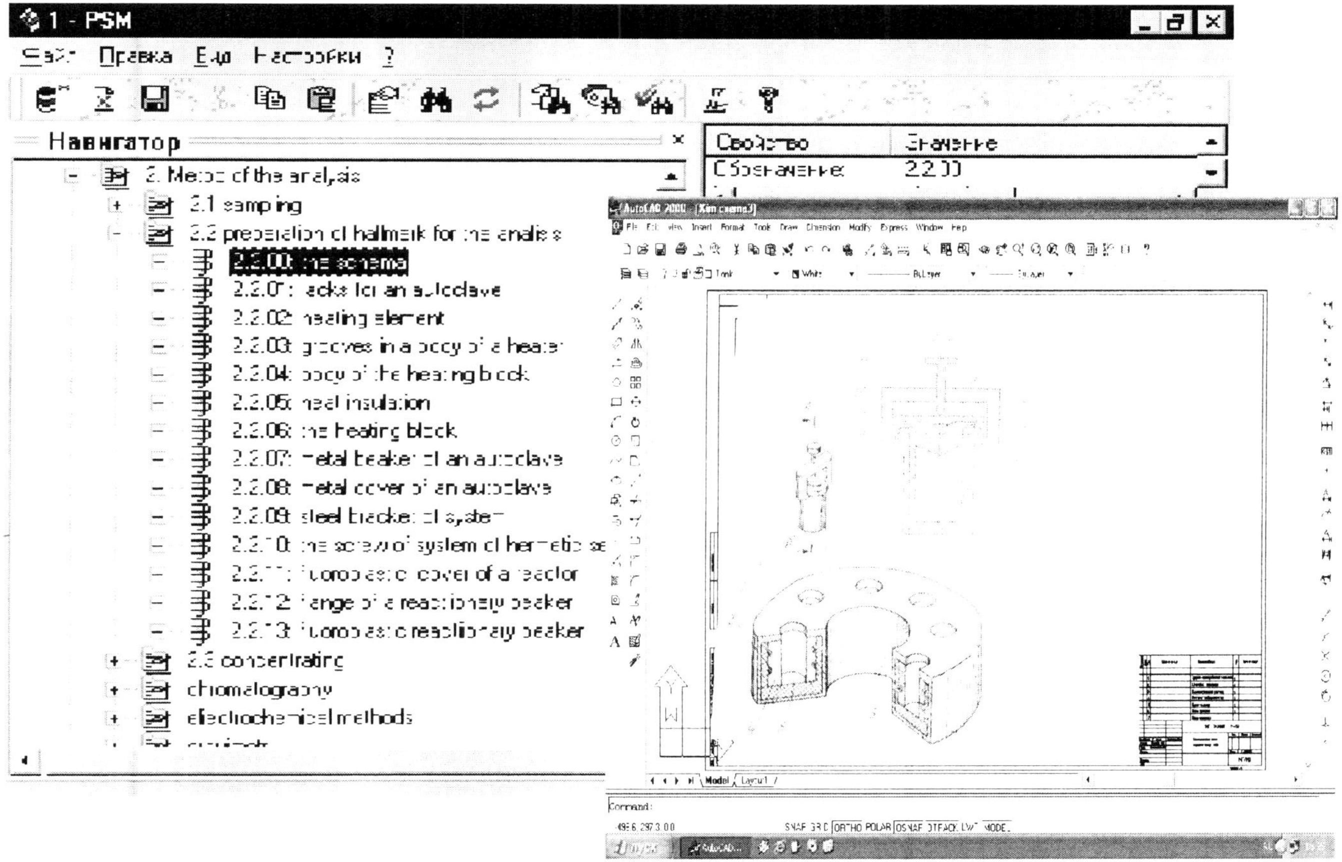

Figure 3. Pilot CALS Project “Thermal exposure of low-soluble substances”.

In the basis of the CALS concept there is a complex of uniform informational models, standardization of methods to access information and its correct interpretation according to international standards (ISO-10303 STEP). These standards have found their application in development of perspective processes of obtaining high-pure materials. In our work, the CALS concept usage allows to accomplish effective analytical monitoring of chemical reagents and high-pure substances, essentially reduce time of analytical research and to increase quality of performed scientific operations.

Grouping of input information in CALS-system is performed by following categories: analyzable substance; controlled admixture; used method of the analysis. In each category there is a little subcategory for data systematization by criteria, by respective category. Thus, in a category "substance" the following groupings were included: organic - inorganic; acids - salt - oxides etc.

Since, generally, the analysis of liquid-phase systems does not represent significant difficulties, in other cases, subcategories "sampling" (chemical or thermal exposure of low-soluble substances) and "concentrating in microadmixtures definition" (representative solution formation for a given method) are included in the category "methods of the analysis" (fig. 3).

Analytical methods included in CALS-system are subdivided into the following categories: direct (gravimetry, titratimetry), used primarily for basic substance analysis and admixtures of the macrocomponents; indirect, used for different aspects definition of microcomponents: organic compounds, ions, admixtures of transition metals etc. Given category contains the following groups of analytical monitoring methods: chromatographic (fig. 3), optical (extraction, atomic absorbent spectral technology), electrochemical and mass - spectral methods.

Analysis method selection for admixtures definition, first of all, depends on an interval of contents, especially of their low boundary, and also on metrology characteristics of a method, i.e. correctness and reproducibility. Also practical factors play important role in the selection, for example, number of determinate admixtures, duration of the analysis, availability of instrumentation, employee qualification.

All these factors have brought us to designing of the expert system extended with advanced databases [8]. Such databases embrace formalized object – attributes relations alongside with numerous empiric rules, according to which, classification of objects and further selection of preparatory operations and analysis method are performed.

There was developed a shell for the expert system for high-pure substances analysis methods. Let's highlight shell's following basic functional subsystems: input and editing of rules (or simply, rules editor), objects editor, and also the subsystem of advises and explanations (consulting subsystem) [1]. Knowledge in the expert system is represented as objects and rules with cross references. In our case, objects are "substance", "admixture" (fig. 3), and "method of analysis". Objects in system are represented as records: object - attribute - value. Consultations are performed with use of rules from objects knowledge base. Rules editor is a part of the expert system that fills up knowledge base introducing new concepts and new rules. This feature makes users of the expert system independent from developers.

The developed expert system utilizes common chemical knowledge and rules of argumentation, accepted in particular methods of high-pure substances analysis. It essentially eases work of the chemist - analytic. Results of approbation allow to create and certificate a typical modular computer control system of production quality, that gives developers an instrument that provides quality and competitiveness of manufactured production.

REFERENCE

[1] Bessarabov A.M., Avseev A.V., Avseev V.V., and Kutepov A.M., Information Technologies in the Industry of Chemical Reagents and Special-Purity Substances // *Theoretical Foundations of Chemical Engineering*, 2004. 38(2), p. 214-218.

[2] Garanina, E.I., Avseev, V.V., and Bessarabov, A.M., Development of Expert System for Solving the Problem of Deficiency of Chemical Reagents and Special-Purity Substances // *High-Purity Substances*. 1991. 5, p. 69-72.

[3] Kutepov, A.M., Ryabenko, E.A., Blyum, G.Z., et al. Structural Fluoropolymers and Their Permeability for Electrolyte Solutions. // *High-Purity Substances*. 1994. 6, p. 35-39.

[4] Bessarabov, A.M., Yaroshenko, A.M., Ryabenko, E.A., et al. Development of Information Systems on Structural Materials in Technology of Special-Purity Substances. // *Plast. Massy*. 2000. 1, p. 26-31.

[5] Malyshev, R.M., Avseev, V.V., Bessarabov, A.M., et al., Development of Databases on Equipment for Production of Chemical Reagents and Special-Purity Substances, *Khim. Prom-st*. 1992. 6, p. 372-378.

[6] Bessarabov, A.M., Malyshev, R.M., Trefilov, A.V., et al., Development of Databank on Multifunctional Specialized Equipment for Production of Chemical Reagents and Special-Purity Substances. *Khim. Prom-st*. 1994. 9, p. 628-633.

[7] Bessarabov, A.M., Ryabenko, E.A., Gafitulin, M.Yu., et al., Analysis of Technological Level and Raw Material Resources in Production of Chemical Reagents and Special-Purity Substances. *High-Purity Substances*. 1996. 3, p. 79-82.

[8] Riybenko E.A., Bessarabov A.M., Alekseeva O.V., et al., Expert systems application for selection of deep purification method and instrumental provisioning. // *High-Purity Substances*. 1994. 1, p. 48-52.

[9] Bessarabov A.M., Malyshev R.M., and Dem'yanyuk A.Yu., CALS-Based Information Model of the Technology of Biologically Active Additives of a New Generation. // *Theoretical Foundations of Chemical Engineering*. 2004. 38(3), p. 322-327.

In: Synthesis and Properties of Low- and High-Molecular Compounds ISBN 1-59454-716-5
Editor: Gennady E. Zaikov et al., pp. 85-100

Chapter 7

ENERGY OF CHEMICAL BOND AND SPATIAL-ENERGY PRINCIPLES OF HYBRIDIZATION OF ATOM ORBITALS

***G. A. Korablev*[1] *and G. E. Zaikov*[2]**

[1]Basic Research-Educational Center of Chemical Physics and Mesoscopy, Udmurt Research Center, Ural Division, RAS, Izhevsk, E-mail: korablev@udm.net.
[2]Institute of Biochemical Physics after N.M. Emanuel, RAS, Russia, Moscow 119991, 4 Kosygina St., E-mail: chembio@sky.chph.ras.ru.

ABSTRACT

Methods for evaluating energy directedness of atom orbital hybridization and calculating the energy of chemical bonds in simple and complex structures are proposed based on the application of spatial-energy parameter (P-parameter) concept. The appropriate calculations and comparisons for 68 compounds were made.

Key words: spatial-energy parameter, hybridization of atom orbitals, bond energy.

INTRODUCTION

The bond energy is a direct measure of chemical bond strength. Its value is determined by the work necessary to destruct the bond between the atoms of molecular structure (or the gain of energy in the formation process of this structure from atoms). If the molecule contains two or more similar bonds, the break-off energy of this bond differs from its average energy (by all bonds).

The values of bond energy of electrons of free atoms are calculated by quantum-mechanical methods via the wave functions, for instance in [1]. But their practical application for determining the energy values of inter-atomic bonds of actual structures produces significant difficulties since the values of electron bond energy in these structures depend upon the changes in electron and nucleus configuration of the systems, especially during the hybridization of atom orbitals. The prognostic evaluation of such processes is still not properly developed.

Therefore the main computational method for determining the values of chemical bond energy is the use of corresponding thermal-chemical values (enthalpies of formation of reaction products and initial molecule).

It is of interest both in theoretical and practical aspect to arrange a more direct dependence between the character of changes in initial energy characteristics of atom and value of chemical bond energy.

In this respect it is perspective to experimentally study the electron spectra of different (not only molecular) structures by means of X-ray electron spectroscopy (XES) that allows estimating the electron bond energies in complex systems [2].

In this research the attempt is made to estimate the energy of chemical bonds based on initial spatial-energy characteristics of free atoms with the help of the concept on spatial-energy parameter (P-parameter), taking into consideration their changes during the hybridization of atom orbitals.

METHOD SUBSTANTIATION

The analysis of various physical-chemical macro- and microprocesses results in the conclusion that in many cases the inverse values of kinetic or energy parameters of subsystems are added when estimating the resulting interaction of atom-molecular structures. Therefore tabulated (initial) values of spatial-energy parameters can be calculated based on the principle of addition of inverse values of energy components of free atom systems [3]:

$$\frac{1}{P_0} = \frac{1}{q^2} + \frac{1}{(wrn)_i} \qquad (1)$$

$$P_E = \frac{\Sigma P_0}{R} \qquad (2)$$

where: W_i – bond energy of electrons [1]; r_i – orbital radius of *i*-orbital [4]; n_i – number of electrons of the given orbital; $q=Z^*/n^*$, where Z^* and n^* – nucleus effective charge and effective main quantum number [5,6]; R – dimensional characteristics of atom bond.

Values of P_0-parameter are constant for electrons of *i*-orbital of the given atom.

As described in [3] P_E-parameter numerically equals the energy of valence electrons in atom static model, is a direct characteristics of electron density inside the atom at the given distance from the nucleus and, therefore, can be used to estimate the kinetics of chemical reactions and chemical bond energy of structures.

P_0 and P_E-parameters of free atoms were calculated based on equations (1, 2), the results of which are given in Table 1. For hydrogen atom the value of Bohr radius of hydrogen atom equaled to 0.529Å and besides, for some cases – ionic radius (1.36Å) were used as the main dimensional characteristics.

Table 1. P-parameters of atoms calculated via the bond energy of electrons

Atom	Valence electrons	W (eV)	r_i (Å)	q^2_0 (eVÅ)	P_0 (eVÅ)	R (Å)	P_0/R (eV)	k	P_E/k	r_I (Å)	P_0/r_I (eV)
1	2	3	4	5	6	7	8	9	10	11	12
H	$1S^1$	13.595	0.5295	14.394	4.7985	0.5295	9.0624	1	9.0624	1.36	3.528
						0.46	10.426				
	$2P^1$	11.792	0.596 0.596	35.395 35.395	5.8680 10.061	0.77 0.77	7.6208	1	7.6208	2.60	2.2569
	$2P^2$	11.792				0.69	13.066	2	6.533	2.60	3.8696
					13.213		14.581				
	$2P^3_r$				4.4044						
	$2P^1_r$		0.620	37.240	9.0209 14.524	0.77 0.77					
C	$2S^1$	19.201			22.234	0.772	11.715 18.862	1	11.715	2.60 2.60	3.470
	$2S^2$				19.082	0.710	28.801				5.5862
	$2S^1+2P^3_r$				13.425		26.876	4	7.2003		
	$2S^1+2P^2$				24.585	0.710		3	8.9587		
	$2S^1+2P^1_r$					0.77	34.627				
	$2S^2+2P^2$						31.929	4	8.657	2.60	
								4	7.982	0.20	9.456
											122.9
	$2P^1$	15.445	0.4875	52.912	6.5916	0.71	9.2839				
	$2P^2$				11.723						
	$2P^3$				15.830	0.71	22.296	3	5.2767	1.48	10.696
N	$2P^4_r$				19.193	0.55	34.896	3	11.632		
	$2P^5_r$				21.966	0.55	39.938	5	7.9876		
	$2S^1$	25.724	0.521 0.521	53.283 53.283	10.709 17.833	0.71	15.083 25.117				
	$2S^2$	25.724			33.663	0.71	47.413				
	$2S^2+2P^3$					0.71		5	9.4826	1.48	22.745
	$2P^1$	17.195	0.4135 0.4135	71.383 71.383	6.4663 11.858	0.66	9.7979				
O	$2P^2$	17.195				0.66	17.967	2	8.9835	1.36	8.7191
			0.4135	71.383	20.338	0.59	20.048				
	$2P^4$	17.195	0.450 0.450	72.620 72.620	12.594 21.466	0.66	30.815	4		1.36	14.954
O	$2S^1$	33.859			41.804	0.66	19.082				
	$2S^2$	33.859				0.66 0.66	32.524 63.339				
	$2S^2+2P^4$					0.59	70.854			1.36	30.738

Table 1. Continuation

1	2	3	4	5	6	7	8	9	10	11	12
	$3P^1$	8.0848	1.068	29.377	6.6732	1.17	5.7036	4			
						1.34	4.990				
	$3P^2$				10.876	1.34	8.1164	4			
						1.17	9.2974	4			
	$3P^3{}_r$				13.766	1.11	12.402	4			
Si						1.34	10.723				
	$3S^1$	14.690	0.904	38.462	9.8716	1.17	8.4373 7.3669	4			
						1.34	13.428				
	$3S^2$				15.711	1.17	23.952	4			
	$3S^2+3P^2$				26.587	1.11	21.295	4	5.988	0.39	68.172
	$3S^1+3P^3$				23.638	1.11		4	5.3238		
	$4P^1$	7.8190	1.090	41.372	7.0669	1.24	5.6991				
						1.39	5.0841				
	$4P^2$				12.072	1.24	9.7355 8.6649				
						1.39				0.65	18.572
	$4P^3$				15.803		8.7540 7.8094				
Ge	$4S^1$	15.059	0.886	58.223	10.855	1.24	14.756 13.164				
						1.39	24.492 21.849				
	$4S^2$				18.298	1.24					
						1.39					
	$4S^2+4P^2$				30.370	1.24			69.023	0.44	
						1.39					
	$4S^1+4P^3$				26.658						
	$2P^1$	19.864	0.3595	93.625	6.6350	0.64	10.367			1.33	4.9887
	$2P^3$				17.433	0.64					
	$2P^5$				25.648	0.64	40.388			1.33	19.435
F	$2S^1$	42.792	0.396	94.641	14.375	0.64	22.461				
	$2S^2$				24.961	0.64	39.002				
	$2S^1+2P^3$				31.808	0.64	49.700	4	12.425		
	$2S^2+2P^5$				50.809	0.64	79.388			1.33	38.202

Table 1. Continuation

1	2	3	4	5	6	7	8	9	10	11	12
	$5P^1$	7 .2124	1.240	47.714	7.5313	1.42	5.3037 4.7666				
Sn						1.58	9.1613 8.2336				
	$5P^2$				13.0091	1.42	12.094			1.02	12.754
						1.58	7.7838 6.9956				
	$5P^3{}_r$				17.173	1.42	13.307				
	$5S^1$	12.965	1.027	65.062	11.053	1.42	11.959				
						1.58	18.611 16.726				
	$5S^2$				18.896	1.42					
						1.58					
	$5P^2+5S^2$				26.427	1.42			0.67 0.67		38.443
						1.58					
	$3P^1$	13.780	0.7235	59.844	8.5461	1.00	8.5461		1.81	4.7216	
	$3P^3$				19.943						
Cl	$3P^5$	13.780	0.7235 0.660	59.844 79.928	.27.196 15.526	1.00	27.196 15.526				
	$3S^1$	29.196	0.660	79.928	26.002	1.00					
	$3S^2$	29.196			35.468		35.468				
	$3S^1+3P^3$				53.198	1.00	53.198	4	8.867		
	$3S^2+3P^5$					1.00			1.81	29.391	
	$4P^1$	12.438	0.8425	73.346	9.1690	1.14	8.0430		1.96	4.6781	
	$4P^3$				22.005	1.14					
Br	$4P^5$				30.563 16.477		26.809 14.454				
	$4S^1$	27.013	0.730	100.21	28.300		24.825				
	$4S^2$				38.462		33.739				
	$4S^1+4P^3$				58.863	1.14	51.634	4	8.4348		
	$4S^2+4P^5$								(0.39)	150.93	
	$5P^1$	10.971	1.0215	77.651	9.7936	1.35	7.2545		2.20	4.4516	
	$5P^3$				23.462	1.35	13.739	3	4.580		
I	$5P^5$				32.548 16.459		24.109 12.192				
	$5S^1$	22.345	0.876	103.44	28.400 60.948		21.037 45.147				
	$5S^2$										
	$5S^2+5P^5$								0.50	121.90	

Table 2. Computation of bond energy taking into account the hybridization of atom orbitals

Structure	Bond	Hybridization	Orbitals	P_o' (eV)	$\sum P_o'$ (eV)	R_k $R = d/2$ (A^o)	$P_э'$ (eV)	(N/к)$_1$	$P_э''$ (eV)	(N/к)$_2$	P_c (eV)	$E\left(\frac{kJ}{mol}\right)$ calculation	experiment
1	2	3	4	5	6	7	8	9	10	11	12	13	14
Diamond	σ $c-c$	sp^3	$2s^1$ $2p^3{}_r$	9.0209 13.213	22.234	0.772	28.801	1/4	28.801	1/4	3.600	347.5	347.3
Graphite (1)	σ $c-c$	sp^2	$2s^1$ $2p^2$	9.0209 10.061	19.082	0.710	26.876	1/3	26.876	1/3	4.479	432.4	418.7-460.6
Graphite (2)	σ $c-c$	s^2p^2	$2s^2$ $2p^2$	14.524 10.061	24.585	0.710	34.627	1/4	34.627	1/4	4.3283	417.8	418.7
Carbyne $(-c\equiv c-)_m$	single	sp	$2s^1$ $2p'_r$	9.0209 4.4044	13.425* *1/2	0.6895	9.7365	1/4	9.7365	1/4	1.2170	117.5	108.9
Ethylene $H_2C=CH_2$	σ $c-c$	sp^2	$2s^1$ $2p^2$	9.0209 10.061	19.082	0.665	28.695	2/4	28.695	2/4	3.587	346.2	347
Acetylene $HC\equiv CH$	σ $c-c$	sp	$2s^1$ $2p'_r$	9.0209 4.4044	13.425	0.601	22.375	3/4	22.375	3/4	8.391	807.6	782
	π $c-c$		$2s^1$ $2p'_r$	4.4044 4.4044	8.8088	0.601	14.657	1/4	14.657	1/4	1.832	176.8	
	$\sigma+\pi$											984.4	962.3

Table 2. Continuation

1	2	3	4	5	6	7	8	9	10	11	12	13	14
Methane (1) CH_4	σ *C-H*	sp^3	$2s^1$ $2p^3_r$	9.0209 13.213	22.234	0.546	40.722	1/4	$\frac{4.7985}{0.546}$	1/1	4.716	455.3	435.1
Methane (2)	*C-H*	–	$2s^2$ $2p^2$	14.524 10.061	24.585	0.77	31.929	1/4	9.0624	1/1	4.243	409.6	410
Ethane H_3C-CH_3	σ $c-c$	sp^3	$2s^1$ $2p^3_r$	9.0209 13.213	22.234	0.772	28.819	1/4	28.819	1/4	3.6024	347.7	345.6
Nitrogen N_2	*N-N*	–	$2p^1$ $2p^1$	6.5916 6.5916	13.183	0.71	18.658	1/3	18.658	1/3	3.095	298.7	318
	N=N	–	$2p^2$ $2p^2$	11.723 11.723	23.446	0.63	37.216	1/3	37.216	1/3	6.2026	598.7	586
N_2 $N\equiv N$	σ *N-N*	sp	$2p^4_r$	19.193	19.193	0.55	34.896	1/3	34.896	1/3	5.8161	561.4	543.4
	2π *N-N* *N-N*		$2p^5_r$	21.966	21.966	0.55	39.938	1/5	39.938	1/5	3.9938	385.5	
	$\sigma+\pi$											946.9	947.6
Silicon $Si_2 \rightarrow 2Si$	*Si- Si* σ	s^2p^2	$3s^2$ $3p^2$	15.711 10.876	26.587	1.11	23.952	1/4	23.952	1/4	2.994	289	305 ± 3 309.6 ± 13
			$3p^3_r$	13.766	13.766	1.34	10.273	1/3	10.273	1/3	1.712	165.3	176
SiH_4	*Si-H*	sp^3	$3s^1$ $3p^3_r$	9.8716 13.766	23.638	0.738	32.030	1/4	9.0624	1/1	4.251	410.3	395
Germanium $Ge_2 \rightarrow 2Ge$	*Ge-Ge* σ	sp^3	$4s^1$ $4p^3_r$	10.855 15.803	26.658	1.22	21.851	1/4	21.851	1/4	2.7314	263.6	273 278 ± 13
			$4p^3_r$	15.803	15.803	1.39	11.369	1/3	11.369	1/3	1.895	183	168

Table 2. Continuation

1	2	3	4	5	6	7	8	9	10	11	12	13	14
Tin $Sn_2 \rightarrow 2Sn$	*Sn- Sn*	$5p^3_r$	$5p^3_r$	17.173	17.173	1.42	12.094	1/3	12.094	1/3	2.016	194.6	192.5 ± ± 16.7
Sn(II)	*Sn- Sn*	p^2	$5p^2$	13.009	13.009	1.63	7.981	1/2	7.981	1/2	1.995	192.6	192.5
Sn(IV)	*Sn- Sn*	s^2p^2	$5p^2$ $5s^2$	13.009 18.896	26.427	1.58	16.726	1/4	16.726	1/4	2.098	202.5	192.5
HF	σ *F-H*	sp^2	$2s^1$ $2p^3$	14.375 17.433	31.808	0.64	49.700	1/4	4.79851/ 0.438	1/1	5.822	562	566
HCl	σ *Cl-H*	sp^2	$3s^1$ $3p^2$	15.526 19.943	35.468	1.00	35.468	1/4	4.7985/ 0.529	1/1	4.482	432.6	427.8
HBr	σ *Br-H*	sp^2	$4s^1$ $4p^3$	16.477 22.005	38.462	1.14	33.734	1/4	4.7985/ 0.704	1/1	3.769	363.9	362.5
HI	*I -H*	p^3	$5p^3$	23.462	23.462	1.35	17.379	1/3	4.7985/ 0.8045	1/1	2.94	283.7	294.6

Table 3. Dissociation energies of diatomic molecules – $D_0 \left(\frac{kJ}{mol}\right)$

Structure	First atom				Second atom				P_C (eV)	D_0 calculation	D_0 experiment
	Orbitals	N/k	P_E (eV)	$P_E \frac{N}{k}$	Orbitals	N/k	P_E (eV)	$P_E \frac{N}{k}$			
1	2	3	4	5	6	7	8	9	10	11	12
CC*l*	$2P^1$	1/1	7.6208	7.6208	$3P^1$	1/1	8.5461	8.5461	4.0209	388.9	393.3
CBr	$2P^1$	1/1	7.6208	7.6208	$4P^1$	1/1	8.0430	8.0430	3.9130	377.7	364
CJ	$2P^1$	1/1	7.6208	7.6208	$5P^1$	1/1	7.2545	7.2545	2.2523	217.4	209.2
CN	$2P^2$	2/2	13.066	13.066	$2S^22P^3$	2/5	47.413	18.965	7.7358	746.7	755.6
CN	$2P^2$	2/2	14.581	14.581	$2P^3$	2/3	25.127	16.751	7.796	752.5	755.6
C-O	$2P^2$	1/2	13.066	6.533	$2P^2$	1/2	17.967	8.984	3.782	365	356
NO	$2P^1$	1/1	9.2839	9.2839	$2P^2$	2/2	20.048	20.048	6.346	612.5	626.8
CH	$2P^2$	1/2	13.066	6.533	$1S^1$	1/1	9.066	9.066	3.7969	366.5	333±1
OH	$2P^2$	1/2	17.967	8.9835	$1S^1$	1/1	9.066	9.066	4.5118	435.5	423.7
C*l*F	$3S^23P^5$	1/7	29.391*	4.1987	$2S^22P^5$	1/7	38.202*	5.4574	2.5579	246.9	229.1
C*l*O	$3S^23P^5$	1/7	29.391*	4.1987	$2P^2$	2/2	8.7191*	8.7191	2.8337	273.5	264
C*l*O	$3P^1$	1/1	4.7216*	4.7216	$2S^22P^4$	1/6	30.738*	5.123	2.450	237.2	264
FO	$2P^1$	1/1	4.9887*	4.9887	$2P^2$	1/2	8.7191*	4.3596	2.327	224.6	219.2
NF	$2P^3$	1/3	10.696*	3.5653	$2P^1$	1/7	38.202*	5.4574	2.486	239.5	298.9
NC*l*	$2P^3$	1/3	22.296	7.432	$3P^1$	1/1	8.5461	8.5461	3.9751	383.7	384.9
H_2	$1S^1$	1/1	9.0624	9.0624	$1S^1$	1/1	9.066	9.066	4.533	437.5	432.2
Li_2	$2S^1$	1/1	2.2419	2.2419	$2S^1$	1/1	2.2419	2.2419	1.121	108.2	98.99
B_2	$2P^1$	1/1	5.4885	5.4885	$2P^1$	1/1	5.4885	5.4885	2.744	264.9	276±21
C-C	$2P^1$	1/1	7.6208	7.6208	$2P^1$	1/1	7.6208	7.6208	3.810	367.8	376.7
C=C	$2P^2$	2/2	13.066	13.066	$2P^2$	2/2	13.066	13.066	6.533	630.6	611
N-N	$2P^3$	1/3	10.696*	3.5653	$2P^3$	1/3	10.696*	3.5653	1.783	172.1	161
N=N	$2S^22P^3$	2/5	22.745*	9.098	$2S^22P^3$	2/5	22.745*	9.098	4.549	439	418
O-O	$2P^2$	1/2	8.7191	4.3596	$2P^2$	1/2	8.7191	4.3596	2.1798	210.4	213.4
O=O	$2S^22P^4$	2/6	30.738*	10.246	$2S^22P^4$	2/6	30.738*	10.246	5.123	494.5	498.3

Note: * - Calculations of P_E-parameter are given using ion radius based on the equation: $P_E=\Sigma P_0 / r_I$

Table 4. Energy of bond breaking-off in complex structures – E $\left(\frac{kJ}{mol}\right)$

No	Reactions	Bond breaking-off	First atom			Second atom			Calculation	Experim.
			orbitals	N/k	P_E (eV) P_I	orbitals	N/k	P_E (eV)	E	E
	1	2	3	4	5	6	7	8	9	10
1	$CH_2=CH+H$									430±12.6
2	$CH_3=CH_2+H$									457±12.6 >434.8
3	$CH_4=CH_3+H$	C---H	$2S^22P^2$	1/4	7.982	$1S^1$	1/1	9.0624	409.7	435±4.2
4	$C_2H_4=C_2H_3+H$									438.9
5	$C_2H_6=C_2H_5+H$							10.426	436.4	445.2
6	$C_6H_6=C_6H_5+H$									457.3
7	$CH_2=CH+H$	C---H	$2P^2$	1/2	6.533	$1S^1$	1/1	9.0624	366.5	338.9 364
8	$CH_4=CH_2+H_2$	C---(H_2)	$2P^2$	1/2	6.533	$1S^1$	2·1/1	2·9.0624	463.6	432.6
9	$C_2H_5=CH_3+CH_2$									416.7±8.4
10	$C_2H_6=2CH_3$	C---C	$2S^22P^2$	1/4	7.982	$2S^22P^2$	1/4	7.982	385.2	372.4
11	$C_3H_8=C_2H_5+CH_3$									380.7
12	$O_2=O+O$	O=O	$2P^2$	2/2	17.967	$2P^2$	2/2	17.967		—
13	$CH_3O{\cdot}OH=$ CH_3O+OH	-O-O-	$2P^4$	1/4	14.954*	$2P^4$	1/4	14.954*	180.4	181.5±19
14	$H_2O_2=2OH$	-O-O-	$2P^2$	1/2	8.7192	$2P^2$	1/2	8.7192	210.4	231.8±2.5
15	$H_2O_2=2OH$	(OH)-(OH)			4.5118			4.5118	217.8	231.8±2.5
16	$N_2=2N$	N–N	$2S^22P^3$	1/5	22.745	$2S^22P^3$	1/5	22.745	219.5 (2.275 eV)	
17	$N_2H_2=NH+NH$	N=N	$2S^22P^3$	2/5	$22.745\frac{2}{5}=$ 8.898*	$2S^22P^3$	2/5	8.898*	439.1	472.8±33.5

Table 4. Continuation

	1	2	3	4	5	6	7	8	9	10
18	$NH_2=N+H_2$	N=N	$2P^3$	2/3	10.696*	$1S^1$	1/1	9.0624	(P_i-5.118 eV)	
19	$N_2H_4=2(NH_2)$	(NH_2)- (NH_2)			5.118*			5.118*	247	252.7±16.7
20	$CH_3NHNH_2=$ CH_3NH+NH_2	N-N N-N	$2P^3$ $2S^22P^3$	1/3 1/5	10.696* 22.745*	$2P^3$ $2S^22P^3$	1/3 1/5	10.696* 22.745*	172.1 219.5	175.7 217±4
21	$NO_2=NO+O$	(≡N=O)---O	$2S^22P^3$	—	4.4525	$2P^2$	2/2	8.7191*	284.5	305.9
22	$N_2O=NO+N$	N-O	$2P^1$	1/1	9.2839	$2P^1$	1/1	9.7979	460.2	481.8
23	$N_2O=(N_2)+O$	(N_2)=O	—	—	22.745*	—	—	8.7191*	172.5	167.4
24	$NO_2=N+O_2$	(N)-(O_2)	$2S^22P^3$	1/5	9.4826	—	—	8.9835	445.3	439.3

Note: * - calculations of P_E-parameter are done using the ion radius (r_i)

All atoms, covalent and ionic radii were taken basically according to Belov-Bokii. For atoms C, N and O also the possibility to change covalent radii depending upon the bond repetition factor was taken into consideration. For the same elements average statistical values of P-parameters are given as P_E / k – where k – hybridization coefficient, that assumes the possibility to further calculate average value of bond energy.

Spatial-Energy Principles of Hybridization

Hybridization means the mixing of atom orbitals of different types of the given atom in one molecular (or atom) orbital. Hybridization principles are well-developed in accordance with the experimental data in the frames of general theories of valence bond (VB) and molecular orbitals (MO).

But the sources of energy directedness of hybridization processes have to be further investigated and discussed.

In [1] there is a conclusion based on the analysis of multiple computational and experimental data that the most valence-active are the orbitals with minimum values of P_0-parameters. Let us apply this principle to the hybridization of atom orbitals on the example of carbon and nitrogen atoms.

Carbon ($2s^2 2p^2$)

From Table 1 we can see that maximum value of P_0-parameter of $2p^2$-orbital equals 10.061 eVÅ, but the minimum value of P_0-parameter of $2s^1$-orbital is smaller (equaled to 9.029 eVÅ). This means that $2s^1$- orbital is more valence-active than $2p^2$-orbital. This conditions their hybridization. The calculation according to equation (1) produces the value of P_0-parameter of $2p^3$ (hybridized) orbital equaled to 13.213 eVÅ. This is much smaller than P_0-parameter of $2s^2$-orbital (14.524 eVÅ). Therefore, only the following hybridization options can occur: $2p^3 + 2s^1$; $2p^2 + 2s^1$; $2p^1 + 2s^1$; this corresponds to single, double and triple bonds of hybridization of sp^3, sp^2 and sp types.

Nitrogen ($2s^2 2p^3$)

P_0-parameter of $2p^3$-orbital equals 15.830 eVÅ, and $2s^1$-orbital – 10.709 eVÅ. Therefore, they are hybridized with the formation of $2p^4_r$-hybridized orbital responsible for σ-bond sp hybridization where P_o=19.193 eVÅ. But this is still greater than P_0-parameter of $2s^2$-orbitals (17.833 eVÅ). That is the hybridization process will continue due to $2s^2$-

orbital with the formation of $2p^5_r$-orbital (P_o=21.966 eVÅ) responsible for 2π-bond of $s-p$ hybridization.

These are main hybridization options of orbitals in carbon and nitrogen atoms in this approach. Less possible are metastable states with the hybridization of $2s^2+2p^2$ type with carbon and $2s^2+2p^3$ - of nitrogen.

The initial hybridization principle is applied for the analysis of energy directedness of mixing of atom orbitals for some other structures (Table 2). Computational values of P_0-parameter of hybridized orbitals were further used to determine bond energies (E). In the supposition of pair inter-atomic interaction the structural P_C-parameter was calculated [1,7] following the principle of the addition of inverse values of initial values of P-parameters, and in this case – based on the following equation:

$$\frac{1}{E}=\frac{1}{P_C}=\frac{1}{\left(P_E\frac{N}{K}\right)_1}+\frac{1}{\left(P_E\frac{N}{K}\right)_2} \qquad (3).$$

where N – coefficient of bond repetition factor, K – hybridization coefficient that usually equals the number of registered atom valence electrons. The half of inter-nuclear distance was frequently used as a dimensional characteristics R for binary bond. The same – for hydrogen atom in halogen-hydrogen.

The corresponding calculations for several structures are given in Table 2. From Table 2 it is seen that hybridization coefficient (K) in the crystalline carbon structures observed equals the coordination number. And for σ-bond of nitrogen K=3, this corresponds to the number of valence electrons $2p^3$-orbital: $\kappa_1 = n_1$=3.

The comparison of computational values with experimental data by bond energy [8] given in Table 2 characterizes rather high efficiency of this method. Usually a ratio error does not exceed 0.1% and not more than 5% in other cases.

Besides, it should be noted that the given model mainly confirms the approved conclusions and results of the corresponding computational methods of bond energies as applicable to certain structures, the list of which in this paper is limited only by the authors' interests.

Calculation of Chemical Bond Energy via the Average Values of P_0-Parameters

The application of methods of valence bond and molecular orbitals to complex structures meets significant difficulties regarding the prediction of hybridization energy directedness and type of bonds being formed. Let us consider several opportunities of using P_0-parameter method. It is practicable to apply equation (3) to calculate the energy of chemical bonds, where K – mixing or hybridization coefficient that usually equals the number of registered valence electrons, and $P_э$ (N/κ) has a physical sense of averaged energy of spatial-energy parameter falling on one valence electron of registered orbitals. But for complex structures $P_Э$ -parameter is averaged by all main valence orbitals.

Let us first approve such an approach on binary molecules. For binary molecules the dissociation energy (D_o) corresponds to the value of chemical bond energy: D_o=E.

The results of calculating the dissociation energy by equation (3) given in Table 3 showed that P_C=D_0. For some molecules containing F, N and O the values of ion radius (in Table 3 marked with *) were used to register the ionic character of the bond in the process of P_E-parameter calculation. For molecules C_2, N_2, O_2 the calculations were done by divisible bonds. In other cases, the average values of bond energy were calculated. Computational data are not in conflict with the experimental [8].

With similar computation of average values of bond energy in complex structures the average values of P_E-parameters (taken from Table 1) were considered as well, but taking valence sub-levels into account (Table 4). In these cases P_C=E (bond energy).

It is also shown that in most cases, due to the influence of all the valence electrons of atoms, it is possible as a first approximation to be limited with the estimation of interaction only between basic bond atoms (for instance, C-H in hydrocarbon structures). To a greater extent this refers to hydrocarbon organic structures. But for nitrogen oxides and hydrides more accurate results are obtained with preliminary calculations of P_C-parameters of reaction intermediate products following the equation (3).

Then E is calculated according to the following equation:

$$\frac{1}{E} = \frac{1}{P_{C_1}} + \frac{1}{P_{C_2}} \qquad (4)$$

Where P_{C_1} and P_{C_2} - P_C-parameters of complex structure parameters.

Calculations based on equations (3 and 4) are given in Tables 3 and 4. At the same time, in some cases the results of calculations of bond energy for fragments of NH_2, NO_2 and N_2O that are introduced into other complex structures are given. The deviations of computational data from the experimental ones [8] do not exceed 10% for complex structures.

CONCLUSIONS

1. The energy of chemical bond in simple and complex structures can be satisfactorily determined by means of P-parameter method based on initial spatial-energy characteristics of free atoms taking hybridization of their atom orbital into account.
2. The proposed method for estimating the energy directedness of mixing atom orbitals agrees with the experimental data.

REFERENCES

[1] Fischer C.F. Average – Energy of Configuration Hartree – Fock Results for the Atoms Helium to Radon//*Atomic Data*.-1972. №4. p. 301-399.

[2] Klyushnikov O.I., Salnikov V.R., Bogdanovich N.M. Investigation of pyrovakites $La_{0.8-x}Sr_{0.2}MnO_3$ by means of X-ray electron spectroscopy. *Chemical physics and mesoscopy*. 2001. v.3. №2. p. 173-185.

[3] Korablev G.A. Spatial-Energy Principles of Complex Structures Formation. Netherlands. *Brill Academic Publishers and VSP*. 2005. 426 p. (Monograph).

[4] Waber J.T., Cromer D.T. Orbital Radii of Atoms and Ions //*J.Chem. Phys* —1965.-V 42.-№ 12.-p. 4116- 4123.

[5] Clementi E., Raimondi D.L. Atomic Screening constants from S.C.F. Functions. 1.// *J.Chem. Phys*.-1963.-v.38.-№11.-p.2686-2689.

[6] Clementi E., Raimondi D.L. Atomic Screening Constants from S.C.F. Functions. II.//*J. Chem. Phys*.-1967.-V.47. № 4.-p. 1300-1307.

[7] Korablev G.A., Kodolov V.I. Dependence of activation energy of chemical reactions upon spatial-energy characteristics of atoms – *Chemical physics and mesoscopy*. UdRC RAS. Izhevsk. 2001. №2.v.3. p.243-254.

[8] Gurvich L.V., Karachentsev G.V., Kondratjev V.I. et al. Breaking-off energies of chemical bonds. *Ionization potentials and affinity with an electron*. M: Science. 1974. 351 p.

In: Synthesis and Properties of Low- and High-Molecular Compounds ISBN 1-59454-716-5
Editor: Gennady E. Zaikov et al., pp. 101-136

Chapter 8

MODIFICATION OF POLYCYANURATES BY POLYETHERS, POLYESTERS AND POLYURETHANES. HYBRID AND INTERPENETRATING POLYMER NETWORKS

***A. Fainleib**[*1]*, ***O. Grigoryeva**[1]* ***and P. Pissis**[2]*

[1]Institute of Macromolecular Chemistry of the National Academy of Ukraine, 02160 Kyiv, Ukraine.

[2]Department of Physics, National Technical University of Athens, Zografou Campus, 15780 Athens, Greece

1. INTRODUCTION

Polycyanurates (PCN) offer a variety of excellent thermal and good mechanical properties, which commend them for use in high performance technology (e.g. as matrices for composites for high-speed electronic circuitry and transportation). For the electronics market, attractive features of PCN are their low dielectric loss characteristics, dimensional stability at molten solder temperatures (220-270°C), high purity, inherent flame-retardancy (giving the potential to eliminate brominated flame retardants) and excellent adhesion to conductor metals at temperatures up to 250°C [1]. Since the late 1970s, cyanate ester resins have been used with glass or aramid fibers in high-speed multilayer circuit boards and this remains their primary application. Several reviews [2-6] collecting the numerous publications (papers and patents) in the field of PCN synthesis, processing, characterization, modification and application have appeared since 1990s. In addition, like conventional FR-4 diepoxides, cyanate ester laminates retain the desirable (ketone) solution processing characteristics and the ability to be drilled, making possible to employ them in printed circuitboard manufacture. In the last two decades, aerospace composites have evolved into damage-tolerant primary and secondary structures utilizing both thermoset and thermoplastic resins. PCN homopolymers

[*] Address for correspondence: fainleib@i.kiev.ua.

develop approximately twice the fracture toughness of multifunctional epoxies while qualifying for service temperatures of at least 150°C, intermediate between epoxy and bismaleimides capabilities. PCN have already flown in prototype radomes and high gain antennae, with possible applications in primary and secondary structures of the High Speed Civil Transport (HSCT) and European Fighter Aircraft. PCN are also being qualified for satellite truss and tube structures and cryogenic, radiation-resistant components in the Superconducting Supercollider [7]. This is indeed the problem, to convince a traditionally conservative industry that the superior performance of PCN (which surpass the glass transition temperature and hydrophobicity of epoxies while matching their processability and are easily toughened) makes them worthy of further investigation in spite of their price, which is currently higher than the price of the epoxies. PCN must be traditionally cured at high temperatures in order to achieve complete conversion, which increases manufacturing cost, but reactive modification of PCN allows decreasing the high temperature of PCN post-curing. The primary drawback of PCN, which hinders more extensive application of the cured materials, however, is low room temperature toughness.

PCN are synthesized by a polycyclotrimerization reaction of cyanate esters (CER) of bisphenols (cf. Figure1).

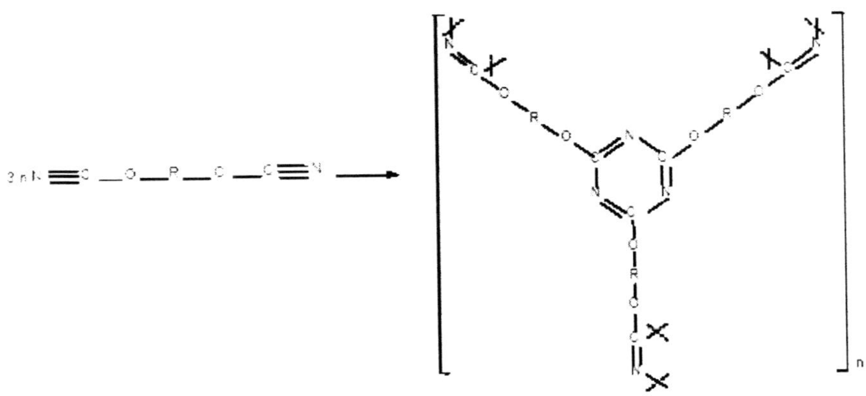

Figure 1. Generalised monomer structure and polycyanurate network formation

Cyanate esters may be modified by co-reaction with monomers or oligomers that contain active hydrogens (e.g., water, phenols, bisphenols, diamines, diepoxides, ethers, esters, etc) [2-6]. The PCN modified with reactive monomers usually have a homogeneous single phase, with properties proportional to the ratio of the two components.

PCN have been toughened, on the other hand, by physical modification through the addition of thermoplastics [2-6], with formation of so-called semi-interpenetrating polymer networks (IPNs) [3]. In this case, the degree of toughening depends on the final morphology of the polymer blends and composites, which, in turn, depends on the rate of phase separation during cure relative to the rate of polymerization [8]. A number of amorphous thermoplastics, including polyetherimides, polysulphones, polyethersulphones, polyarylates and polyimides, have been dissolved in aryl dicyanate formulations, and when they phase separate during cure, toughened systems are achieved [2-6]. Rubbers have also been used to toughen dicyanate esters [2-6]. Disadvantages of physical toughening are large-scale heterogeneity for interpenetrating polymer systems, difficulty in controlling domain size and poor processability. Some results have been published [9-11] where the researchers had used the combination of chemical and physical methods of modification. There are two possibilities to combine those kinds of modification: simultaneous use of reactive co-monomer and inert rubber or thermoplastics to change the chemical structure and phase morphology of polycyanurates and use of a rubber or a thermoplastic containing reactive chain ends. In the combined method, the ability of additives to react with the matrix is often of great interest since the effect is to improve the adhesion between phases in the case of a biphasic material, and in any case they ensure a chemical linkage between the oligomeric modifier and the network. Polycyanurates with well-defined morphology and improved characteristics have been synthesized [9-11].

2. Hybrid Networks from Cyanate Esters and Polyethers (Polyesters)

Last years several papers describing synthesis, structure and properties of polycyanurates modified with commercial polyethers [12-15] and polyesters [16] have been published.

Several series' of polycyanurate networks (PCN), based on the dicyanate of bisphenol A monomer (DCBA), were synthesized in the presence of different contents of hydroxyl-terminated polyethers (PEth), such as polyoxypropylene glycol (PPG) [12,13,15] and polyoxytetramethylene glycol (PTMG) [14,15]. The influence of the nature of the oligomeric modifier, initially miscible with DCBA, on the chemical structure, glass transition behaviour, phase morphology and mechanical properties of modified PCN was studied. The possibility of PEth incorporation into the PCN structure through mixed cyanurate ring formation has been discussed. A maximum PEth incorporated content of 0.1 mol of PEth per 1 mol of DCBA (~26-28 wt. %) irrespective of PEth type has been detected by comparison of calculated and experimental values of gel-fraction content. The theoretical value of gel fraction ($w_{g\ theor}$) was calculated using equation 1 and with the conjecture that the PEth was completely extracted.

$$w_{g\ theor} = (1-w_{PEth}) \times (2\alpha-1)/\alpha^2 \ , \qquad (1)$$

where α is the OCN-conversion (determined by both FTIR and DSC methods) and w_{PEth} is the weight fraction of PEth in the initial composition.

Based on the knowledge from Organic Chemistry [16,17] relating to reactions of organic cyanates with active hydrogen containing compounds and taking in account the results of investigations on modification of PCN by phenols [2], the authors of refs. [12,13] have proposed a scheme (cf. Figure 2) of chemical incorporation of hydroxyl-terminated modifiers into the PCN structure.

DMTA analysis has shown the formation of multiphase polymer compositions due to microphase separation of the components occurring during DCBA/PPG curing. The formation of very finely divided morphologies with highly interpenetrated phases, i.e. a PCN-rich phase, a mixed phase of PCN/PPG components and a PPG-rich phase can be clearly seen from the temperature dependence of loss modulus, E'' (cf. Figure 3).

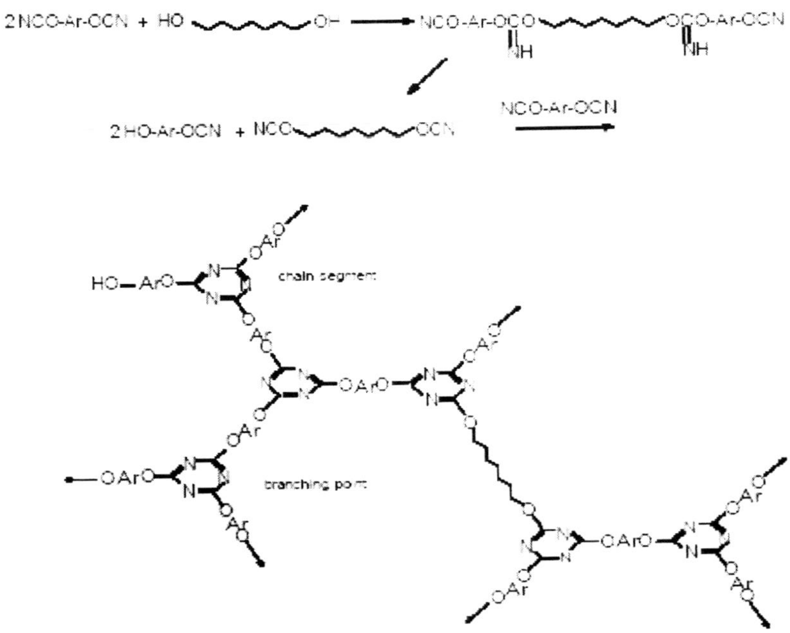

Figure 2. Scheme of chemical modification of PCN with hydroxyl-terminated polymer

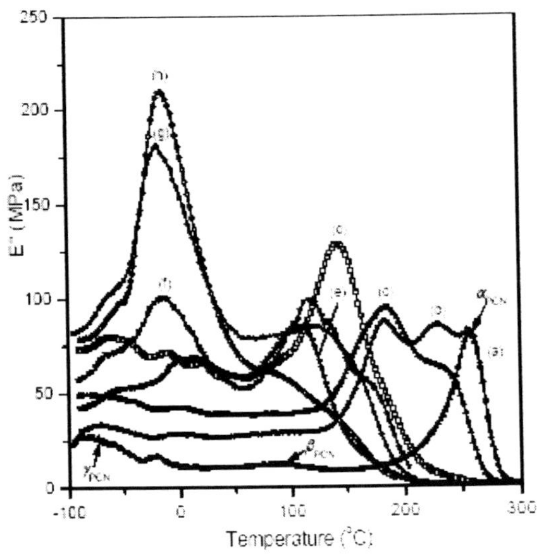

Figure 3. Loss modulus (E'') *versus* temperature for PCN/PPG composition (bending mode, 1Hz). (a) Pure PCN; (b) 98:2; (c) 95:5; (d) 90:10; (e) 85:15; (f) 74:26; (g) 69:31 and (h) 63:37 PCN/PPG (wt.%).

On the other hand, all PCN/PTMG cured compositions exhibited a single, broad glass transition (cf. Figure 4) that shifted to lower temperature as the modifier content was increased and the experimental T_g versus modifier content showed a slight positive deviation from the Fox equation (cf. Figure 5) for miscible polymer systems.

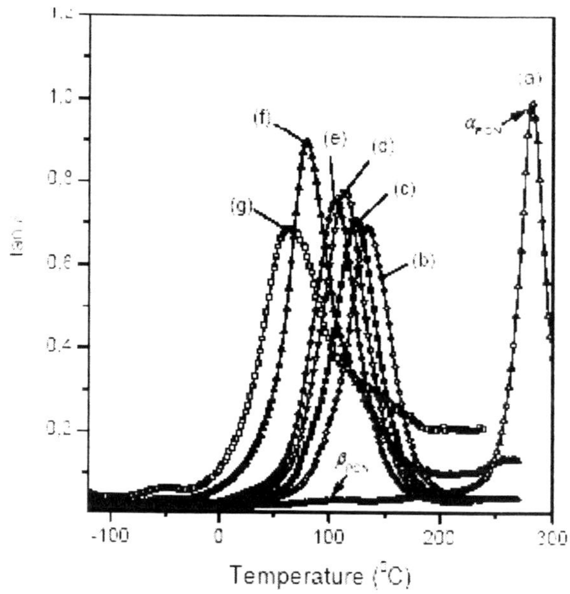

Figure 4. Loss factor (tan δ) *versus* temperature for the PCN/PTMG blends (bending mode, 10 Hz). (a) Pure PCN; (b) 74:26; (c) 71:29; (d) 69:31; (e) 66:34; (f) 62:38 and (g) 58:42 PCN/PTMG (wt.%).

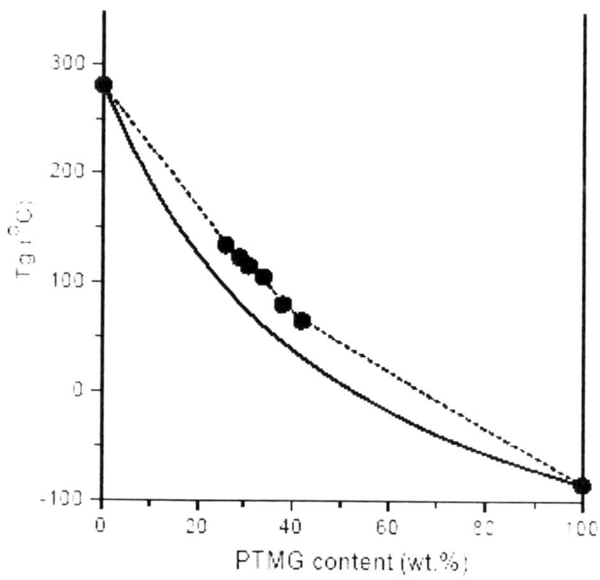

Figure 5. Tg values determined by (--●--) DMTA and calculated from the Fox's equation (—) for the PCN/PTMG compositions.

It was concluded [12] that PCN and PTMG have a higher degree of compatibility than PCN and PPG and, further, that the rate of the incorporation reaction in the case of PTMG is faster than in the case of PPG. Thus, the growing PCN/PTMG network has no time to phase separate. This conclusion, certainly, requires additional experimental verification.

The introduction of PEth into PCN improves the mechanical properties of the latter to maximum extent at the PEth content of 26-28% (cf. Figure 6), corresponding to the maximum PEth incorporation degree determined [12]. The higher values of tensile strength for PCN/PTMG can be explained by higher mixing of the components.

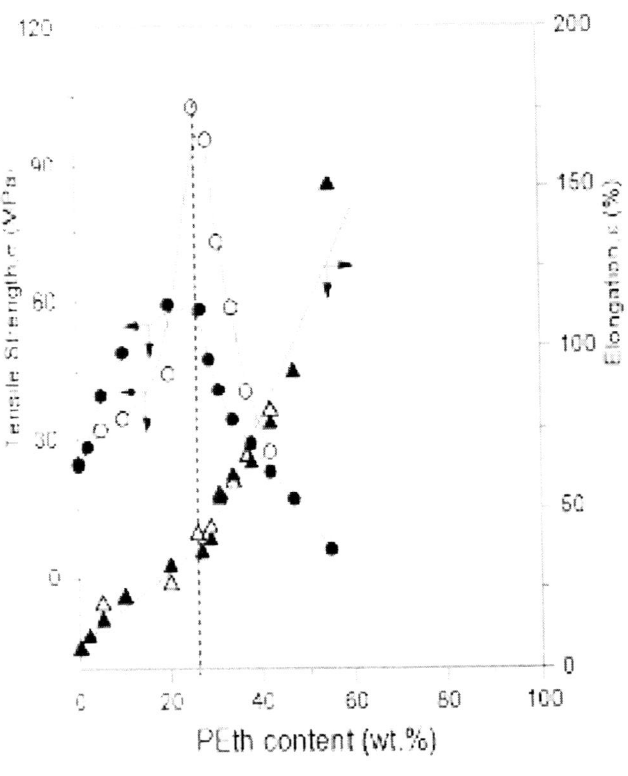

Figure 6. Tensile strength, σ(●,○) and elongation at break, ε (▲,△) for the PCN/PEth compositions as a function of modifier (PEth) content. (●,▲) PPG; (○,△) PTMG.

Polycyanurate network was modified with hydroxyl–terminated polyester, poly(butylene glycol adipate), PBGA, by polycyclotrimerization of bisphenol A dicyanate in the immediate presence of PBGA [18]. The modified networks with PBGA content from 5 to 20 wt. % were characterized by a combination of FTIR, DSC, TMA, TGA, impact testing and sol-gel analysis. It has been established that almost the whole PBGA was chemically incorporated into the PCN structure. It is supposed that the chemistry of such incorporation is the same as that shown in Figure 2. The Tg values for the compositions studied were determined from TMA using two static loads, 100 and 1900 mN, as well as from DSC data. The concentration dependence of Tg determined is presented in Figure 7.

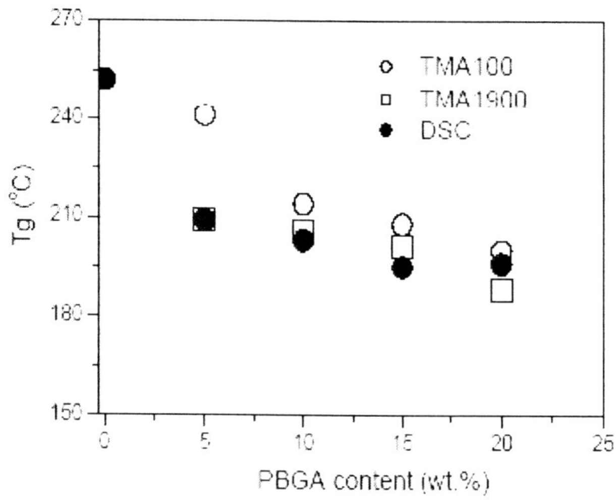

Figure 7. Composition dependence of glass transition temperature, Tg for PCN/PBGA

We can observe a quite sharp reduction of T_g for PCN modified with 5 % of PBGA (reduction of T_g by 17 %). However, further increase of PBGA content up to 20 % reduces T_g just by 5 % more. The authors of ref. [18] suppose that the sharp decrease of T_g by introducing 5 % of PBGA is connected with significant destruction of the regularity of the polycyanurate network structure. The further increase of PBGA content does not reduce the T_g value strongly because, as it was noted above, almost the whole PBGA is chemically incorporated into the network and cannot act as a usual plasticizer. It is worth to note a high convergence of the results obtained by different methods.

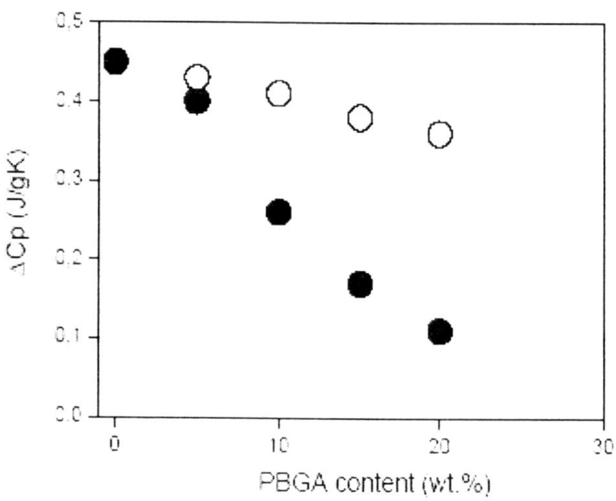

Figure 8. Composition dependence of ΔC_P at glass transition; • experimental (DSC) and o calculated for PCN/PBGA assuming both additivity and no interactions between the components.

Figure 8 reports simultaneously the measured values of ΔCp as a function of the concentration of PBGA and the calculated variations of ΔCp determined from pure PCN on the basis of the law of additive assuming that PCN and PBGA do not interact. We can see that the higher the content of PBGA, the higher the difference between experimental and calculated values of ΔC_P. Thus, according to the "strong-glass" glass former liquid concept proposed by Angell [19, 20], the authors of ref. [18] conclude that the higher the content of PBGA, the stronger the interaction between the components.

It is shown [18] that the introduction of PBGA does not drastically reduce the thermal stability of the PCN network while the impact properties are improved significantly. It is seen from Figure 9 that by introducing even 20 % of PBGA into PCN the temperature of onset of degradation of the latter decreases just by 5 %, while the impact strength decreases by 86 %. It is concluded [16] that the modified PCN developed can be successfully used simultaneously at high temperatures and high loading.

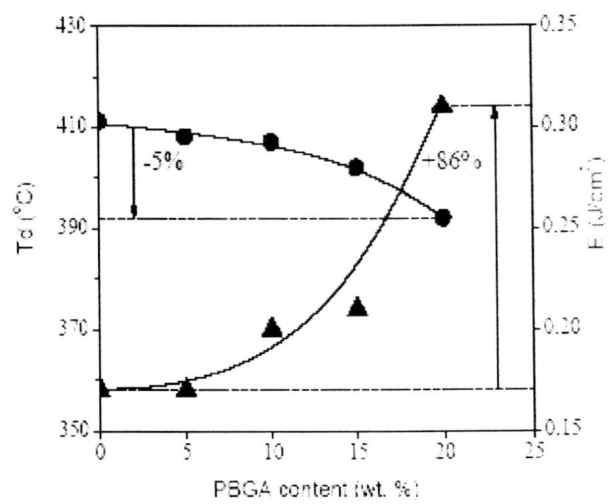

Figure 9. Composition dependence of temperature of degradation, Td (onset) and adsorbed energy, E for PCN/PBGA.

3. Polycyanurate-Polyurethane Grafted Semi-IPNs

In 1992-1994 the first papers [21-25] on synthesis, kinetic peculiarities and characterization of structure-property relationships of polycyanurate-polyurethane semi-IPNs were published. The idea behind these semi-IPNs was to synthesize a new material from widely used linear polyurethane as a thermoplastic elastomer and to intensively develop high performance cyanate ester resins (CER) as a thermoset. Linear segmented polyurethanes (LPU) exhibit rubbery characteristics and thermoplasticity that is directly connected with their structure. Linear segmented polyurethanes are characterized by internal heterogeneity specified by phase separation of soft and hard block of polymer chain. CER formulations offer a variety of excellent thermal and other properties (see section 1), which commend them for use in high performance technology (e.g. high speed electronic circuitry and aerospace composite matrices).

3.1. Synthesis, Chemical Interaction between Components, Reactive Grafting and Compatibilization

The attempt was undertaken to combine the best properties of both materials (polycyanurate and polyurethane) in their semi-IPN. First the suggestions about possible chemical interaction between components in polyurethane-polycyanurate semi-IPNs leading to formation of chemically grafted semi-IPNs were published by Fainleib and co-authors [21] and then confirmed in later works [22-25].

Polycyanurate-polyurethane semi-IPNs were prepared by polycyclotrimerization of dicyanate ester of bisphenol A (DCEBA) in the immediate presence of segmented linear polyurethane, LPU (molar mass 40000 g/mol) synthesized from 4,4'-diphenylmethane diisocyanate, oligobuthylene glycol adipate (molar mass 1000 g/mol) and 1,4-butane diol as a chain extender. Calculations made [21] by comparison of the polycyclotrimerization kinetics (analysis of infra-red spectra) of pure DCEBA and in the blend with LPU have shown that, with increase of LPU content from 10 to 80 %, the portion of the cyanate groups consumption for the polycyclotrimerization decreases from 90 to 33 %. It was concluded that during semi-IPN synthesis at least two competitive chemical processes coexist: 1) formation of the polycyanurate network by polycyclotrimerization (see Figure 1) of DCEBA in the presence of linear LPU leading to components microphase separation, which begins at a certain reaction time due to incompatibility of the resulting components that is typical for IPN systems, and 2) chemical interaction between the forming network and polyurethane that prevents the components microphase separation. By that time, no references concerning the cyanate – urethane chemical reaction were found. The chemical interaction between cyanate and urethane was first investigated with model monofunctional low molar mass organic compounds [26]. As model compounds 4-tert-butylpheny cyanate (BPC) and phenyldodecanol urethane (PDU) were used.

Chromatograms obtained by HPLC for BPC/PDU=5:1 after heating at 150°C is plotted in Figure 10 [26]. The elution times are 9,2 min and 25,4 min for BPC and PDU, respectively. One can see a decrease of the height of the mentioned peaks with increasing reaction time. Simultaneously at t_e=5,3 min, t_e=17,3 min, and t_e=26,9 min three main products are eluted, as well as two additional products at t_e=30,0 min and t_e=31,3 min. The products with elution time 5,3 min and 26,9 min were identified as 4-tert-butylphenol (BP) and 4-tert-butylphenoxytriazine (BPT), respectively. As far as separate heating of BPC and PDU at the same conditions has not led to formation of the product eluted at t_e=17,3 min, it is reasonable to suppose that this one is the reaction product of an immediate interaction between BPC and PDU.

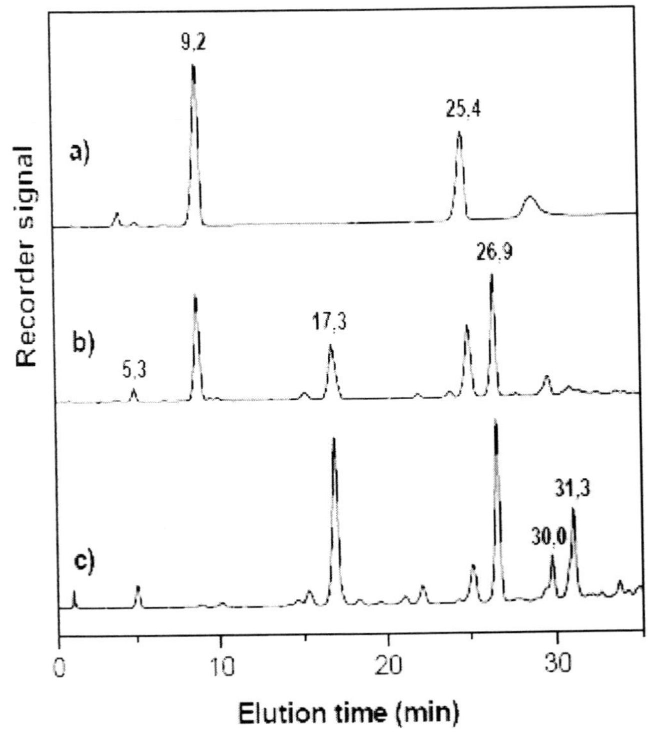

Figure 10. Chromatograms of BPC/PDU=5:1 (mol) after heating at 150°C. 0 min; b) 60 min; c) 180 min.

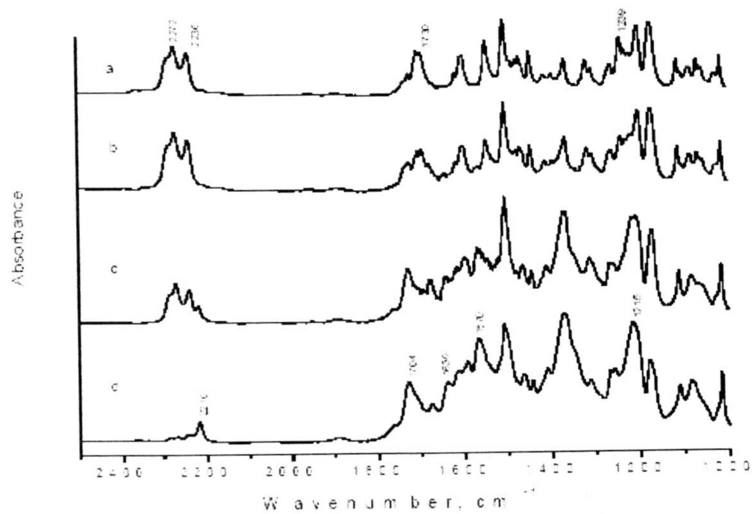

Figure 11. FTIR spectra of BPC/PDU=5:1 (mol) after heating at 150°C. a) 0 min; b) 60 min; c) 120 min; d) 180 min.

The normalized FTIR spectra for BPC/PDU=5:1 are presented in Figure 11. One can see the significant changes in spectra of this composition during heating at 150°C. The decrease of the normalized intensity of the 2236-2272 cm^{-1}-bands of cyanate groups confirms the participation of BPC in the chemical process. On the other hand, there are changes in position and intensity of the bands, which are attributed to the urethane group.

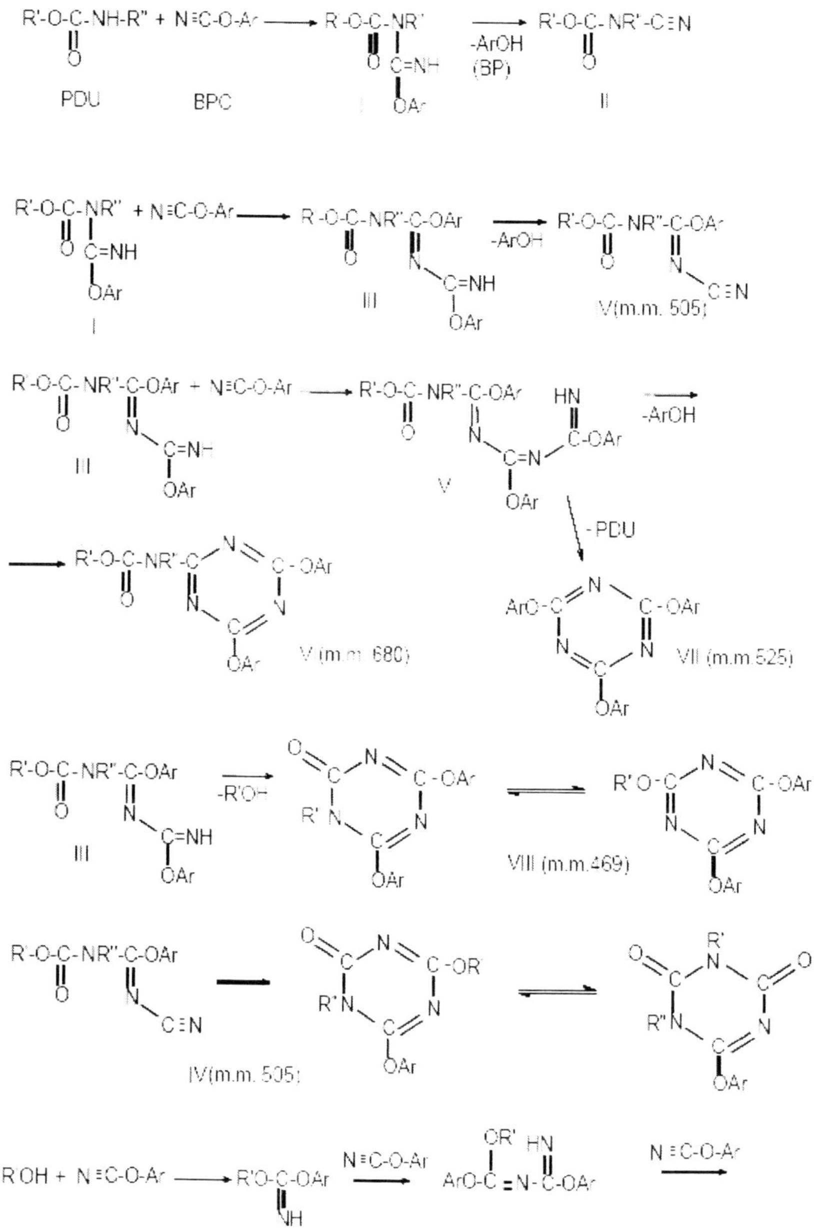

Figure 12 continued on next page

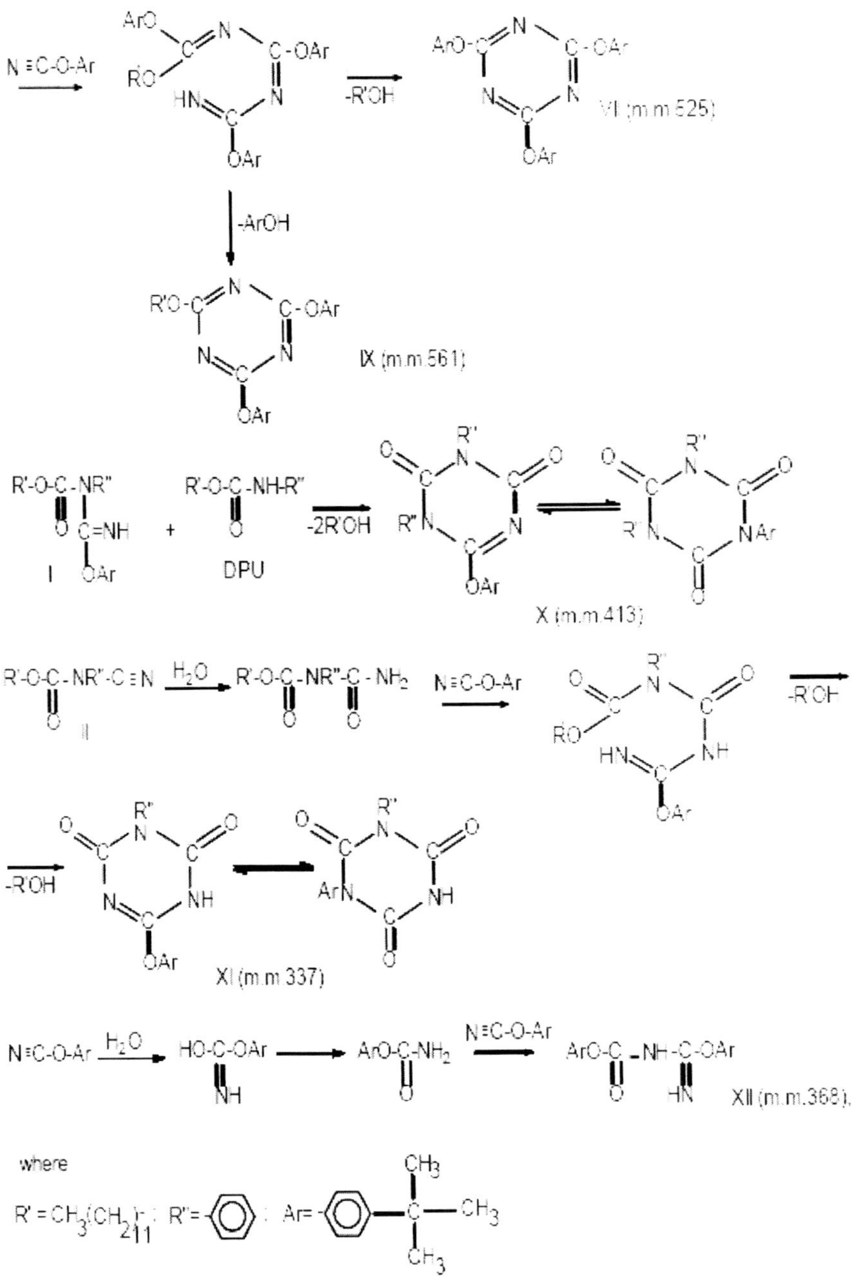

Figure 12. Chemical reactions and transformations in the mixture BPC/PDU.

As it can be seen, the intensity of the 1704 cm^{-1}-band ($\nu_{C=0}$ bonded) decreases with increasing intensity of the absorbance of the band at 1730 cm^{-1} ($\nu_{C=0}$ free), whereas the intensity of the 1239 cm^{-1}-band (δ_{N-H}) decreases with increasing intensity of the peak at 1215 cm^{-1}, which is attributed to aromatic OH. Besides, the appearance of peaks at 2216 and 1639 cm^{-1} characteristic for the nitrile group and at 1570 cm^{-1} of C=N for the cyanurate cycle (see

Figure 1) [2-4] followed by an increase of their intensity can be noted. MALDI-TOF experiments gave the following mass peaks (M^+): 300, 336, 369, 412, 470, 505, 526, 562, 680.

A scheme of the chemistry of the process studied (cf. Figure 12) with the formation of BP, BPT, some intermediate and additional products, including possible substituted cyanurate, isocyanurate and mixed triazine cycles, is presented.

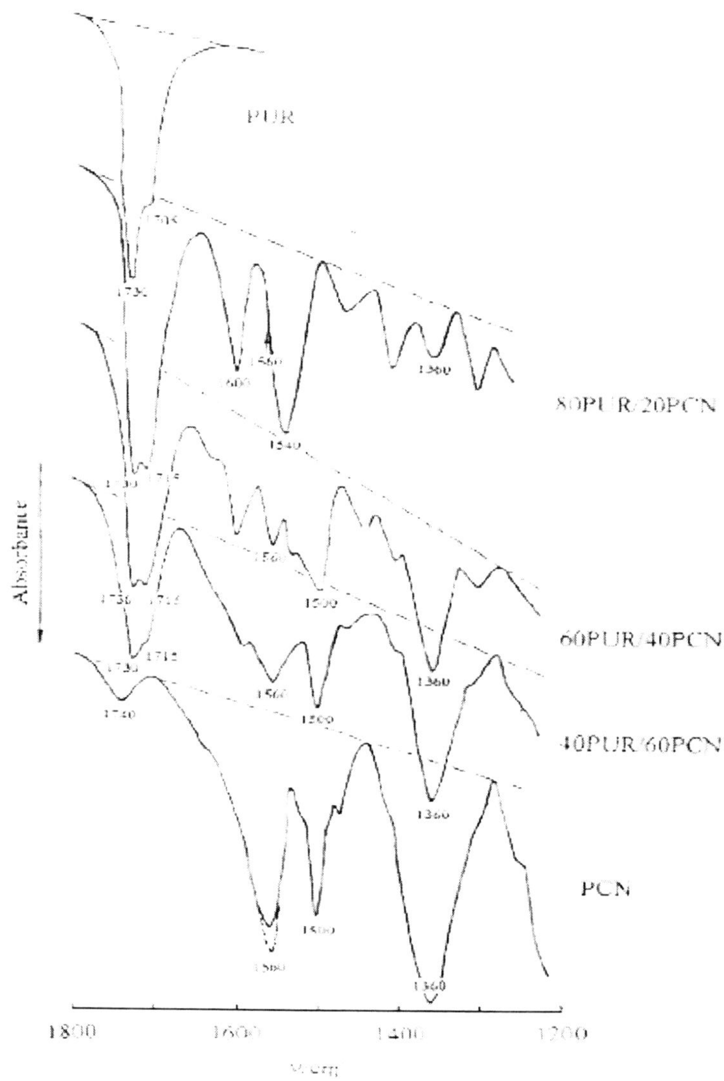

Figure 13. Multiple ATR spectra for individual PCN and PUR components, and some of the PCN/PUR IPNs. KRS crystal light guide, incidence angle $\Theta = 45^o$, $N = 5$ reflections. Dashed line at 1560 cm^{-1} indicates the absorption band after PCN post-curing treatment for 20 min at 560 K.

The existence of hybridisation effect via cyanate/urethane groups chemical interaction was evidenced in polycyanurate-polyurethane semi-IPNs by the method of multiple attenuated total reflection (ATR) infrared spectroscopy [27]. The ATR infrared spectra for some of the samples studied are given in Figure 13. The disappearance of the 2240-2270 cm^{-1} doublet in the spectra of properly prepared samples was accompanied by characteristic spectral changes depending on the polyurethane (PUR) content of the sample. These changes refer especially to appearance and enhancement of the 1560 and 1360 cm^{-1} bands of C=N and to absorption of polyurethane at 1700-1740 cm^{-1}.

One can see that pure PCN is characterized by intense 1560 and 1360 cm^{-1} absorption bands as a consequence of C≡N → C=N transformation. In PCN/PUR compositions, the intensity of these two bands decreases with PUR content but differently. Figure 14 shows these changes related to the intensity of the 1500 cm^{-1} band (benzene rings). The D_{1360}/D_{1500} ratio remained constant (~1.6) for all of compositions with 0-60% PU; for 80PUR/20PCN and 90PUR/10PCN networks, the 1500 cm^{-1} band could not be identified because of its overlapping with more intense PUR absorption at 1540 cm^{-1}. Contrarily, the D_{1560}/D_{1500} ratio certainly diminished with PUR content of the sample. There was no trace of the 1560 cm^{-1} band in the compositions with 80-90% PUR.

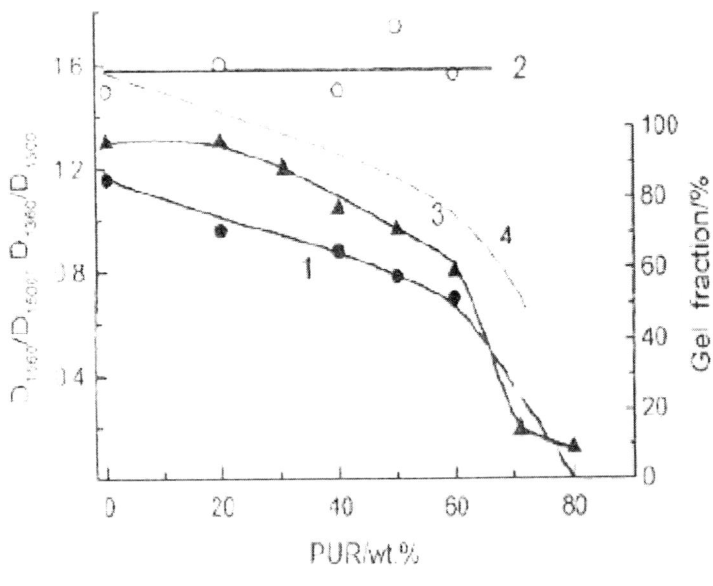

Figure 14. PCN/LPU semi-IPNs: compositional dependencies of the ratios of the band optical densities D_{1560}/D_{1500} (1) and D_{1360}/D_{1500} (2) in the ATR spectra, and the gel fraction value (3) as estimated in (4). Dashed curve 4 corresponds to the hypothetical dependence of the D_{1360}/D_{1500} ratio in the case the 1360 cm^{-1} band would be attributed to C=N groups in polycyanurate rings only.

Figure 14 compares also the plot of the D_{1560}/D_{1500} ratio versus composition with the compositional dependence of the gel fraction estimated before [24]. Practically similar dependence is observed for the curves 1 and 3, which is consistent with the generally adopted assignment of the 1560 cm^{-1} band to triazine ring vibrations, i.e. to insoluble PCN network domains. At the same time, the invariability of the D_{1360}/D_{1500} ratio (curve 2) validates the assignment of the 1360 cm^{-1} band to all of the -O-C=N- groups formed, irrespectively of their position in the network structure , triazine rings (conjugated C=N bonds) or substituted urethane (non-conjugated C=N bonds).

In fact, in case that the 1360 cm^{-1} band would be attributed to O-C=N groups in polytriazine structure only, the D_{1360}/D_{1500} ratio had to follow not to curve 2 but to the dashed curve 4 in Figure 14. Intercomparison of the curves 2 and 4 shows that at least 10-30% of the cyanate groups were spent for the reaction with PU at 20-60% PUR content in a composition. Besides, the small gel fraction for the compositions with 70-80% PUR (curve 3) correlates well with the absence of any indication of the 1560 cm^{-1} band in the ATR spectrum of the 80PUR/20 PCN composition. This result suggests an obvious predominance of simple grafting of DCEBA to urethane groups over polytriazine network formation. Such small contribution of the cyclotrimerization process may be explained by insufficient cyanate concentration and low probability for the elementary act of trimerization because of the 'dilution effect'.

It is noteworthy that the above estimates agree well with recent IR/HPLC experiments performed by one of the authors on low-molecular model cyanate/urethane blends [26]. It was found that, besides polycyclotrimerization, ca.20-30% cyanate formed co-products with urethane.

Finally, the notion about hybridization effect in PCN/PUR semi-IPNs is confirmed also by the carbonyl absorption behavior (Figure 13). Weak absorption at 1740 cm^{-1} in pure PCN is associated with some side, e.g., oxidative, reaction, which is just best registered for a surface layer analyzed by using the ATR technique. For pure PUR, as extensively hydrogen-bonded segmented elastomer, typical $\nu_{C=O}$ absorption splits into 1730 and 1705 cm^{-1} doublet corresponding to 'free' and 'H-bonded' carbonyls, respectively [28]. In PCN/PUR networks, $\nu_{C=O}$ absorption manifests itself at 1730 and 1715 cm^{-1} (Figure 13). This result is consistent with the hybridization idea. Really, cyanate/urethane reaction leads evidently to better mixing of the components, destruction of the interurethane hydrogen bonds, and to formation of the substituted urethanes (carbamates) as indicated above. According to [29], for substituted urethanes the $\nu_{C=O}$ bands are typically displaced by ~15±5 cm^{-1} to lower frequencies compared to those for urethane. Consequently, the 1715 cm^{-1} band may just correspond to substituted urethane groups deprived of hydrogen bonding (1730 cm^{-1}→ 1715 cm^{-1}).

3.2. Kinetic Peculiarities

The kinetic curves of polyurethane-polycyanurate semi-IPNs synthesis [21, 22] are presented in Figures 15 and 16. As it can be seen from Figure 15, the process of polycyclotrimerization of DCEBA is characterized by induction period, which strongly decreases at introducing LPU in the reaction system and disappears at LPU content in the composition higher than 20 %. We can also see that the higher the content of LPU in the system, the higher the rate of increase of cyanate groups conversion.

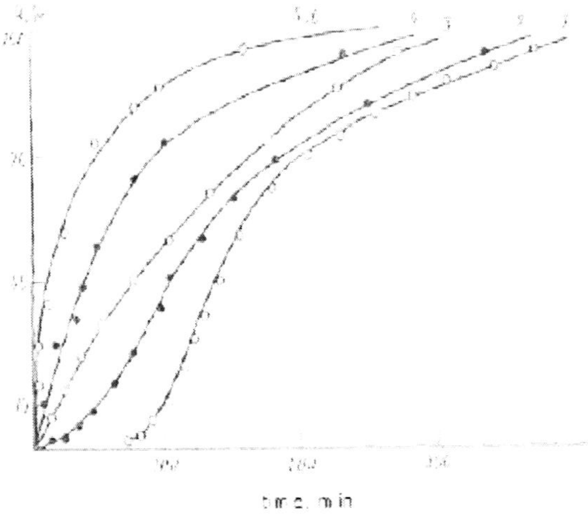

Figure 15. Conversion (Q) of cyanate groups *versus* time for PCN/LPU semi-IPNs. 100/0 (1), 80/20 (2), 60/40 (3), 50/50 (4), 40/60 (5) and 20/80 (6).

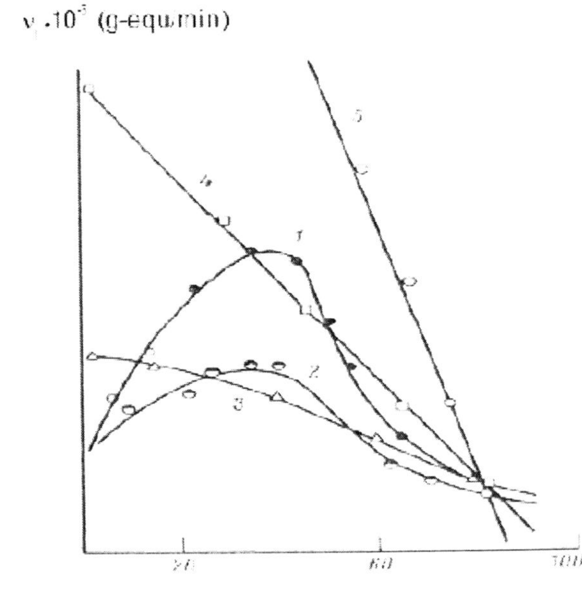

Figure 16. Reaction rate versus conversion of cyanate groups for PCN/LPU semi-IPNs. 100/0 (1), 80/20 (2), 60/40 (3), 50/50 (4), 40/60 (5)

Figure 16 presents the dependence of the reaction rate on cyanate groups conversion. One can see from Figure 16 that a low content of LPU (up to 20 %) does not change the kinetic curve shape, the maximal rate corresponding to 40% of cyanate groups conversion. For the compositions with higher LPU percentage the shape of kinetics curves changes – the reaction rate is observed to be maximal at the beginning (at no conversion of cyanate groups).

Vilensky and co-authors [30] have studied the kinetic peculiarities of DCEBA polycyclotrimerization in the presence of two linear polyurethanes: LPU-1 of mol. mass 40 kg/mol, based on polybutylene glycol adipate (PBGA, molar mass 1 kg/mol), 4,4'-diphenylmethane diisocyanate (DFMDI) and 1,4-butane diol (BD) with co-monomers ratio 1:2:1 and LPU-2 of mol. mass 40 kg/mol, based on polyoxytetramethylene glycol (PTMG, molar mass 1 kg/mol), DFMDI and BD with co-monomers ratio 1:2:1. Thermodynamic affinity and miscibility of LPUs used towards DCEBA were estimated by calculation of solubility parameters (δ, J/cm^3), polarities, interaction parameters and Krause's criterion.

Based on calculations, the authors concluded [30] that DCEBA had to be thermodynamically miscible with LPU-2 and immiscible with LPU-1. For both cases the chemical interactions between the components of IPNs studied have been confirmed.

3.3. Relaxation Behaviour and Phase Structure

The solubility parameters for PCN and LPU-1 were also calculated in [31]. In general, for polymer blends, if the values of δ for two components are similar, this implies that they will be miscible in the blends [32]. The calculated solubility parameters were δ=26.65 $(J/cm^3)^{1/2}$ for PCN component and δ=23.42 $(J/cm^3)^{1/2}$ for LPU-1 component. The authors noted that the values of solubility parameters for LPU-1 and PCN are not very close; thus one can conclude that PCN has to be thermodynamically immiscible with LPU-1 and the PCN/LPU-1 compositions should have a microheterogeneous structure.

In series of publications [23,25,27,33-38] several methods were used for characterization of the microphase structure of the semi-IPNs studied. Small-angle X-ray scattering (SAXS), differential scanning calorimetry (DSC) [25, 33-35], dynamic mechanical thermal analysis (DMTA) [25, 28-30], dielectric relaxation spectroscopy (DRS), and thermally stimulated depolarization currents (TSDC) [23, 37, 38] measurements have shown that pure PCN is characterized by a typical homogeneous structure, but for segmented LPU the microphase separation on the level of hard and soft domains due to their thermodynamic immiscibility was denoted. As for semi-IPNs, the destruction of the microphase separated morphology of LPU was observed and the microphase separation between PCN and LPU phases, expected from the difference of solubility parameters, was not found.

The miscible polyblends are characterized by a single glass transition temperature (T_g), which depends on the relative weight fractions of components and their respective T_g values. As an example, Figure 17 shows the Arrhenius plots for the α relaxation associated with glass transition for four IPNs and LPU based on DRS, TSDC and DSC data [37]. For comparison, a plot of the β relaxation in LPU is also shown. The lines are fits of the Vogel-Tammann-Fulcher equation and of the Arrhenius equation to the data for the α and the β relaxation, respectively, with reasonable values of the fitting parameters [37]. The α relaxation in Figure 17 shifts systematically to longer relaxation times/higher temperatures with increasing PCN content. For the β relaxation, on the contrary, the data for the IPNs (not shown in the figure) practically coincide with those for LPU, indicating that local motions in LPU are not significantly affected by the presence of PCN.

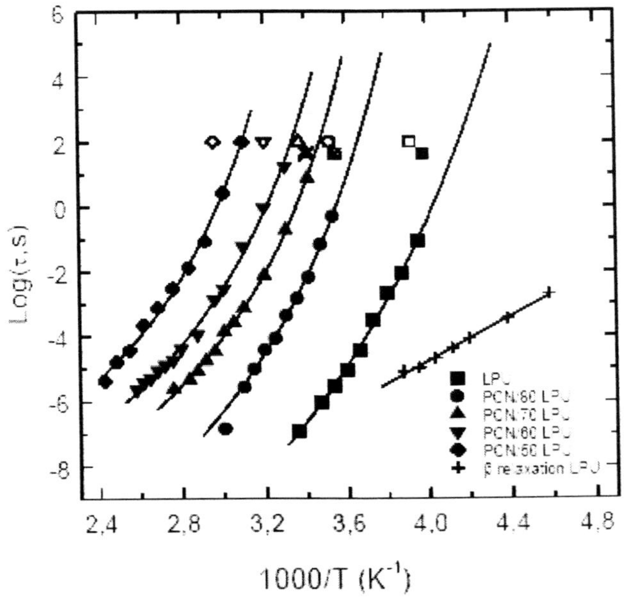

Figure 17. Arrhenius plot of the semi-IPNs indicated on the plot. Full symbols are DRS data for the α relaxation, crosses are DRS data for the β relaxation in LPU, open symbols are DSC data and centered-crossed symbols are TSDC data.

Such a "large-scale" homogeneity is confirmed by the existence of a single T_g in PCN/LPU semi-IPNs, estimated by DMTA, DSC [33-35], DRS and TSDC [37, 38] techniques, common data being presented in Figure 18. All presented T_g values show the same trend with composition. The theoretical compositional dependence of T_g of the PCN/LPU semi-IPNs can be obtained for DMTA data [25] according to the Fox [32] equation:

$$1/T_g = x_1/T_{g1} + x_2/T_{g2} \tag{2}$$

and for DSC data [27] according to the Couchman – Karasz [39] equation:

$$T_g = \frac{x_1 \Delta C_{p1} T_{g1} + x_2 \Delta C_{p2} T_{g2}}{x_1 \Delta C_{p1} + x_2 \Delta C_{p2}} \tag{3}$$

where x_1 is the weight fraction of LPU in the semi-IPNs, T_{g1} the glass transition temperature of LPU, ΔC_{p1} the specific heat increment at the glass transition of LPU and x_2, T_{g2} and ΔC_{p2} the corresponding quantities of PCN. Figure 18 shows the concentration dependence of T_g obtained from the prediction based on the Fox and Couchman – Karasz equations.

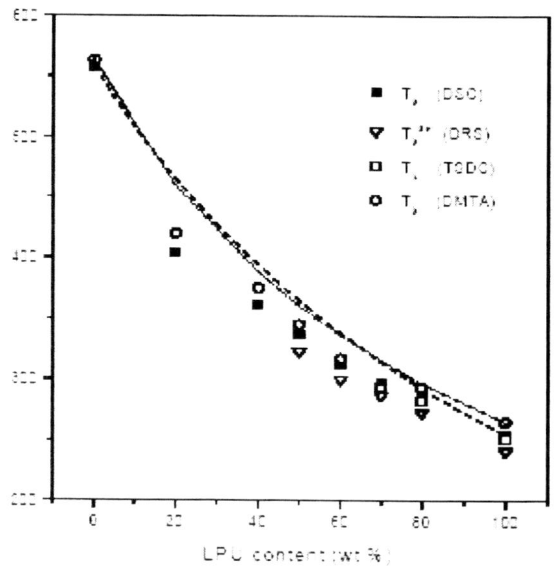

Figure 18. T_g values determined by DSC, DMTA, DRS, and TSDC versus LPU content. The dotted line is a fit of Fox's equation (eq. 2) to the DMTA data and the dashed line is a fit of the Couchman-Karasz equation (eq. 3) to the DSC data.

It can be seen that a slight negative deviation from both equations is observed. Such a deviation indicates that there is some interaction between the components in the system [40].

Interestingly, at the same time, combined CRS/DSC analysis [27] indicated the pronounced nanoscale ($\leq$ 2 nm) dynamic heterogeneity within or below the extraordinarily broad glass transition in these single-phase materials. The authors of ref. [27] noted that, despite the attainment of homogeneous structure in the hybrids, the combined CRS/DSC approach permitted to resolve a few kinds of motion that constitute the relaxation region within or close to the broad glass transition. Their molecular assignments could be safely made, and separate contributions of the PCN network and LPU to the relaxation spectra were estimated. On this basis, first of all, owing to the analysis of creep rate spectra, besides segmental dynamics heterogeneity, also some information concerning the nanoscale heterogeneity of network cross-linking was obtained.

3.4. Influence of Carbon Fiber Filler on Formation and Phase Structure

The influence of two carbon fiber (CF) fillers: basic and with a surface modified by orthophosphoric acid residuals (PCF) on kinetics of epoxypolycyanurate-polyurethane semi-IPNs formation and phase structure has been studied [41-43].

In Figure 19 the kinetic curves for the formation of pure epoxypolycyanurate (EPCN) and semi-IPNs with 20 and 50 % of polyurethane have been plotted. It can be seen that the reactions of cyanate and epoxy groups are accelerated with increasing LPU content in the system. For example, the time to achieve the same conversion of the cyanate and epoxy groups as for pure epoxypolycyanurate decreases for semi-IPNs with 20 % of LPU by 2 and 4 times respectively (Figure 19a, curves 2, 3) and for semi-IPNs with 50 % of LPU by 1,5 and 3 times respectively (Figure 19b, curves 2, 3). The additional accelerating effect for the above mentioned reactions is observed at introducing both carbon fiber fillers into the semi-IPNs studied. This can be seen from the kinetic curves given for semi-IPNs with 20 % of polyurethane component in Figure 19. The authors of refs. [42, 43] associate the acceleration of chemical processes with the additional chemical reactions between the components described in [21-23, 26, 27] and by interactions of polymers with the filler surface discussed earlier in [41].

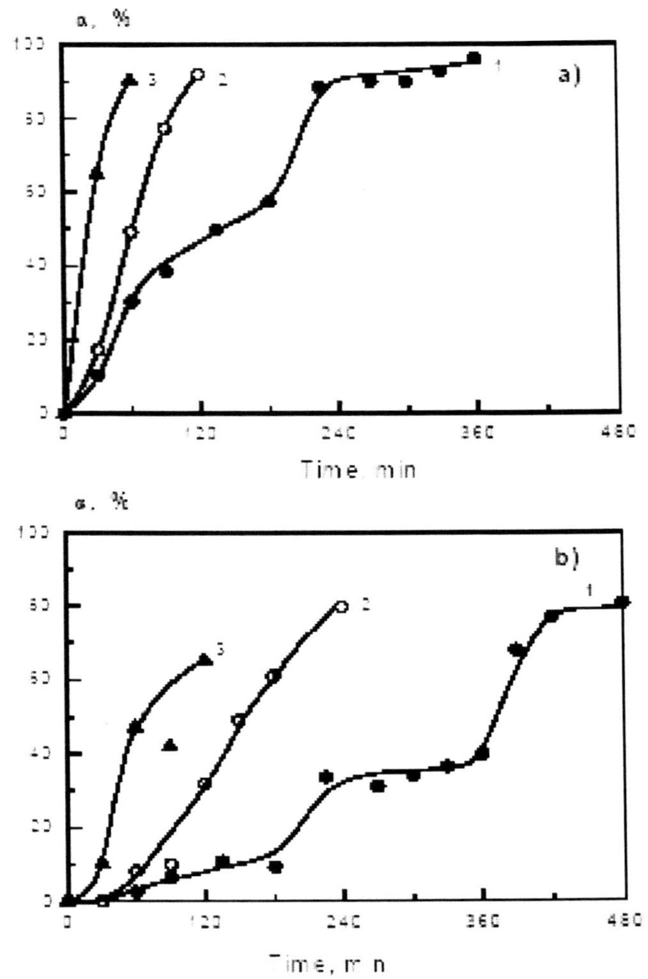

Figure 19. Kinetic curves of conversion of (a) cyanate and (b) epoxy groups for semi-IPNs with EPCN content: 100 (1), 80 (2), 50 (3) wt. % .

The influence of the fillers on the phase structure of the obtained semi-IPNs was studied by DMA. For the 50/50 semi-IPN a wide single peak on the temperature dependence of E'' has been observed. The authors of [42, 43] explain this fact by forced compatibility of the components. This apparent compatibility appears as a result of a competition between the rates of the chemical processes between the components and phase separation (diffusion). As it was shown above, the rate of polycyanurate network formation increases by 4 times by introducing the LPU to the cyanate monomer. Thus, phase separation does not occur.

The authors of references [42, 43] have investigated the influence of the introduction of filler, as well as of its surface modification on the degree of microphase separation in the semi-IPNs studied. In Figure 20 the mechanic spectra of unfilled 50/50 semi-IPNs and those containing from 4 to 24 vol.% of CF are presented.

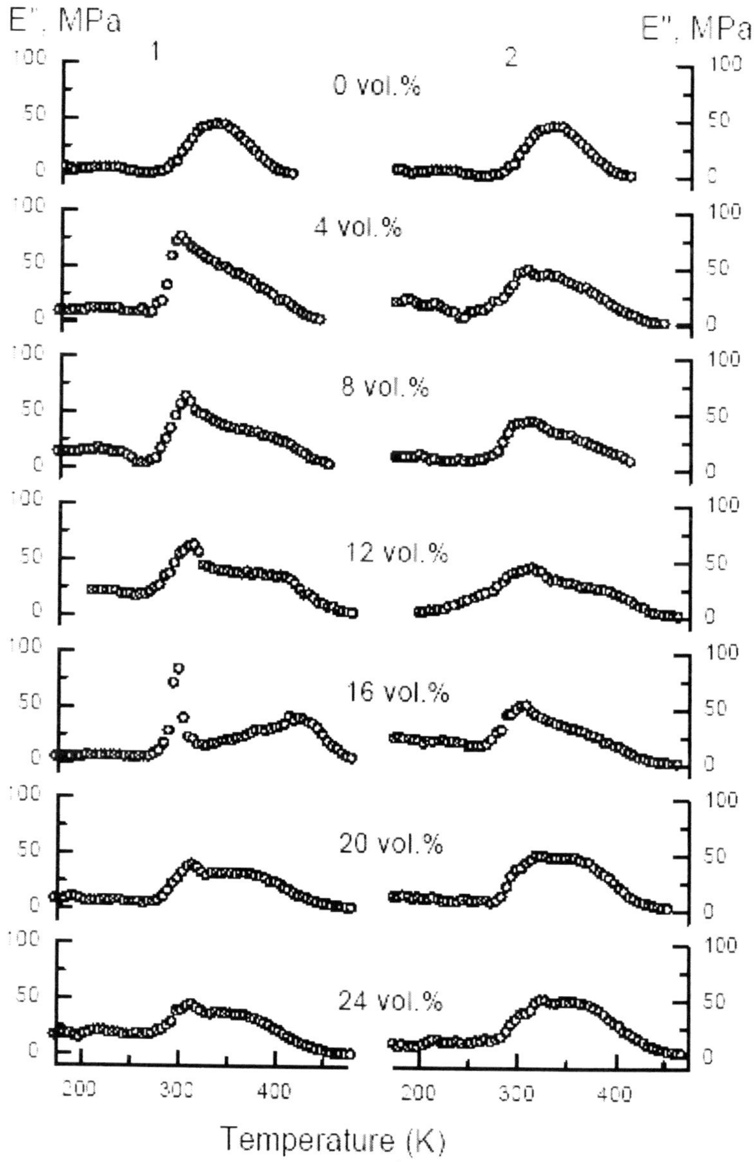

Figure 20. Temperature dependence of loss modulus for semi-IPNs 50/50 filled with CF (1) and PCF (2).

As can be seen from Figure 20, the introduction of small additions (4 vol.%) of CF into semi-IPNs leads to the appearance of a clearly observed relaxation maximum in the mechanical spectrum related to LPU and to a downward shoulder in the temperature interval from 325 to 425 K related to relaxation processes conditioned by molecular mobility in the interface. Thus, the introduction of CF filler generates a microphase separation in the semi-IPNs studied. The further increase of filler content leads to extension of the microphase separation. As it is seen from Figure 20, the intensity of the peak in the region of 325-425 K increases and two peaks with the maxima close to T_g of LPU and EPCN are observed in the mechanical spectrum of semi-IPNs filled with 16 vol.% of CF. At concentrations of CF 20 – 24 vol.% the spectrum looks rather like a curve with one wide peak in the temperature region between T_g of LPU and EPCN. Analyzing the mechanical spectra shown in Figure 20 the authors of refs. [42, 43] supposed a preemptive adsorption of LPU onto CF surface and formation of 2 phases: a polymer phase reach in EPCN and a phase rich in LPU adsorbed onto filler particles at small concentrations of the filler. At higher content of the filler it is supposed that both components adsorb onto the filler surface that decreases the degree of phase separation in the system. Comparative analysis of the influence of the filler surface activity on the phase structure of the semi-IPNs filled with CF and PCF has shown that the system filled by the latter is characterized by lower level of heterogeneity. As far as the filler was introduced into the system on the stage of network formation, the physical adsorption of the LPU onto PCF surface is perhaps compensated by competitive chemisorption of EPCN due to chemical reactions of epoxy and cyanate groups of epoxycyanate oligomer with PCF surface functional groups that hampers the phase separation process.

Additionally, an essential increase of specific electrical resistance, reduction of combustibility and existence of piezoelectric effect have been found [44] for polycyanurate-polyurethane semi-IPNs filled with PCF.

3.5. Properties. Adhesion to Metals

The adhesion characteristics of polycyanurate modified with linear polyurethane based on the principle of semi-IPNs have been studied [31]. Aluminum and titanium plates were used as substrates to prepare the joints bonded by DCEBA curing in the presence of PU. Two clear dependencies of adhesive strength, on adhesive layer thickness and on PU content, have been observed (see Figures 21 and 22). The dependence of adhesive strength value on adhesive layer thickness has been observed for all of the compositions studied. Generally, the thicker the adhesive layer, the higher the adhesive strength for the systems studied. Introduction of LPU first increases the shear strength of PCN to aluminium and titanium. The maximal values of adhesive (shear) strength are achieved at LPU content of 20-25 wt.%, corresponding to formation of the hybrid PCN/LPU network only, owing to the chemical incorporation of LPU into PCN. At higher LPU contents semi-IPNs based on the hybrid network and a non-incorporated LPU are formed. The presence of non-incorporated LPU in the adhesive layer leads to reduction of the adhesive strength. Polycyanurates modified with polyurethanes could be used potentially as high-temperature heating-melt adhesives, coatings, and sealants, as well as matrices for high-performance composites [45].

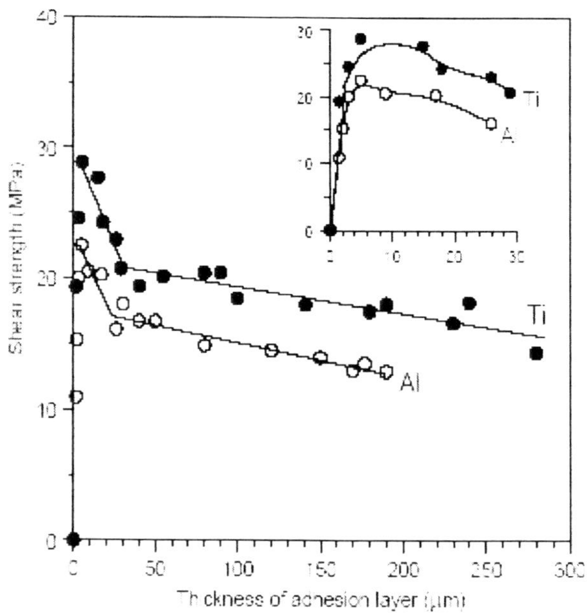

Figure 21. Adhesive strength versus adhesive layer thickness for pure PCN network (metal substrates – Al and Ti).

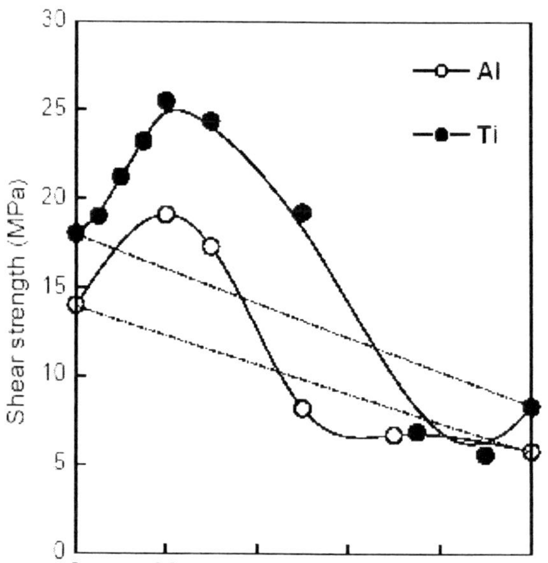

Figure 22. Composition dependence of adhesive strength for aluminium (○) and titanium (•) (layer thickness h ≈150 μm).

4. Polycyanurate-Polyurethane Linked Full-IPNs

The first publication related to synthesis and characterization of polycyanurate-polyurethane full IPNs has appeared in 2000 [46, 47]. Full sequential interpenetrating polymer networks (seq-IPNs) of cross-linked polyurethane (CPU) and cyanurate (PCN) based on thermally cured dicyanic ether of Bisphenol A (DCEBA) were characterized by small-angle X-ray diffraction, dynamic mechanical analysis, stretching calorimetry and microhardness measurements. Neat CPU was shown to be a microphase-separated system characterized by a regular, three-dimensional macrolattice of network junctions, embedded in uniform-size microdomains of stiff chain fragments, which spanned the continuous matrix of soft chain fragments. In contrast, no large-scale structural heterogeneities were detected in the PCN. The X-ray long spacing (L), the degree of microphase segregation (DMS), the α-relaxation temperature and the mechanical properties (elastic modulus, E and microhardness, H) were studied as functions of PCN content. Results were explained [46] in the light of a model that discussed the maximum degree of CPU swelling by molten DCEBA as a function of composition. It has been suggested that predominantly chemical interactions between the molten DCEBA and the stiff chain fragment microdomains, reinforcing primary physical interactions, are responsible for the observed transition at 40% PCN content to more homogeneous phase morphology of seq-IPNs.

The characteristic dependence of L, DMS, Tg, *E* and *H* of a series of full, seq-IPNs upon composition has been explained according to the following model. The maximum degree of the CPU swelling by molten DCE is reached already in the first composition interval $\varphi<0.15$. However, the volume increment of the swollen CPU exceeds, by far, the actual content of the PCN within corresponding seq-IPNs. Hence, in the second composition interval $0.15\leq\varphi\leq0.5$ only a relatively small fraction (i.e. of the order of $\varphi\approx0.15$ of the available molten DCEBA) was in a direct interaction with the expanded soft chain fragments of the CPU, whereas the remaining DCEBA simply filled the empty space created by swelling. This, according to the authors of ref. [46], facilitated the accessability of unreacted functional groups at the periphery of stiff domains of the CPU to strong interactions with the excess of molten DCEBA. As a result, with increasing PCN content the sharp interface between components is gradually smeared out until a completely homogeneous structure is developed in the composition interval $\varphi>0.5$. Predominantly, chemical interactions between the molten DCEBA and the stiff chain fragments microdomains of the CPU complementing primary physical interactions (dilution) are suggested [46] to be responsible for the observed cross-over to a more homogeneous phase morphology of seq-IPNs at $\varphi>0.4$. The main physical characteristics determined for these seq-IPNs are presented in Table 1.

The temperature dependences of heat capacity of the same full seq-IPNs in the 6-340 K range were studied [48] using adiabatic vacuum calorimetry. Using a calorimeter equipped with a static bomb and an isothermal shell, the energies of combustion of the CPU and of the three samples seq-IPNs containing 10, 30 and 50 wt. % of the PCN were measured. On the basis of the experimental data the thermodynamic functions of the research subjects $H^o(T)-H^o(0)$, $S^o(T)-S^o(0)$ and $G^o(T)-H^o(0)$ for the range from $T\rightarrow0$ to $T=340$ K were calculated and the standard enthalpies of combustion and the thermodynamic parameters of formation ΔH^o_f, ΔS^o_f and ΔG^o_f at 298.15 K were determined. The data obtained were used to calculate enthalpy, entropy and the Gibbs functions for the seq-IPNs synthesis. It was shown that the isotherms of diverse thermodynamic properties of interpenetrating polymer networks plotted versus their composition, in particular the molar fraction of the CPU per conditional mole, can be described by straight lines. This makes it possible to estimate the thermodynamic behavior of the seq-IPNs of any compositions at standard pressure within a wide temperature range. It was determined [48] that at molar content > 0.50 of PCN in seq-IPNs studied ΔG^{o}_{p} (ΔG^{o} of process) < 0 and this has allowed authors to conclude about thermodynamical miscibility of the components for seq-IPNs of these composition.

Table 1. Physical properties of polycyanurate-polyurerthane full seq-IPNs

CPU/PCN	Tg (K)	E (GPa)	10^5 x α_L (K^{-1})	H (MPa)
100/0	365	0.20	18.4	43.6
88/12	360	0.26	10.0	31.6
78/22	375	0.52	6.1	63.6
62/38	405	1.10	5.3	178.1
51/49	435	2.60	4.0	247.1
37/63	455/540	3.50	3.2	236.2
0/100	485/570	4.05	2.2	241.7

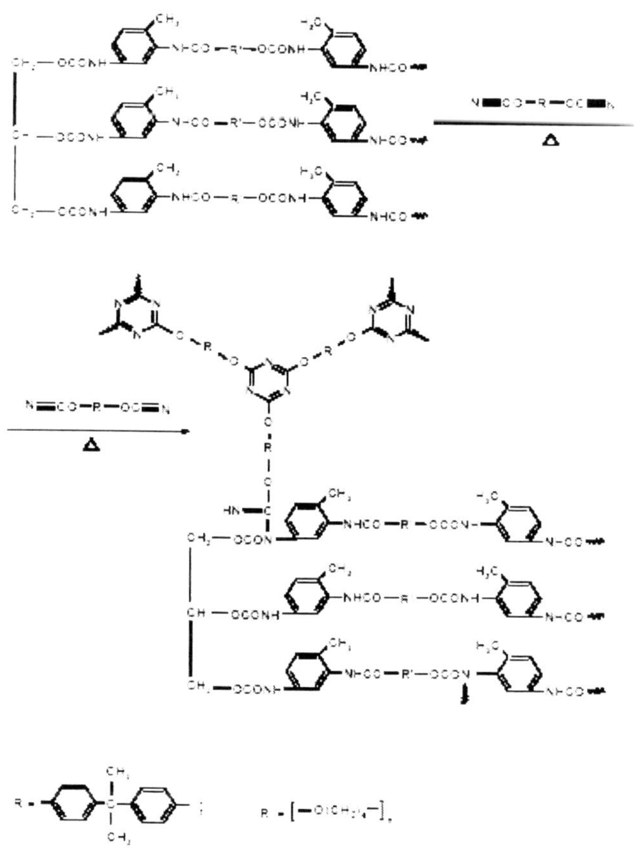

Figure 23. Scheme of chemical linking of PCN and CPU in full seq-IPNs.

The authors of ref. [48] have confirmed the high homogeneity of these full seq-IPNs with PCN content > 40 wt. % of PCN. They explained this fact by strong chemical interactions (linking) of the components in these seq-IPNs, especially in ones with high PCN content and confirmed their conclusions by the FTIR data. They have proposed a scheme of covalent links formation during polycyanurate-polyurethane full seq-IPNs synthesis (cf. Figure 23).

Using the method of thermogravimetry (TGA), the authors of ref. [49] have studied the stages of thermal oxidative degradation (cf. Figure 24) occurring in polycyanurate-polyurethane full seq-IPNs of different composition. Based on FTIR and TGA results they have established the formation of a new structure, a so-called hybrid network. They have shown that the coexistence of CPU, PCN and hybrid structures in these linked full seq-IPNs depends on the ratio of the components. According to the number of degradation stages three structures were found for the 90/10 CPU/PCN; PCN and hybrid structures were observed in the 70/30 seq-IPNs and the hybrid network is supposed [49] to be the main structure detected for the 50/50 seq-IPNs.

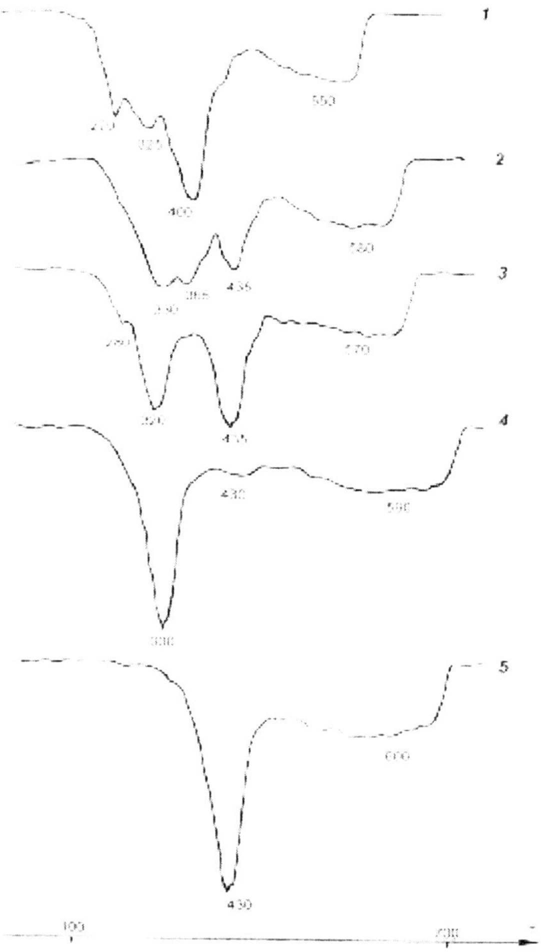

Figure 24. DTG curves. CPU (1), CPU/PCN = 90/10 (2), CPU/PCN = 70/30 (3), CPU/PCN = 50/50 wt. % (4), PCN (5).

Broadband dielectric relaxation spectroscopy (DRS) and thermally stimulated depolarization currents (TSDC) techniques were employed [38] to investigate molecular mobility in relation to morphology in PCN/CPU full seq-IPNs in comparison to semi-IPNs from PCN and linear LPU. As it was mentioned above [31] the semi-IPNs were found to be homogeneous at length scales larger than about 2 nm, whereas heterogeneity was suggested [27] at shorter length scales. The full IPNs are characterized [38] by microphase separation. Non-additivity of several physical properties with composition in both systems was explained in terms of increased free volume due to loosened segmental packing of chains confined to nanovolumes and of chemical bonds between the components. For example, Figure 25 shows in a log-log plot the real part of dielectric permittivity ε' against frequency f of the full PCN/CPU seq-IPNs at room temperature (298 K). The decrease of ε' with increasing f, observed for all the samples except for pure PCN, corresponds to the segmental (α)

relaxation, associated with the glass transition of the CPU phase, as indicated by measurements at various temperatures not shown here. The main result in Figure 25 is the observed non-additivity, i.e. ε′ does not change with composition as predicted by mean field theories for non-interacting PCN and CPU phases.

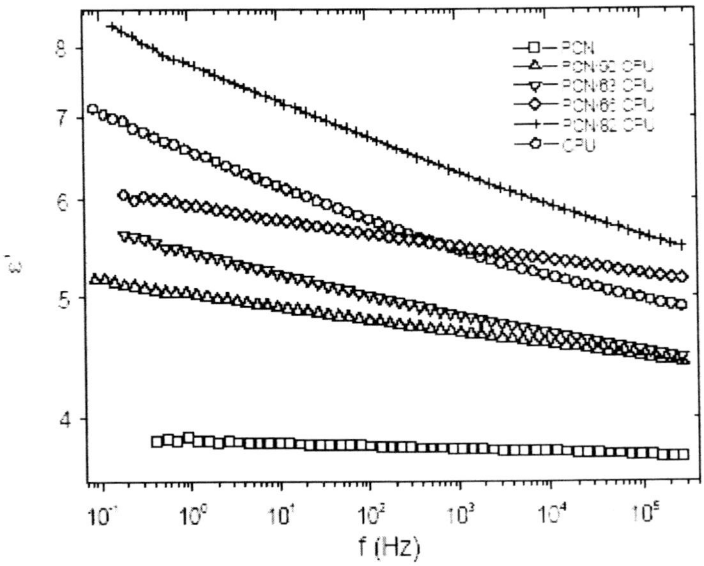

Figure 25. Log-log frequency plot of real part of dielectric permittivity, ε′ (f), at 298 K for the PCN/CPU IPNs indicated on the plot.

The authors of references [50, 51] have synthesized new sequential and *in-situ* sequential polycyanurate-polyurethane full IPNs and studied their structure-properties relationship. PCN based on 1,1-bis-4-cyanatophenyl-ethane (CPE) and CPU synthesized from an adduct of 1,1,1-trimethylolpropane with 2,4-toluene diisocyanate (1:3, mol) and poly(tetramethylene) glycol were used as the components for IPNs.

Sequential and *in-situ* sequential full IPNs with different weight composition (PCN/CPU = 100/0, 75/25, 50/50, 25/75) were prepared. Sequential IPNs were prepared by swelling of a film of preliminarily synthesized CPU by CPE followed by thermal polycyclotrimerization of the latter inside CPU. On the contrary, the *in-situ* method (some kind of simultaneous one) consisted of mixing all the monomers together, then synthesis of CPU in the presence of CPE monomer at low temperature and next synthesis of PCN by polycyclotrimerization of CPE inside CPU at higher temperature.

The investigation of the thermal and mechanical characteristics of full-IPNs synthesized was performed in the temperature regions above and below the glass transition. It has been observed that *in-situ* full IPNs exhibit higher values of density (cf. Figure 26) than seq-IPNs, as a consequence of enhanced intermolecular packing. In blends characterized by adhesion between interfaces and no molecular mixing at the boundary, the density of the blend would be expected to follow the rule of mixtures (dotted line in Figure 26). Generally, an abrupt variation of density values implies significant morphology changes. *In-situ* IPNs possess densities higher than those predicted by additive volume law and also systematically larger than those of the corresponding *seq*-IPNs. This result indicates unambiguously that *in-situ* synthesis improves the degree of interpenetration and chain packing leading to a marked reduction of free volume in the network.

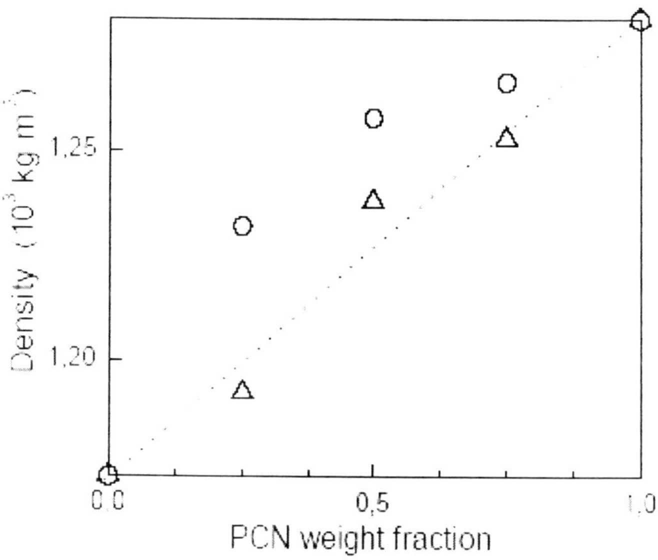

Figure 26. Dependence of the density ρ on the PCN weight ratio in *in-situ* (○) and sequential (Δ) full-IPNs. The diagonal dashed line represents the behavior predicted by the law of additive volumes.

Two well-defined Tg's are observed in all the IPNs samples (cf. Figures 27) revealing that microsegregation of CPU and PCN phases takes place. A significant convergence of Tg of CPU and PCN components in IPNs can bee seen from Table 2. It is very easy to calculate that the difference between the Tg values of the individual networks is 131 K while it is around 52-62 K between the components in IPNs. This can be explained by interpenetration process, as well as by the above mentioned chemical linking between the individual networks in IPNs. Thus, it emerges that PCN/CPU blends have a structure where the PCN phase is plasticized (α_a-peaks at increasingly lower temperatures than in pure PCN) while CPU soft segments are partially locked (α_a-peaks at increasingly higher temperatures than in pure CPU). According to the authors of ref. [51], it is believed that, in the interpenetration process, the junctions of PCN network between CPU soft segments can lock CPU chains by making disentanglement very difficult. Moreover, the hard-segment domains of PCN act as cross-links and filler particles to the soft segment matrix of CPU. This should lead to a decreasing mobility of CPU molecular groups and to a corresponding increase of the energy required for cooperative motions. On the contrary, the CPU phase, increasingly soft with increasing temperature, acts as a sort of internal diluent for the PCN matrix and lowers its Tg.

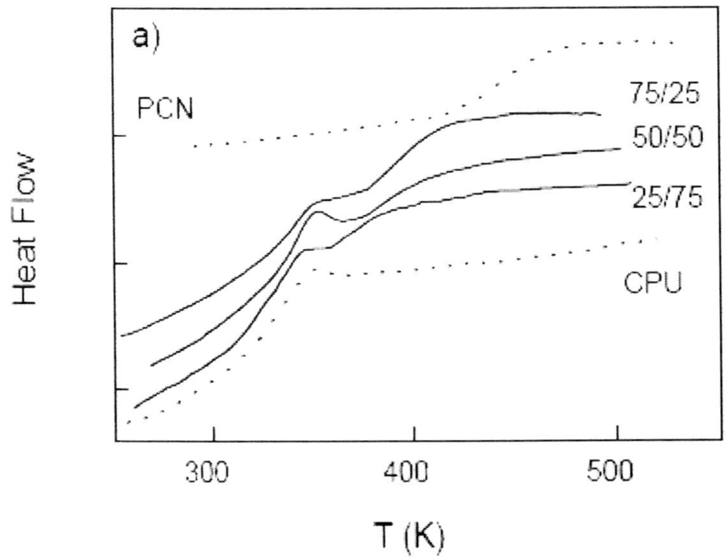

Figure 27. DSC traces through the glass transition region for the neat CPU and PCN and for the three samples of *in-situ* IPNs. The curves have been duly shifted for easier com

Table 2. Calorimetric glass transition temperatures Tg and activation energies Ei of the mechanical γ_1 and γ_2-relaxation in *in-situ* and *seq*-IPNs

PCN/CPU weight ratio	T_g (K)		E_i (kJ/mol^{-1})	
	CPU	PCN	E_1	E_2
0/100	314	-	39	-
seq-25/75	320	377	40	61
seq-50/50	326	387	35	66
seq-75/25	333	395	40	60
in-situ-25/75	333	385	41	61
in-situ-50/50	340	392	42	67
in-situ-75/25	345	400	43	60
100/0	-	445	-	55

Figures 28 and 29 show the comparison between the mechanical spectra of two samples containing the same PCN/CPU ratio (25/75), but prepared by sequential or by *in-situ* sequential method, demonstrating significant differences between the width and the temperature locations of the primary relaxation curves.

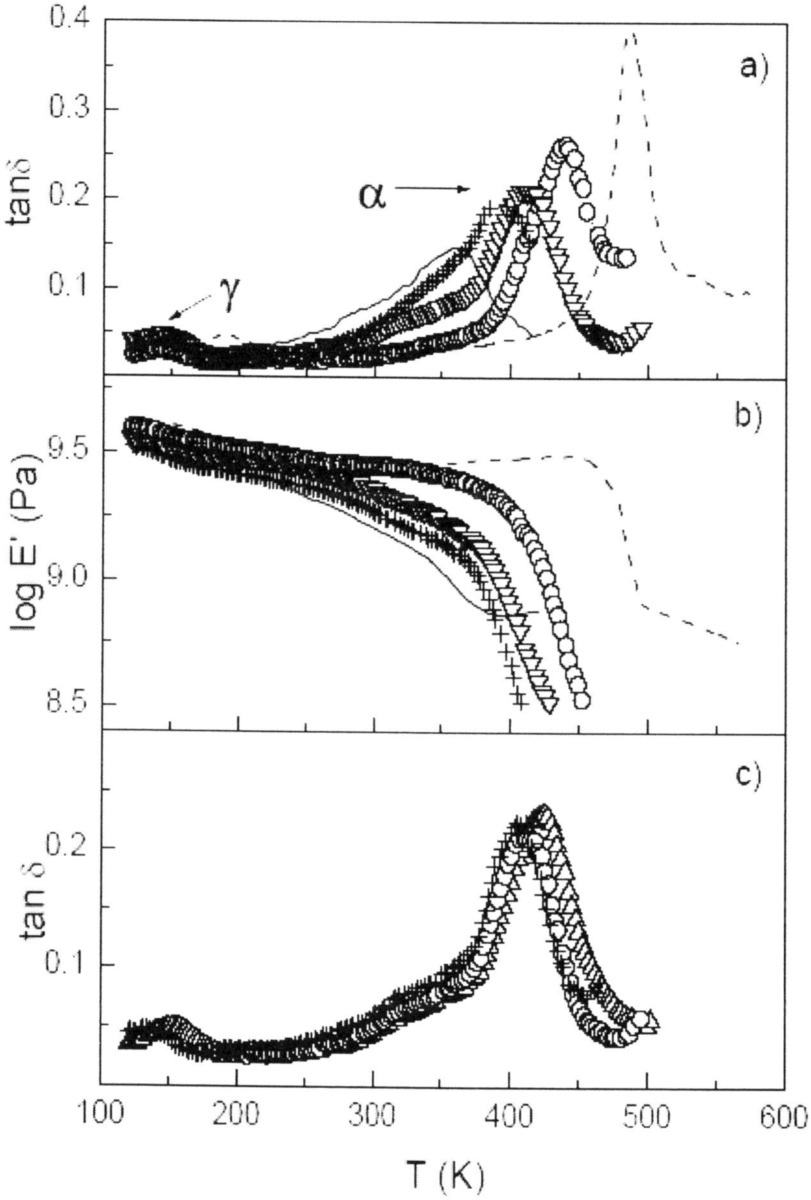

Figure 28. Temperature dependencies of (a) the internal friction tan δ and (b) the dynamic modulus E in pure CPU and PCN and *in-situ* IPNs at selected frequency of 3 Hz: continuous line, pure CPU; (+), PCN/CPU =25/75; (∇), PCN/CPU =50/50; (o), PCN/CPU =75/25; (---) pure PCN. (c) The effect of the driving frequency on the temperature dependence of tan δ in the 50/50 *in-situ IPN*:(+), 0.3 Hz; (∇), 3 Hz; (o), 30 Hz.

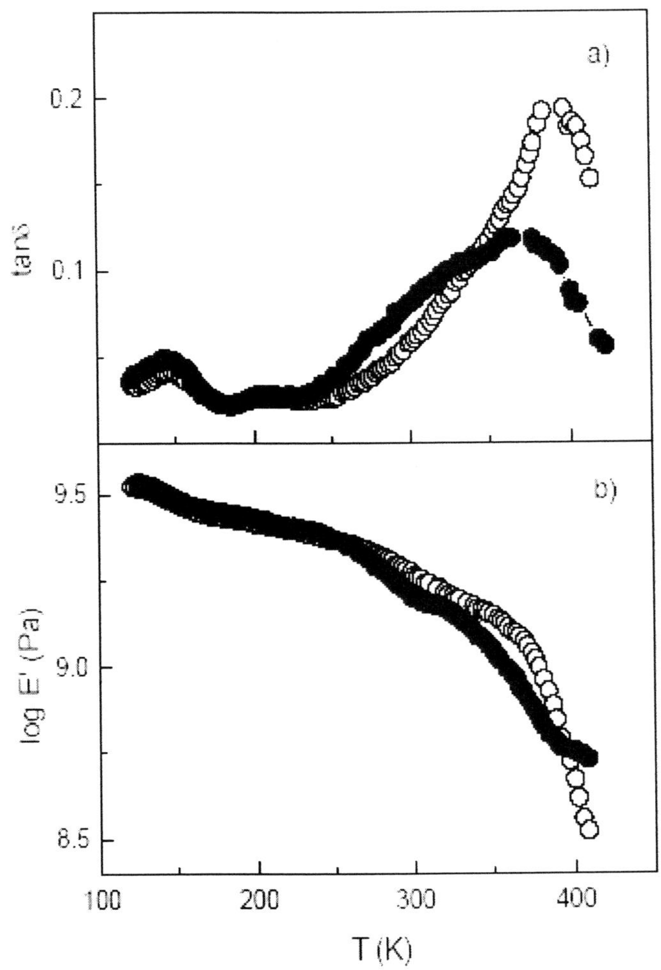

Figure 29. Comparison between the temperature dependencies of (a) the dynamic modulus E' and (b) *tan* δ data in *in-situ* (○) and *seq*-(●) *IPNs* samples having the same weight ratio (25/75).

In-situ IPNs show higher calorimetric (cf. Table 2) and mechanical (cf. Figure 29) glass transition temperatures, Tg than *se*q-IPNs, having the same composition. In the glassy region, the relaxation dynamics of *in-situ* IPNs probed by dynamical mechanical analysis reveals the existence of distinct local segmental motions associated to the individual components. It has been proved that the interpenetration process associated to the *in-situ* synthesis reduces markedly the free-volume in the system, giving rise to significant differences between the local and cooperative molecular mobilities of *in-situ* and *se*q-IPNs. In particular it has been observed a larger "γ-suppression" effect for the γ_2-relaxation of PCN phenylene units, as a consequence of enhanced local intermolecular packing, which prevents the group rearrangements.

5. Conclusions

The development of high-performance, high-temperature composites is an application area where cyanate esters are pitted directly against the epoxy resins, a class of materials, which has earned a reputation for combining both high load-bearing characteristics together with ease of processing. Cyanate esters exhibit all the characteristics inherent to epoxy systems: excellent adhesion to most metallic alloys and to various other substrate types, wide range of processing, cure and property characteristics, absence of volatile products during curing, easy processing without the necessity for applying high pressures during bonding operations, good wetting properties and relatively low shrinkage during cure. Since cyanate esters also have a much better hot/wet performance, much lower moisture and solvent uptake, much lower dielectric loss properties and no shrinkage during cure, this makes them outstanding candidates to challenge the dominance of epoxy resin systems. However, the polycyanurate networks (PCN) often display poor toughness due to their high crosslink density that along with a high price limits their industrial application.

Modification of PCN by reactive oligomers and polymers with formation of hybrid or interpenetrating (semi- and full grafted or linked IPNs) polymer networks with controlled degree of phase separation (often nano-scale) of the components provides development of composites with an optimal combination of mechanical and thermal characteristics for transportation and electronics industries. Curing the cyanate ester resins in the presence of monomers, oligomers or polymers of certain reactivity (the known content of the functional groups of the known reactivity) towards them provides the needful limited concentration of chemical bonding between the components (reactive compatibilization) leading to formation of fine morphology. The chemical grafting of polymer chains of modifiers during network formation reduces the heterogeneity of the system to the degree depending on the concentration of graftings (interbondings). Selection of modifiers with the required content of the functional groups of the correct reactivity allows achieving the lowest level of heterogeneity, nano-scale heterogeneity, producing a nanostructure.

Certainly, using of the additional components and additional reactions at PCN composites processing requires control of selective physical and chemical adsorption of the polymer components into the filler surface, which will lead to improved adhesion at the polymer matrix / filler interface and correspondingly to improved operating characteristics.

Finally, the fine morphology described provides improved properties; in particular, a toughened material of cost effective formulation with good thermal stability for electronics and structural composite applications.

References

[1] Shimp DA, Christenson JR, Ising SJ. *Proc 34th SAMPE,* 1989, p.222.

[2] Fainleib A.M., Shantalii T.A., Pankratov V.A. Copolymers of cyanate esters and plastics based on them. *Compos. Polym. Mat.* (Kiev, in Russian), 49, 39-53 (1991).

[3] Fainleib A.M., Sergeeva L.M., Shantalii T.A. Triazinecontaining interpenetrating polymer networks. *Compos. Polym. Mat.* (Kiev, in Russian), 50, 63-72 (1991).

[4] Hamerton I, editor. *Chemistry and Technology of Cyanate Ester Resins*. Glasgow: Chapman and Hall, 1994.
[5] Hamerton I., J.N. Hay. High Perform Polym. 10, 163 (1998).
[6] Nair CPR, Mathew D, Ninan KN. Advantages in cyanate ester resins. *Adv. Polym. Sci.*, 155, 1-99 (2000).
[7] McConnel V.P. *Advanced Composites* 1992, May/June issue, 28.
[8] Pascault, J.P. *Macromol.Chem., Macromol Symp*. 1995, 93, 43-51.
[9] Cao ZQ, Mechin F, Pascault JP. *Polym Int* 1994;34:41-48.
[10] Uhlig C, Bauer J, Bauer M. *Macromol Chem Macromol Symp* 1995;93:69-79.
[11] Srinivasan SA, Joardar SS, Kranbeuhl D, Ward TC, McGrath JE. *J Appl Polym Sci* 1997, 64, 179-190.
[12] Fainleib A., Grigoryeva O., Hourston D. Synthesis of inhomogeneous modified polycyanurates by reactive blending of bisphenol A dicyanate ester and polyoxypropylene glycol. *Macromol. Symp.,* 164, 429-442 (2001).
[13] Fainleib A., Hourston D., Grigoryeva O., Shantalii T., Sergeeva L. Structure development in aromatic polycyanurate networks modified with hydroxyl-terminated polyethers. *Polymer,* 42, 8361-8372 (2001).
[14] Fainleib A.M., Grigoryeva O.P., Hourston D.J. Structure-Properties Relationships for Bisphenol A Polycyanurate Network Modified with Polyoxytetramethylene Glycol. *Int. J. Polym. Mat.,* 2001, 51(1-2), 57-75.
[15] Fainleib A.M., Shantalii T.A., Klochok O.O., Galatenko N.A. Synthesis and some properties of poly(bisphenol A)cyanurate modified with oligoethers. *Compos. Polym. Mat.*, Kyiv, 23(1), 14-19 (2001).
[16] Martin D, Bacaloglu R. Organishe Synthesen mit Cyansäureestern. Berlin: Akademie-Verlag, 1980.
[17] Martin D, Schwarz KH, Rackow S, Reich P, Gründemann E. Chem Ber 1966;99:2302-2308.
[18] Fainleib A, Grenet J., Garda M.R., Saiter J.M , Grigoryeva O., Grytsenko V., Popescu N., Enescu M. C. Poly(bisphenol A)cyanurate network modified with poly(butylene glycol adipate). Thermal and mechanical properties. *Polym. Degr. Stab*, 81(3), 423-430 (2003).
[19] ANGELL CA. J NON-CRYST SOLIDS 1999;131-133:13-31.
[20] ANGELL CA. IN: NGAI KL, WRIGHT GB, EDITORS. RELAXATION IN COMPLEX SYSTEMS. WASHINGTON DC: NAVAL RESEARCH LABARATORY, 1984. P.3.
[21] Fainleib A M, Novikova T I, Shantalii T A and Sergeeva L M (1992) Kinetic of formation semi-interpenetrating polymer networks based on crosslinked polycyanurate and linear polyurethane, *Polym. Sci., Ser B* 33:60-67.
[22] Fainleib A M, Novikova T I, Shantalii T A and Sergeeva L M (1992) Synthesis, structure and some properties of the polycyanurate-polyurethane semi-IPNs, *Polym Mater Sci Eng* 66:131-132.
[23] Lipatov S Yu, Fainleib A M, Shantalii T A and Sergeeva L M (1992) Semi-interpenetrating networks based on the oligomers of dicyanates and linear polyurethanes, *Polym Sci* 34:407-410.
[24] Fainleib A M, Shantalii T A and Sergeeva L M (1993) Polycyanurate-polyurethane semi-IPNs, *Compos Polym Mat* 54:14-16.

[25] Brovko A A, Fainleib A M, Shantalii T A, Sergeeva L M and Davidenko V V (1994) Structure and viscoelastic properties of polycyanurate-polyurethane semiinterpenetrating polymer networks, *Polym Sci* 36:934-938.
[26] Fainleib A M, Kay M, Buffel K, Bauer J and Bauer M (2000) Chemical transformations in blends of monofunctional organic cyanate and urethane, *Reports of the National Academy of Sciences of Ukraine* N12:170-174.
[27] Bershtein V A, Egorova L M, Ryzhov V P, Yakushev P N, Fainleib A M, Shantalii T A and Pissis P (2001) Structure and segmental dynamics heterogeneity in hybrid polycyanurate-polyurethane networks, *J Macromol Sci Phys, B* 40:105-131.
[28] Srichatrapimuk V.W.and Cooper S.L., *J. Macromol. Sci.-Phys., B15,* 267 (1978).
[29] Bellamy L.J. The Infra-Red Spectra of Complex Molecules. Wiley, New York, 1954.
[30] Vilensky V A, Fainleib A M, Goncharenko L A and Danilenko I Yu (2002) Influence of "inclusion" polymer and components thermodynamic affinity on bisphenol A dicyanate ester polycyclotrimerization, *Reports of the National Academy of Sciences of Ukraine* N1:142-148.
[31] Grigoryeva O., Fainleib A., Pissis P, Boiteux G. Effect of hybrid network formation on adhesion properties of polycyanurate/polyurethane semi-interpenetrating polymer networks. *Polym. Eng. Sci.*, 42 (12), 2440-2448 (2002).
[32] Van Krevelen D.W. Properties of polymers. Their correlation with chemical structure; their numerical estimation and prediction from additive group contributions , Elsevier, Amsterdam, 189 (1990).
[33] Bartolotta A, Di Marco G, Lanza M, Carini G, D'Angelo G, Tripodo G, Fainleib A M, Slinchenko E A and Privalko V P (1997) Molecular mobility in semi-IPNs of linear polyurethane and heterocyclic polymer networks, *J Adhesion* 64:269-286.
[34] Bartolotta A, Di Marco G, Carini G, D'Angelo G, Tripodo G, Fainleib A, and Privalko V (1998) Relaxation in semi-interpenetrating polymer networks of linear polyurethane and heterocyclic polymer networks, *J Non-Cryst Solids* 235-237:600-604.
[35] Bartolotta A, Di Marco G, Lanza M, Carini G, D'Angelo G, Tripodo G, Fainleib A M, Slinchenko E A, Shtompel V I and Privalko V P. (1999) Synthesis and physical characterization of semi-IPNs of linear polyurethane and heterocyclic polymer network, *Polym Eng Sci* 39:549-558.
[36] Balta Calleja F J, Privalko E G, Fainleib A M, Shantalii T A, and Privalko V P (2000) Structure-microhardness relationships for semi-interpenetrating polymer networks, *J Macromol Sci Phys, B* 39:131-141.
[37] Georgoussis G, Kyritsis A, Bershtein V A, Fainleib A M and Pissis P (2000) Dielectric studies of chain dynamics in homogeneous semi-interpenetrating polymer networks, *J Polym Sci, B Polym Phys* 38:3070-3087.
[38] Pissis P, Georgoussis G, Bershtein V A, Neagu E and Fainleib A M (2002) Dielectric studies in homogeneous and heterogeneous polyurethane / polycyanurate interpenetrating polymer networks, *J Non-Cryst Solids* 305:150-158.
[39] Couchman R. P. *Macromolecules*, 11, 1156 (1978).
[40] Zhang Y. and Hourston D.J. *J.Appl.Polym.Sci.,* 69, 271 (1998).
[41] Seminovych G M, Fainleib A M, Slinchenko E A, Brovko A A, Sergeeva L M and Dubkova V I (1999) Influence of carbon fibre on formation kinetics of cross-linked copolymer from bisphenol A dicyanate and epoxy oligomer, *React Funct Polym* 40:281-288

[42] Brovko O O, Fainleib A M, Slinchenko E A, Dubkova V I and Sergeeva L M (2001) Filled semi-interpenetrating polymer networks: formation kinetics and properties, *Compos Polym Mat* 23(2):85-91.

[43] Fainleib A.M, Brovko O.O., Slinchenko E.A., Sergeeva L.M. Compatibilization of components in interpenetrating polymer networks. Influence of carbon fiber filler on formation kinetiks and phase structure. *Nonlinear Optics. Quantum Optics*, 32, 149-160 (2004).

[44] Sergeeva L M, Dubkova V I, Fainleib A M, Alekseenko V I, Brovko O O and Maevskaya O I (2000) The role of active carbon-fibrous filler in decrease of combustibility of semi-interpenetrating polymer networks, *Intern J Polym Mat* 47:31-41.

[45] *Pat.USSR* N1807066, 1992. Composition for coating/ Fainleib A.M., Shantalii T.A., Sergeeva L.M.

[46] Balta Calleja F.J.,.Privalko E.G., Sukhorukov D.I., Fainleib A.M., Sergeeva L.M., Shantalii T.A., Shtompel V.I., Monleon Pradas M., Gallego Ferrer G., Privalko V.P. Structure-properties relationships for cyanurate-containing, full interpenetrating polymer networks. *Polymer*, 41(12), 4699-4707 (2000).

[47] Fainleib A.M, Shantalii T.A., Shtompel V.I., Monleon Pradas M., Sergeeva L.M., Privalko Y.P. Polycyanurate-polyurethane interpenetrating polymer networks. Synthesis and phase structure. *Reports of the NAS of Ukraine*, 2002, N7, 155-160.

[48] Lebedev B.V., Kulagina T.G., Bykova T.A., Fainleib A.M., Grytsenko V.V., Sergeeva L.M. Thermodynamics of interpenetrating polymer networks based on crosslinked polycyanurate and polyurethane in region from T $\rightarrow$0 to 340K. *Polym. Sci.* A, 45(4), 649-659 (2003).

[49] Fainleib A., Kozak N., Grigoryeva O., Nizelskii Yu., Gritsenko V., Pissis P., Boiteux G. Structure-thermal property relationships for polycyanurate-polyurethane linked interpenetrating polymer networks. *Polym. Degr. Stab.*, 76(3), 393-399 (2002).

[50] Bartolotta A., Di Marco G., Lanza M., Carini G., D'Angelo G., Tripodo G., Fainleib A., Danilenko I., Sergeeva L. Mechanical behavior of polycyanurate-polyurethane sequential full-Interpenetrating polymer networks. *J. Non-Crystal. Solid,* 307-310, 698-704 (2002).

[51] Bartolotta A., Di Marco G., Lanza M., Carini G., D'Angelo G., Tripodo G., Fainleib A., Danilenko I., Grytsenko V., Sergeeva L. Thermal and mechanical properties of simultaneous and sequential full-interpenetrating polymer networks. *Mat. Sci. and Eng. A.*, (2004).

In: Synthesis and Properties of Low- and High-Molecular Compounds ISBN 1-59454-716-5
Editor: Gennady E. Zaikov et al., pp. 137-181

Chapter 9

FRACTAL PHYSICAL CHEMISTRY OF POLYMER SOLUTIONS

G. V. Kozlov*[1], *I. V. Dolbin*[2] *and G. E. Zaikov
[1]Researching Institute of Applied Mathematics and Automatization
of Kabardino-Balkarian Scientific Center of Russian Academy of Science
Nal'chik – 360000, Shortanov st., 89 "a", Russian Federation
[2]Institute of Biochemical Physics of Russian Academy of Science
Moscow – 119991, Kosygin st., 4, Russian Federation

ABSTRACT

The main aspects of the application of the fractal analysis for the description of the behavior of macromolecular coils in the diluted solutions are considered. The coil structure is quantitatively described with the help of its fractal (Hausdorff) dimension characterizing the distribution of coil elements in space. A number of the experimental methods of the determination this dimension is offered. The interrelation of the classical and fractal (structural) characteristics of macromolecular coils is shown. The fractal model is used for the description of such phenomena as film formation from polymer solutions, flocculation and self-diffusion of macromolecular coils. The example of the application of the theory of fractional derivatives for the description of macromolecular coil the main parameters of a in solution is give.

Key words: Polymer solution, macromolecular coil, structure, fractal analysis, polymer film, flocculation, self-diffusion.

1. INTRODUCTION

Developed in the physical chemistry of polymer solutions the basic ideas are the basis of our understanding of the peculiar properties of polymers. Therefore, this problem is always given much attention and a great number of the monograph summed up these studies exist.

The principal feature of the offered review is the introduction of the idea of macromolecular coil structure within the framework of the fractal analysis. Such an approach allows to receive the direct correlations "structure-properties", that is the main task of any physical domain including the physical chemistry of polymer solutions.

2. Experimental Methods of Determintion of Fractal Dimension of Macromolecular Coils in Solution

For quantitative characterization of macromolecular coil structure are required estimation methods of its fractal dimension D_f. Most simply the value D_f is determined from its interrelation with known and easy defined properties [1] and number of such methods in present chapter will be considered.

Linear polymer macromolecules are known to occur in various conformational and/or phase states, depending on their molecular weight, the quality of solvent, temperature, concentration, and other are a random coil in an ideal (θ) solvent, an impermeable coil in a good solvent, and a permeable coil. In each of these states, a macromolecular coil in solution is a fractal, i.e., a self-similar object with dimension D_f, which is uncoincided to its topological dimension. The fractal dimension D_f characterizes the volume distribution of its constituent elements in space [3]. Determination of D_f is the first step of studying macromolecular coils within the framework of the fractal analysis, and D_f is usually estimated by finding the exponents in equations of the Mark-Kuhn-Houwink type, which relate the intrinsic viscosity $[\eta]$, the translational diffusion coefficient D_0, or the rate sedimentation coefficient S_0 with the molecular weight M of polymers [4]:

$$[\eta] \sim M^{b_\eta}, \tag{1}$$

$$D_0 \sim M^{-b_D}, \tag{2}$$

$$S_0 \sim M^{b_S}. \tag{3}$$

The D_f value can be calculated according to the following relationship [4]:

$$D_{f_\eta} = \frac{3}{b_\eta + 1}, \tag{4}$$

$$D_{f_D} = \frac{1}{b_D}, \tag{5}$$

$$D_{fs} = \frac{1}{1-b_S}. \tag{6}$$

All considered methods require quite complex and laborious measurements [4-6]. The simplest of these methods, which requires no complicated instrumentation, is measurement of [η]. Therefore, in papers [7, 8] are proposed a simple rapid method of estimating D_f of macromolecular coils in solutions, which is based on the same principles as those applied in deriving the equations (4)-(6).

The coefficient of swelling α of a macromolecular coil is known to be defined as [9]:

$$\alpha = \left(\frac{\left\langle \bar{r}^2 \right\rangle}{\left\langle \bar{r}^2 \right\rangle_\theta} \right)^{1/2}, \tag{7}$$

where $\left\langle \bar{r}^2 \right\rangle^{1/2}$ and $\left\langle \bar{r}^2 \right\rangle_\theta^{1/2}$ are the root-meansquare distances between the ends of the macromolecule in an arbitrary solvent and an ideal (θ) solvent, respectively.

In its turn, the value of α is related with the intrinsic viscosities [η] and $[\eta]_\theta$ of the polymer in arbitrary and ideal solvents, respectively, so [9]:

$$\alpha^3 = \frac{[\eta]}{[\eta]_\theta}. \tag{8}$$

The parameter ε of the bulk interactions (which cause a deviation of the coil shape from the ideal, Gaussian shape) is found according to the relationship [9]:

$$\varepsilon = \frac{d\ln\alpha^2}{d\ln M} = \frac{\alpha^2 - 1}{5\alpha^2 - 3}. \tag{9}$$

In its turn, both ε and D_f depend on the exponent b_η in Mark-Kuhn-Houwink equation (1) [6]:

$$\varepsilon = \frac{2b_\eta - 1}{3}, \tag{10}$$

and the dependence of D_f on b_η is given by the equation (4).

Combining the equations (4) and (7)-(10), one can obtain the following relationship, which enables one to determine D_f only from the intrinsic viscosities [η] and $[\eta]_\theta$ [7]:

$$D_f = \frac{5([\eta]/[\eta]_\theta)^{2/3} - 3}{3([\eta]/[\eta]_\theta)^{2/3} - 2}. \tag{11}$$

Table 1 offers a comparison between experimental and calculated data for biopolymer of polysaccharide class (rodexman). The D_f calculation according to the equation(4) the value ~ 1,71 is give. Estimations of D_f according to the equation (11) are listed in Table 1 for eight fractions of rodexman with the molecular weights in the range (27-103)$\times10^3$. Table 1 also presents the [η] values [5] and the $[\eta]_\theta$ values, calculated according to the equation (1) at condition b_η=0,5 [2]. As can be see from the data of this Table, the value of D_f varies within a very narrow range 1,68-1,70, which agrees well with the estimation according to the equation (4). There is a certain increase in D_f (a coil compactness increase) with decreasing *M*, which is also consistent with the known data [6].

The authors [10] for obtaining of D_f estimation method are used two-component model of solubility parameter, according to which [11]:

$$\vec{\delta}^2 = \delta_f^2 + \delta_c^2, \tag{12}$$

where component δ_f of solubility parameter includes a dispersion interaction energy and interaction energy of dipole bonding and component δ_c – hydrogen bonding interaction energy and the interaction energy between an electron-deficient atom of one molecule (acceptor) and an electron-rich atom of another molecule (donor), which requires a certain orientation of these two molecules. In this treatment is no need to have separate component for description of interactions between polar molecules [11].

Table 1. Comparison between the fractal dimensions D_f calculated by two methods for a macromolecular coil of rodexman in aqueous solution [7]

$M\times10^3$ [5]	$[\eta]\times10^3$, m^3/kg [5]	$[\eta]_\theta\times10^3$ m^3/kg, the equation (1)	D_f, the equation (4)	D_f, the equation (11)
103	135	7,48	-	1,68
93	115	7,11	-	1,69
90	104	6,99	-	1,69
72	98	6,25	1,71	1,69
67	82	6,03	-	1,69
45	62	4,94	-	1,69
32	51	4,17	-	1,69
27	37	3,83	-	1,70

Within the framework of this model the following equation was obtained [10]:

$$D_f = 1{,}50 + 0{,}2(\Delta\delta_f)^{2/(1+\delta_c)}, \tag{13}$$

where $\Delta\delta_f$ is the difference of values δ_f for polymer and solvent.

The equation (13) gives a good correspondence with calculation according to the equation (4) for selection including 7 polymers and 9 solvents (the average dispersion ~ 4 %) [10].

As it is known [12], the value of D_f is determined by two interactions groups: an interactions polymer-solvent and interactions amongs coil elements. Can be supposed, that second group is determined by molecular characteristics of polymer, for example, its characteristic ratio C_∞ (the characteristic of chain statistical flexibility [13]) and cross-sectional area of macromolecule S. To remove of influence of interactions of first group the authors [14] were obtained the equation for D_f calculation in good solvent, i.e., the minimal value D_f [2], which has form:

$$D_f = 2 - 4\left(\frac{2}{C_\infty^2 S}\right)^{1/2}, \qquad (14)$$

where S gives in Å.

The equation (14) gives also good correspondence with calculation according to the equation (4) for 9 pairs of polymer-solvent (the average dispersion ~ 4,3 %) [14].

3. The Interrelation of the Classical and Fractal Characteristics of Polymer Solutions

As noted above, the value of the fractal dimension of a macromolecular coil in solution is determined by two groups of factors: interactions polymer-solvent and interactions among coil elements [12]. The dependence of the reduced viscosity η_{red} on the concentration c for the dilute polymeric solutions is usually described by the equation of Huggins [13]:

$$\eta_{red} = [\eta] + k_x[\eta]^2 c + \ldots, \qquad (15)$$

where k_x is a Huggins constant, characterizing the level of polymer-solvent interactions.

In Fig. 1 there is the dependence of value D_f, calculated according to the equation (4), on the parameter k_x^{-2} (such a form of the dependence is chosen with the purpose of the obtaining of the linear correlation) for polymers having M=5×10^5. As we can see there is, the good linear correlation for 30 various pairs of polymer-solvent (the correlation 0,930), which allows to predict quite simply the value of D_f. It is expected that for the other M values the correlation $D_f(k_x^{-2})$ will have an analogous form, but another slope. This dependence allows to make some important conclusions.

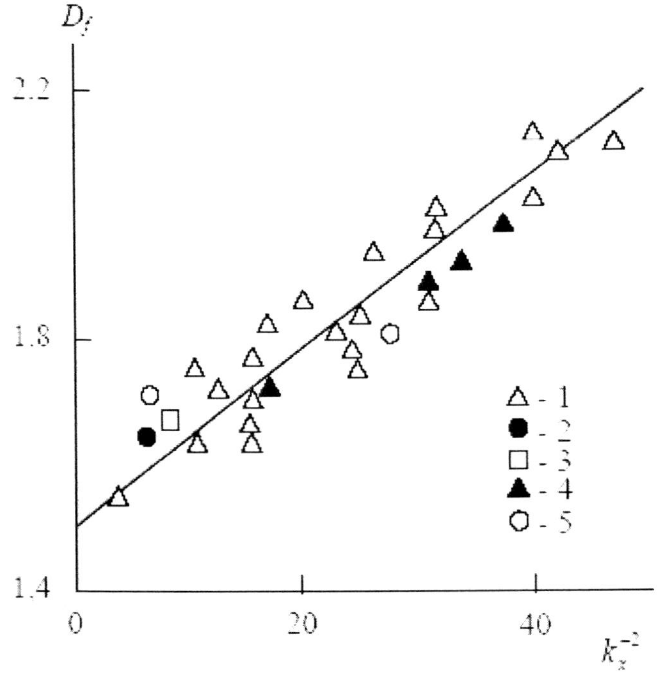

Figure 1. The relationship between a macromolecular coil fractal dimension D_f and parameter k_x^{-2} for polyarylate (1), polymethylmethacrylate (2), polyvynil chloride (3), polysulfone (4) and polycarbonate (5) [15].

First, it seems that this correlation describes the dependence of D_f only on the interactions polymer-solvent, characterized by a Huggins parameter k_x, and not take into consideration the interactions among coil elements. However, the linearity itself of this correlation supposes that it includes the factors of the second group, mentioned above. For example, it is well known [16] that the increase of the chain rigidity results to the increase of exponent b_η in Mark-Kuhn-Houwink equation and, consequently, to D_f reduction (the equation (4)). At the same time the increase of the chain rigidity results to [η] the growth at the other equal conditions. Thus, both the increase of the chain rigidity and the improvement of the solvent thermodynamic quality give the same effect – [η] the increase and, correspondingly, the k_x growth according to the equation (15). This, in its turn, results to k_x^{-2} decrease and D_f reduction that is expected. This supposition is confirmed experimentally – in paper [17] the increase of Kuhn statistical segment length A, characterizing the chain thermodynamical rigidity, at the improvement of the solvent thermodynamical quality for two polyarylates, is shown.

Second, as it is shown in paper [15], the minimal value k_x=0,14 (or maximal value k_x^{-2} ≈ 51) reaches at [η]=0. From the graph of Fig. 1 is follows that $D_f \approx 2{,}25$ is corresponds to this value k_x. As it is known [12], the screening of the interactions of the exluded volume results to D_f increase and at the complete screening (the compensation of the pointed effects) the value D_f^c corresponds to so called compensated state. Within the framework of Flory's theory, when the compensation is realized by the interactions with the other coils, D_f^c=2,5 (for the three-dimensional Euclidean space). The other method of the decrease of repulsive interactions among coil elements is the introduction of the attractive interactions. For this case, corresponding to an isolated coil (a dilute solution) can be written [12]:

$$D_f^c = \frac{4(d+1)}{7}, \tag{16}$$

where d is dimension of an Euclidean space, in which the fractal is considered. It is obvious, in our case d=3 and then D_f^c=2,286, that practically exactly corresponds to the limiting D_f value, obtained according to the graph of Fig. 1.

Another limiting case, corresponding only to the repulsive interactions, corresponds to the condition k_x^{-2}=0. In this case the extrapolation of the graph of Fig. 1 to k_x^{-2}=0 gives D_f=1,50, that corresponds to the dimension of a permeable coil [2]. Thus, obtained from the graph of Fig. 1 the limiting values of D_f completely correspond to the theoretical conclusions.

Third, as noted above, the decrease of exponent b_η at M growth is observed. The authors [15] obtained the following relationship:

$$D_f = \frac{3\ln M}{\ln M + \ln(7{,}14k_x - 1) - \ln K_\eta - \ln k_x}, \tag{17}$$

where K_η is a coefficient of the proportionality in Mark-Kuhn-Houwink equation (1).

The equation (17) gives the analytical interrelation between D_f and M and, in essence, is one more method of D_f estimation [15].

The common aspects of the dependence of D_f on a parameter of the solvent solubility δ_s (or, more exactly, on the difference δ_s and a parameter δ_p of the polymer solubility, $\Delta\delta=\delta_s-\delta_p$) were considered in papers [18-20]. They allow to obtain the following tendencies of the change of the fractal dimension of a macromolecular coil in solution as the function of a number of factors [19]:

1. a poorness of the thermodynamic quality of a solvent in respect of polymer (an increase $|\Delta\delta|$) always results to increase D_f;
2. the bigger the flexibility of a polymer main chain is, the weaker the tendency of D_f growth is at $|\Delta\delta|$ increase;
3. in addition to point 2) we note that the introduction of the rigid para-links instead of more flexible metha-links in the main chain results to the sharp decrease D_f at the other equal conditions;
4. the polymers with the bulk side groups and a flexible main chain will have D_f values, which are bigger on approximately constant value $\Delta D_f \approx 0{,}17$ (representing itself the

difference of coil dimensions in a good solvent and a permeable coil) in comparison with the polymers, which doesn't have the noted features;

5. the existence of the hydrogen bonding polymer-solvent results to much faster growth D_f at $|\Delta\delta|$ increase (approximately twice) in comparison with the solvent, which is not capable to the formation of the mentioned bonds.

These common rules allow to choose purposely the solvent for the synthesis of any polymer. As it was shown before [21, 22], the D_f decrease results to the essential acceleration of the reaction at the other equal conditions.

As it is noted above, between the length of Kuhn segment A, characterizing statistical rigidity of chain, and D_f the certain correlation is observed, analytically expressed in such a way [23, 24]:

$$D_f = 2{,}0 - 1{,}32 \times 10^{-2} A, \tag{18}$$

for the flexible chain polymers and

$$D_f = 1{,}667 - 4{,}45 \times 10^{-4} A, \tag{19}$$

for the rigid chain polymers. In the equations (18) and (19) the value A is expressed in Å.

The equations (18) and (19) have the expected from the most general ideas form: the increase A, i.e., the increase of chain rigidity, results to D_f decrease, i.e., the decrease of the compactness degree of a macromolecular coil in solution [23]. As it is known [13], for Gaussian chain in an ideal solvent the condition is carried out:

$$\left\langle \overline{r^2} \right\rangle_\theta^{1/2} = NA, \tag{20}$$

where N is a number of the statistical segments of a chain.

For the nonideal solvents the condition (20) is broken and the conformation of a macromolecular coil in solution differs from the Gaussian one. This results to the variation of A as a function of the thermodynamical quality of a solvent in respect to the polymer. Let's draw attention to the principal difference of the equations (20), on the one hand, and (18), (19) on the other hand. The equation (20) doesn't allow the condition of the infinitely flexible chain, i.e., A=0, then the equations (18) and (19) give such condition at $D_f > 2{,}0$ (i.e., in the ideal θ-solvent) and $D_f = 1{,}667$, respectively. This supposes that the equations (18) and (19) give the dependence of A on two interactions groups: polymer-solvent and coil elements between themselves, i.e., those groups of the interactions, which define D_f value [12]. It is possible that more exact dependences $D_f(A)$ will be extrapolated for the flexible chain polymers at $D_f = 2{,}0$ to A value for θ-solvent, for which the macromolecular coil has the Gaussian conformation. However, the equation (18) and (19) allow to make the estimation of value A even in terms of the obtained approximations in papers [23, 24].

In Fig. 2 and 3 the comparison of dependences $A(D_f)$, calculated according to the equations (18) and (19) for the flexible and rigid chain polymers, respectively, and cited in papers [25, 26] is shown. As we can see, in both cases the expected tendency of $A(D_f)$ variation is obtained and for the most part of polymer-solvent pairs the good quantitative correspondence is obtained. The substantial dispersion of A values for two used methods of the estimation in the case 5 out of 19 shown in Fig. 2 and 3 polymer-solvent pairs is due to the corresponding dispersion of the literary values A, which can be fourfold [27] for the rigid chain polymers. It is specific that the authors [28] made the correction of A value for three rigid chain polymers in the terms of the fractal analysis that allows to obtain the most probable values of this parameter for the noted polymers.

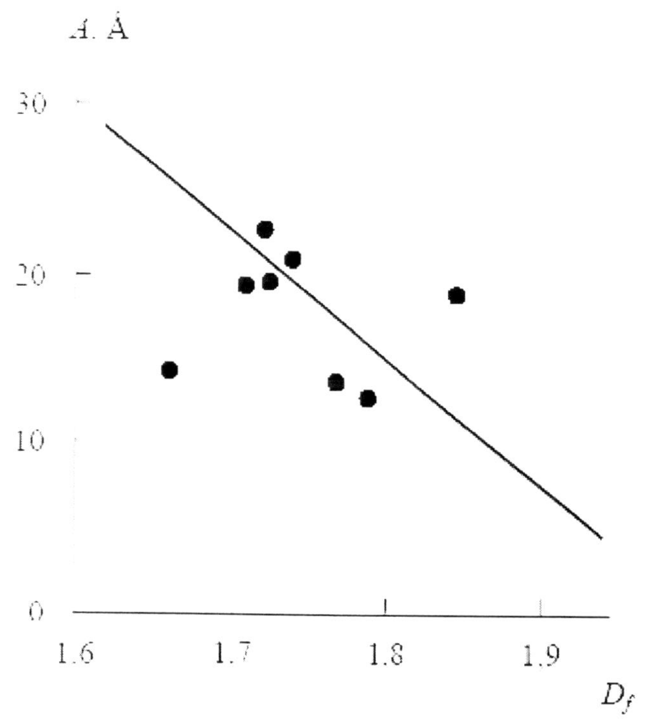

Figure 2. The dependence of Kuhn segment length A on a macromolecular coil fractal dimension D_f for flexible chain polymers.

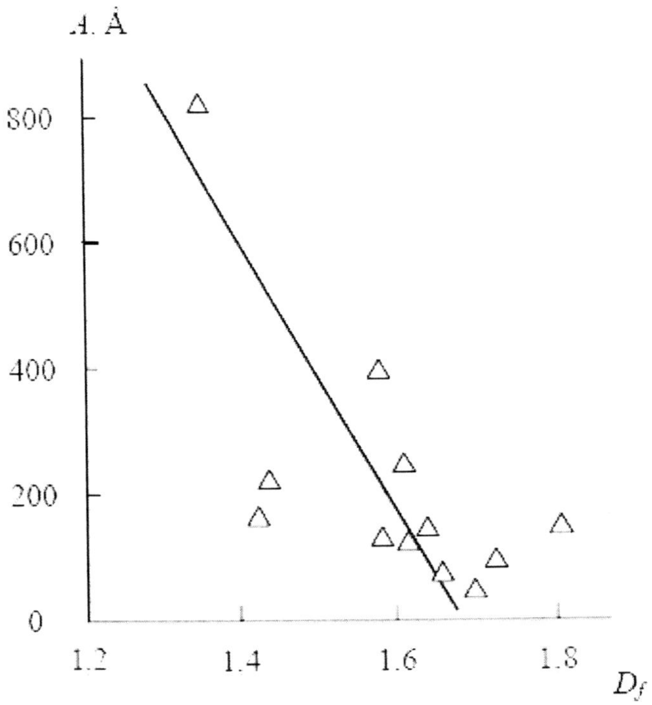

Figure 3. The dependence of Kuhn segment length *A* on a macromolecular coil fractal dimension D_f for rigid chain polymers. The straight line – the calculation according to the equation (19), points – data of paper [26] [24].

Let's note some more important aspect. The comparison of the equations (18) and (19) allow to give one more definition of the flexible and rigid chain polymers. The mentioned equations suppose that the maximal dimensions D_f of a macromolecular coil of the linear polymers are equal to 2,0 (i.e., coil in ideal θ-solvent [2]) for the flexible polymers and 1,667 (i.e., coil in good solvent [2]) – for the rigid polymers. Therefore, to the rigid chain polymers it is necessary to refer such polymers, the rigidity of chain of which (intramolecular interactions) allows to compensate it by the interactions polymer-solvent (intermolecular interactions) only to the certain degree, i.e., to $D_f = 1{,}667$. The other criterion follows from the equation (18): at minimal D_f value 1,0 we obtain the value $A \approx 75$Å. Differently speaking, the polymers with $A \leq 75$ Å are the flexible chain (for them it can be reached $D_f = 2{,}0$ by the screening of the intramolecular interactions), and with $A > 75$ Å are the rigid chain polymers.

As the value of D_f of a macromolecular coil in solution is determined by two noted above groups of the interactions, then such definition allows to the authors [29] to connect D_f and the parameter χ_1 of Flory-Huggins interaction, which is defined as follows [13]:

$$\chi_1 = \frac{E_{vap}}{RT}\left(1 - \frac{\delta_p}{\delta_s}\right)^2 + \chi_s, \tag{21}$$

where E_{vap} is molar energy of solvent vaporization, R is a universal gas constant, T is temperature, χ_s is an empirical parameter.

Sometimes the value χ_1 is defined so [13]:

$$\chi_1 = \chi_H + \chi_s, \tag{22}$$

where χ_H and χ_s are enthalpic and entropic components of Flory-Huggins parameter, respectively.

The equation (21) assumes that with the help of parameter δ_p it is possible to determine the interactions of coil elements among themselves, and with the help of the ratio δ_p/δ_s – the interactions polymer-solvent. Besides, the entropic component χ_s takes into account the effects of ordering of the interacting elements of system.

The set of the experimental data for the various polymers has allowed to receive an empirical correlation $D_f(\chi_1)$ of the following form [29]:

$$D_f = 1{,}50 + 0{,}45\chi_1. \tag{23}$$

The theoretical estimations suppose that the rise of temperature makes the fractal (macromolecular coil) less compact, i.e., that leads to the D_f decrease. However, the experimental confirmation of this supposition is absent in the present time. The authors [30] considered the D_f change with T variation on the example of the solutions of polyarylate on the basis of phenolphtalein and isophthalic acid dichloroanhydride (F-1) [16].

As it is known [31], the reason of changes of the macromolecular coil structure in the diluted solution with varying the temperature can be the effects of long-range interaction (effects of exluded volume) as well as the effects of close-range interaction leading to the specific influence of the solvent on the undisturbed dimensions of a coil [16]. For the semirigid chain polymers to which itis necessary to refer polyarilates the macromolecules in the solution are characterized by the significant transparency, and therefore the effects of the long-range interaction can be neglected. For these polymers it is assumed [32], that the temperature coefficient of the viscosity for them $d \ln [\eta]/dT$ is negative according to the sign, and according to the absolute value it excesses the one for the flexible chain polymers of the same M. The temperature dependences of $[\eta]$ for the solution of F-1 in three solvents are given in Fig. 4. These dependences have the expected character, i.e., the decrease of $[\eta]$ with the increase of T is observed. As it has been already noted, it supposes that the macromolecular coil structure is mainly controlled by the close-range interaction effects, that is the interaction polymer-solvent. The value $d \ln [\eta]/dT$ is equal about to – 0,0053, what agrees with the corresponding parameter for the more rigid chain polyamides [31].

The dependences η_{red}/c (where η_{red} is reduced viscosity, c is polymer's concentration) on c for the solutions F-1 correspond to the Huggins's equation (15), that allows to obtain the values k_x=0,397, 0,314 and 0,294 for T=293, 323 and 353 K, respectively. It means that the interaction polymer-solvent decreases with the temperature increase and the graph of Fig. 4 allows to estimate D_f from ~ 1,60 to 1,68 due by this increase.

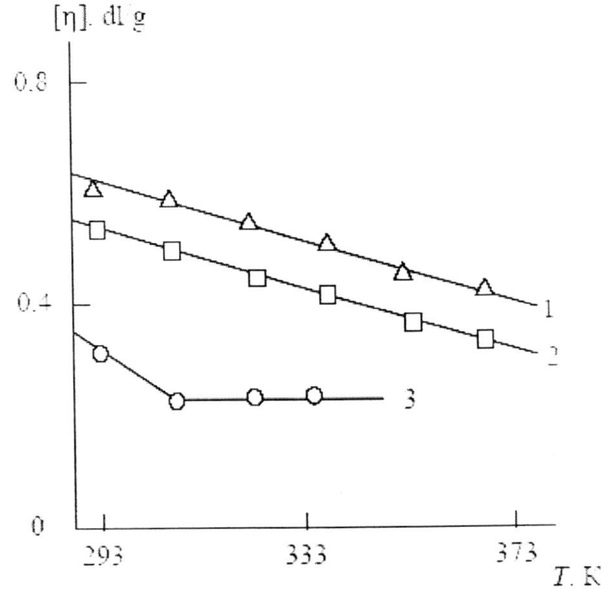

Figure 4. The dependence of the intrinsic viscosity [η] on temperature T for the solutions of polyarylate F-1 in and tetrahydrofurane (3) [30].

Fig. 5 shows the dependences $D_f(T)$ for solutions F-1 in tetrachloroethane and N,N-dimethylformamide (c=0,5 weight %), where the value D_f is determined according to the equation (11). As we can see, the monotonous increase of D_f with T rise is observed, that is the increase of the compactness of a macromolecular coil [12]. The extrapolation of the graphs in Fig. 5 to D_f=2,0 [2] allows to estimate the values of θ-temperature for the indicated solvents. It should be noted, that the achievement of θ-conditions doesn't mean any critical state of the coil. Such state for the coil in the diluted solutions (practically the isolated macromolecule) can be achieved at the critical value of the fractal dimension D_f^c, estimated according to the equation (16). We should note, that about at $D_f = D_f^c$=2,285 the dependence [η](T) for F-1 in tetrahydrofurane (Fig. 4) becomes parallel to abscissa axis, i.e., this D_f value is critical [30].

Generally the dependence $D_f(T)$ is expected to be rather complicated. So, for the flexible chain polymers one can observe at first the increase of [η] with the T rise and then its decrease [13]. This assumes at first the decrease D_f with the T rise for these polymers and then its increase. In Fig. 6 the dependence $D_f(T)$ for the solution of the triacetate cellulose in benzyle spirite [33] is shown, where the D_f value is calculated according to the equation (4). As one can see at first the D_f decrease is observed and in the interval T=363-423 K the D_f increase takes place. Such change of the dependence $D_f(T)$ for the triacetate cellulose can be explained by the complex interaction polymer-solvent: the D_f decrease at $T \leq 363$ K is explained by the desolvation process due to "squeezing" of the solvent out of the macromolecular coil at the pairwise interactions increase, and the D_f increase at $T > 363$ K is connected with the destruction of the solvent structure [33]. For the diacetate cellulose in the various solvents the decrease of [η] with the T rise is observed [34], that supposes the corresponding D_f increase according to the equation (11).

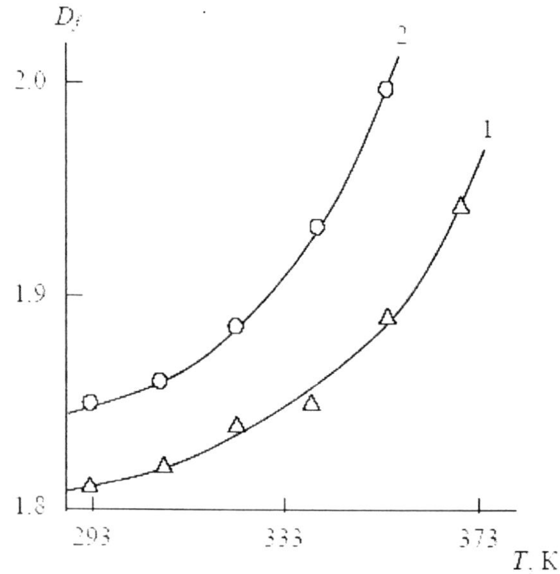

Figure 5. The dependence of the fractal dimension D_f of a macromolecular coil on temperature T for the solutions of polyarylate F-1 in symm-tetrachloroethane (1) and N,N-dimethylformamide (2) [30].

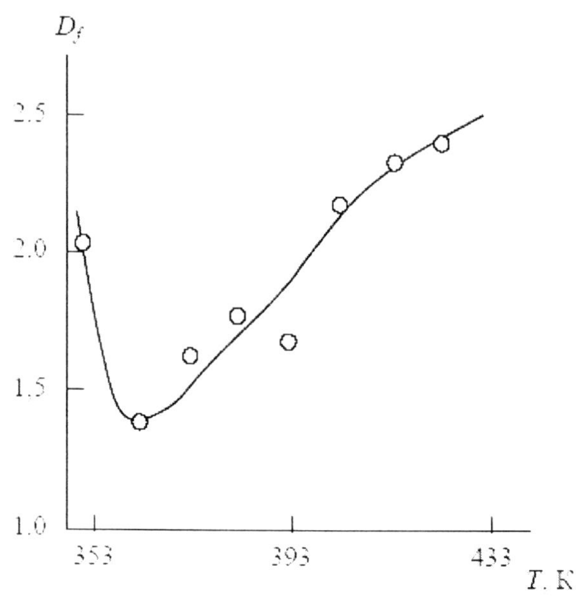

Figure 6. The dependence of the fractal dimension D_f of a macromolecular coil on temperature T for the solutions of triacetate cellulose in benzyle spirite according to the data of paper [33] [30].

Thus, the cited above results suppose, that the dependence $D_f(T)$ for the diluted solutions has rather complex character and for the semirigid and rigid chain polymers the D_f increase with T rise is observed in general [30].

A branching degree (and/or the existence of bulk side substituents) is the important property of a polymer chain, which defined in many things the polymer behaviour in solutions. It is shown [16, 35], that the increase of the molecular weight side substituents and of a branching degree results to the systematic decrease of exponent b_η in Mark-Kuhn-Houwink equation, that at the other equal conditions it means the decrease of a coil gyration radius, i.e., its rise of compactness. For the quantitative estimation of polymer branching degree the branching factor g is usually used, defined as follows [16]:

$$g^{2-b_\eta} = \frac{[\eta]_b}{[\eta]_l}, \tag{24}$$

where subseripts "b" and "l" mean the branched and linear macromolecules, respectively.

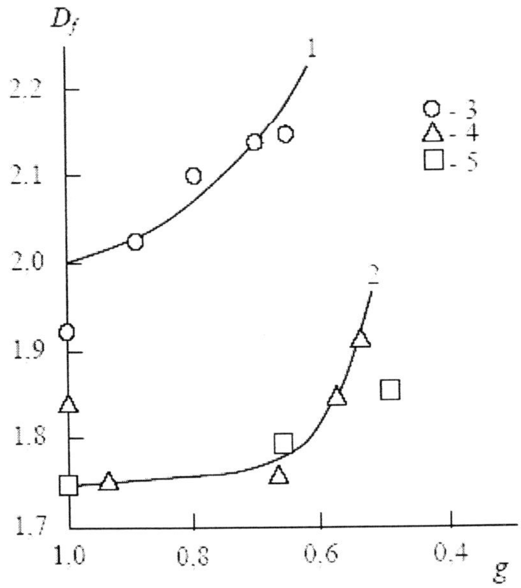

Figure 7. The dependences of the fractal dimension D_f of a macromolecular coil on branching factor g for PPQX (1-4) and B-PES (5). The solvents: N-methylpyrrolydone (1, 3) and chloroform (2, 4, 5). 1, 2 – the calculation according to the equation (25), 3-5 – experimental data [38].

In Fig. 7 there are the dependences D_f on g (points) for polyphenylquinoxaline (PPQX, solvents-chloroform and N-methylpyrrolydone) [35] and bromine-containing aromatic polyethersulfones (B-PES, solvent-chloroform) [36]. As one can see in any case the increase of branching degree, characterized the g decrease [16, 35], results to D_f rise, i.e., the increase of a coil compactness degree [37, 38]. Another factor influencing on the D_f value is the solvent thermodynamical quality in respect to polymer. As follows from the data of Fig. 7, a poor solvent for PPQX (N-methylpyrrolydone) results to much greater values D_f in comparison with a good solvent (chloroform) for both considered polymers. We should note, that the data for the linear analogues of these polymers (at $g=1$) do not lie on the dependences for the branched polymers, therewith the law for the relationship of the values D_f for the branched and linear analogues is absent [37].

The graphs of Fig. 7 allow to make two important conclusions. First, as it should be expected [12], the value D_f of the branched polymers is controlled by two factors: polymer-solvent interactions and the interactions among the coil elements. Second, the dominant parameter in the determination of the second factor is a branching degree g, as it is not observed any correspondence with the linear analogues.

In order to obtain the analytical dependence D_f on g the equations (4) and (24) can be used. Their combination allows to obtain the following relationship [38]:

$$D_f = \frac{3\ln g}{3\ln g - \left(\ln[\eta]_b - \ln[\eta]_l\right)}. \tag{25}$$

In Fig. 7 the comparison between the dependences $D_f(g)$, obtained according to the equations (4) and (24) (points) and the equation (25) (full curves) is shown. From this comparison the good correspondence of dependences $D_f(g)$, obtained by both noted methods [37, 38] follows.

As it is known [13], widely used now the traditional methods of the determination of macromolecular coil structural features of the branched polymers are connected with the necessity of the comparison of their hydrodynamic properties with the properties of the linear analogue of the same molecular weight. Theories used for this purpose are complicated, often nonunique and sometimes they do not allow the quantitative estimations of the branched polymers structure. Therefore the authors [39] used for these purposes the methods of a fractal analysis.

As it is known [40], the phantom (which does not account for the interactions of the exluded volume) fractal dimension of a macromolecular coil d_f is given by

$$d_f = \frac{2d_s}{2 - d_s}, \tag{26}$$

and the swollen (which accounts for the exluded volume effects) fractal dimension of the same coil D_f is determined as follows [40]:

$$D_f = \frac{d_s(d+2)}{d_s + 2}. \tag{27}$$

In the equations (26) and (27) d_s there is a spectral (fracton) dimension characterizing the connectivity of the object [41].

The equation (27) gives the value D_f in solvents consisting of the point (zero-dimensional) molecules, which have the fractal dimension $\delta_f=0$ [40]. Generally, the value δ_f can be estimated according to the equation [42]:

$$\delta_f = 1{,}58\left(\delta_s^{1/2} - 2{,}83\right), \tag{28}$$

where δ_s is in $(cal/cm^3)^{1/2}$. The discussion of the equation (28) will be giveh in chapter 4.

From the equation (28) it follows, that the condition $\delta_f=0$ is achieved for $\delta_s \le 8{,}0$ $(cal/cm^3)^{1/2}$. As the values δ_f for the used solvents are higher than this value, for them $\delta_f > 0$. According to the equation (28) it can be estimated that the value δ_f is equal to ~ 0,19 for chloroform and ~ 0,91 for N-methylpyrrolydone. In this case the value D_f is determined according to the equation [40]:

$$D_f = \frac{d+2}{2-\left(\delta_f - 2\right)/d_s}. \tag{29}$$

In Fig. 8 the dependences D_f and d_f on d_s for all considered above cases are shown. The dependences $D_f(d_s)$ for the real polymers should be settled down between the curves $d_f(d_s)$ and $D_f(d_s)$, where the value D_f is determined according to the equation (27) (curves 1 and 2, respectively). For the macromolecular coils PPQX in N-methylpyrrolydone this condition is really carried out and what's more the experimental values D_f (the equation (4)) are excellently agreed to the calculation D_f according to the equation (29), where $\delta_f=0{,}91$, and the value d_s is calculated according to the equation (27). At the same time the data for the macromolecular coils PPQX in chloroform estimated according to the equation (4), are lower than the dependence $D_f(d_s)$ for the swollen coils, though the equation (27) assumes the minimal value D_f for them ($\delta_f=0$). The dependence $D_f(d_s)$ for the swollen coils (curve 2 in Fig. 8) is not agreed to the experimental results. For the explanation of this disagreement, let's consider the definition of the equation (29), cited in [40]. It is assumed that the fractal molecules of the solvent screen the interactions of the exluded volume between the macromolecule elements. Therefore, the increase δ_f leads to D_f rise. Then the value α, which is equal to [40]:

$$\alpha = \frac{\delta_f}{d_f}, \tag{30}$$

is incorporated. In the equation (30) δ_f is a phantom fractal dimension of the solvent molecules.

The final result of this treatment is the equation (29) or, if the spectral dimension d_s is used, the following equation is obtained [40]:

$$D_f = \frac{d_s(d+2)}{(1-\alpha)d_s + 2}. \quad (31)$$

It is easy to see that in this treatment the possibility of screening of the interactions of the attraction between the macromolecule elements is not allowed. This effect should give the decrease of a coil compactness and the reduction of D_f value that is observed for PPQX coils in chloroform (Fig 8). The simplest method of the incorporation of this effect is the replacement of the sign "plus" before δ_f in the equation (29) by "minus" or the replacement of the sign "minus" before α in the equation (31) by "plus". The calculation D_f according to the modified by the mentioned method equations (29) and (31) gave the excellent correspondence with the experiment (curve 5, Fig. 8). This allows to assume that the chloroform molecules screen the interactions of the attraction between the branches of PPQX macromolecule, but they do not screen them for the main chain of polymer (the experimental value D_f for linear PPQX corresponds well to the calculation according to the equation (29) or the equation (31) at d_s=1,0 [41], Fig. 8) [39].

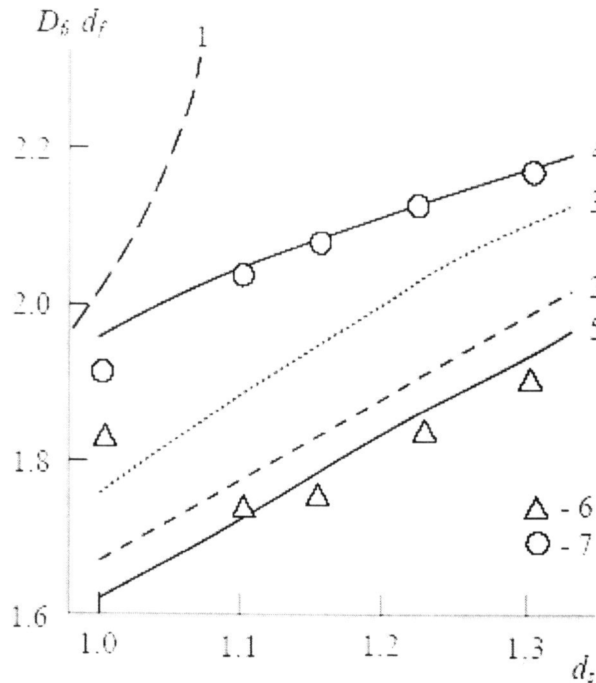

Figure 8. The dependences of swollen D_f and phantom d_f fractal dimensions of a macromolecular coil PPQX on spectral dimension d_s. The calculation according to: the equations (26) (1) and (27) (2), the equation (29) for chloroform (3) and N-methylpyrrolydone (4); the modified equation (29) for chloroform (5); the equation (4) for chloroform (6) and N-methylpyrrolydone (7) [39].

The offered above data suppose, the substantial role of the dimension d_s for the characteristic of the macromolecular coil structure of branched polymers (the equations (26),

(27), (29), (31)). Therefore, the authors [43] considered the dependence d_s on a branching degree of PPQX chain more strictly. For the estimation of a branching degree the number of the nodes of branching m were used [13]. The value m can be determined by two methods. First of them is given in paper [35]:

$$m = \frac{N\gamma}{(2+\gamma)}, \tag{32}$$

where N is a polymerization degree, γ is a fraction of a functional branching component.

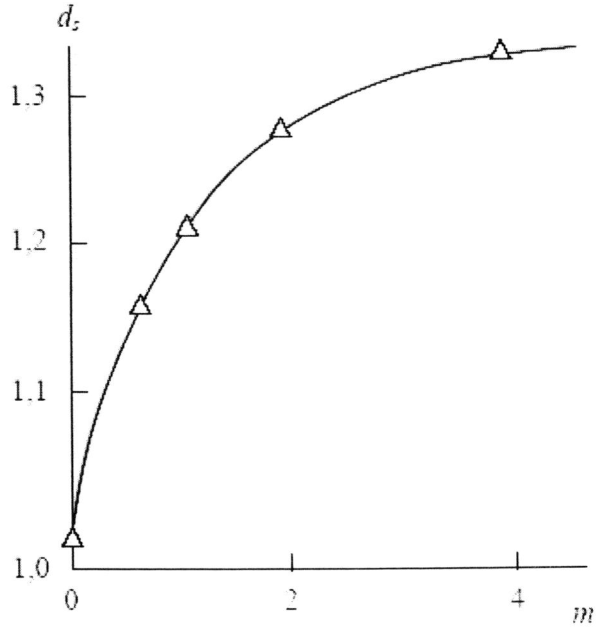

Figure 9. The dependence of the spectral dimension d_s, calculated according to the equation (31), on number branching nodes m for PPQX [43].

The second method uses the formula for the trifunctional branching nodes [13, 35]:

$$g = \left[\left(1+\frac{m}{7}\right)^{0,5} + \frac{4m}{9\pi}\right]^{-0,5}. \tag{33}$$

In Fig. 9 the dependence $d_s(m)$ for PPQX is shown. As it should be expected from the most common considerations, the value d_s monotonously rises at m increase, approaching to the asymptotic magnitude $d_s \approx 1{,}33$ [41] at $m \approx 4$. This dependence is approximately quadric and it can be linearized d_s with written as a function of $m^{1/2}$. Then the analytical form of the dependence $d_s(m)$ will have the form [43]:

$$d_s = 1 + 0{,}17m^{0{,}5}, \quad m \le 4,$$
$$d_s = 1{,}33, \qquad m > 4. \tag{34}$$

The equation (34) assumes that the degree of a chain branching reaches the saturation and the farther increase of γ (or m) does not change the macromolecular coil structure, i.e., the dimensions d_s and D_f [43].

Thus, the considered in chapters 2 and 3 results showed the interrelation of the macromolecular coil structure in solution, characterized by the dimension D_f, with practically all basic parameters of the classical physical chemistry of polymer solutions. This fact can be treated as the defining influence of the coil structure on these parameters. Besides, these correlations give a number of the simple and convenient methods for D_f estimation.

4. A Fractal Variant of the Mark-Kuhn- Houwink Equation

The Mark-Kuhn-Houwink equation derived from the analysis of a great body of experimental data is widely used for determining M_η from the measured intrinsic viscosity $[\eta]$ of polymer solutions (the equation (1)) [13].

Analysis of experimental data revealed [44] that the K_η and b_η constants involved in equation (1) correlate with one another for many flexible chain polymers dissolved in good solvents. Thus, it was found that

$$K_\eta \approx \frac{21}{m_0}\left(\frac{4\times10^{-4}M}{m_0}\right)^{b_\eta}, \tag{35}$$

where m_0 is the molecular mass of a monomer unit.

In some cases, the use of empirical relationships such as equation (35) enables molecular weight evaluation to be performed without detailed study of the samples. A more exact relationship for K_η was proposed by Budtov [13]:

$$K_\eta = \frac{0{,}46}{m_0}\cdot\frac{A^2 l\times10^{24}}{(7{,}3sm_0)^{b_\eta}} \tag{36}$$

where l is the length of a monomer unit, and s is the number of monomer units per segment.

For polymers with the same chain rigidity, the relationship (36) is very close to empirical formula [35]. Relationships (1), (35) and (36) were noted [13] to be very useful in the analysis of solitary polymer samples when they have not been characterized in a relevant solvent but their structural parameters are known.

For the derivation of the fractal variant of the Mark-Kuhn-Houwink equation authors [45, 46] started from the following well-known formula [13]:

$$[\eta] = 6^{1/2}\Phi(\alpha)\frac{\langle R_g^3 \rangle}{M}, \qquad (5)$$

where $\Phi(\alpha)$ is the form factor of a macromolecular coil under rotational friction and R_g is coil gyration radius.

For the sake of convenience, α is adopted to be equal to the viscous swelling ratio defined according to the equation (8). The simplest relationship between Φ and α is [13]:

$$\Phi(\alpha) = \Phi_\theta\left(0{,}753 + \frac{0{,}247}{\alpha^3}\right), \qquad (38)$$

where Φ_θ is Φ for a equal to unity.

The relationship between R_g and M can be expressed as an following approximate [45]:

$$R_g \approx 37{,}5N^{1/D_f} = 37{,}5\left(\frac{M}{m_0}\right)^{1/D_f}, \qquad (39)$$

where R_g is give in Å.

The combination of the equations (8), (37)-(39) allows to obtain a relationship between $[\eta]$ and M, which is similar to the Mark-Kuhn-Houwink equation [45, 46]:

$$[\eta] = c(\alpha)\frac{M^{(3-D_f)/D_f}}{m_0^{3/D_f}}, \qquad (40)$$

where c is some constant depending on α, because it contains the parameter $\Phi(\alpha)$. This circumstance makes it possible to evaluate the coefficient $c(\alpha)$ at α variation in accordance with the equation (37). The value α itself can be evaluated by the equations (1), (8) and (35), if $[\eta]_\theta$ is determined at b_η=0.5 (or D_f=2,0) [2]. We should to note one important aspect. As it is known [47], the ratio $([\eta]/[\eta]_\theta)$ is a single-valued function of D_f, as follows from the equation (11).

Thus, the equation (40) suggests that the proportionality coefficient K_η depends only on two parameters: D_f and m_0. The final equation for calculating the K_η value takes on the form [45, 46]:

$$K_\eta = \frac{8{,}1\left(0{,}753 + 0{,}247/\alpha^3\right)}{m_0^{3/D_f}}. \qquad (41)$$

Fig. 10 compares theoretical K_η values K_η^T calculated according to the equation (41) with corresponding experimental values K_η^e [16] for polyarylates. This plot demonstrates good agreement between K_η^T and K_η^e. Such agreement between K_η^T and K_η^e is obtained in paper [48] for series of cationic polyelectrolytes-copolymers of acrylamide with trimethyl ammonium methylmethacryate.

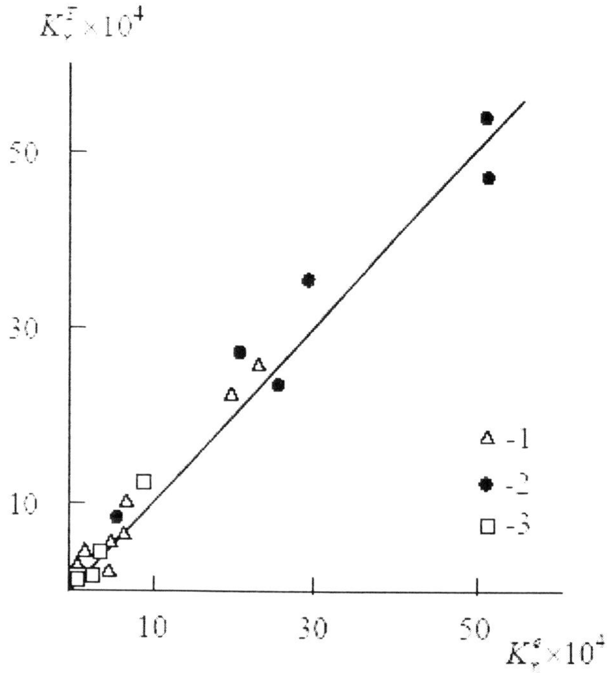

Figure 10. The correlation between experimental (K_η^e) Mark-Kuhn-Houwink constants and those calculated according to the equation (41) for the solutions of polyarylates [16] in symm-tetrachloroethane (1), tetrahydrofurane (2) and 1,4-dioxane (3) [46].

Another method of exponent b_η evaluation is proposed by the authors [49]. It is based on the usage of solubility parameters δ_s and δ_p. From the equation (29) follows, that the value $D_f = 1{,}67$ for good solvent is achieved at $\delta_f = 0$ and $D_f = 2{,}0$ for poor (θ) solvent – at $\delta_f = 1$. At the same time great number of experimental observations are shown the general tendency – the closer the values δ_p and δ_s the better a polymer is dissolved in this solvent [50]. This allows to suppose following form of correlation δ_f, δ_p and δ_s [49]:

$$\delta_f \sim \left| \delta_p - \delta_s \right|. \tag{42}$$

The proportionality coefficient in (42) can be obtained from following simple considerations. As it is known [50], a polymer is not dissolved in a solvent, if $|\delta_p-\delta_s| \geq 2,5$ (cal/cm^3)$^{1/2}$. This criterion for poor solvent with $\delta_f = 1$, that allows to adopted mentioned coefficient equal to ~ 0,4 and calculate D_f according to the equation (29) and b_η - according to the equation (4). The comparison of theoretical and experimental b_η values for 18 pairs of polymer-solvent their good agreement is shown [49].

5. Physical Sense of the Structural Parameters of Low-Molecular Solvents

The representation δ_f was used above as the dimension of a molecule of low-molecular solvent [40]. However, another treatment [51], which will be considered below, is possible. At the derivation of the equation (29) the supposition, that the cluster sizes of polymer and solvent are comparable, was made [40]. As in the case of the low-molecular solvents, the macromolecular coil size is much bigger then the solvent molecule size, we should make the conclusion that it is necessary to consider the structure of the solvent molecules set interacting with a macromolecular coil ("swarm" of the solvent molecules), but not a separate molecule. In favour of such a conclusion there exists the fact that the value δ_f for one and the same solvent, but for the various polymers adopts the different magnitudes [10]. Therefore, it should be supposed, that the dimension δ_f characterizes the polymer-solvent interactions. In Fig. 11 the dependence δ_f on Flory-Huggins interaction parameter χ_1 for 4 polymers in the various solvents is shown, which confirms this assumption. The indicated correlation is found approximately linear and it approximates by the following empirical equation [51]:

$$\delta_f \approx 1{,}15\chi_1 - 0{,}3. \tag{43}$$

The most interest feature of the equation (43) is the possibility of the obtaining of δ_f negative values. As it is known [3, 52], the classical fractal analysis assumes only positive fractal dimensions, describing that or another structure. Therefore, the natural question about the physical sense of dimension δ_f appears. The certain similarity can be given by the equation, describing the number N_{is} of the intersections of two fractals with the arbitrary dimensions D_1 and D_2 [40]:

$$N_{is} \sim R^{D_1+D_2-d}, \tag{44}$$

where R is a radius of the biggest fractal.

At $D_1+D_2>d$ the fractals are opaque for each other, at $D_1+D_2<d$ are permeable for each other. It should be noted, that the relationship (44) gives the condition of the permeability (transparency) of macromolecular coils with $D_1=D_2$ at $d=3$ [51]:

$$2D = 3 \ or \ D_1 = D_2 = 1{,}50. \tag{45}$$

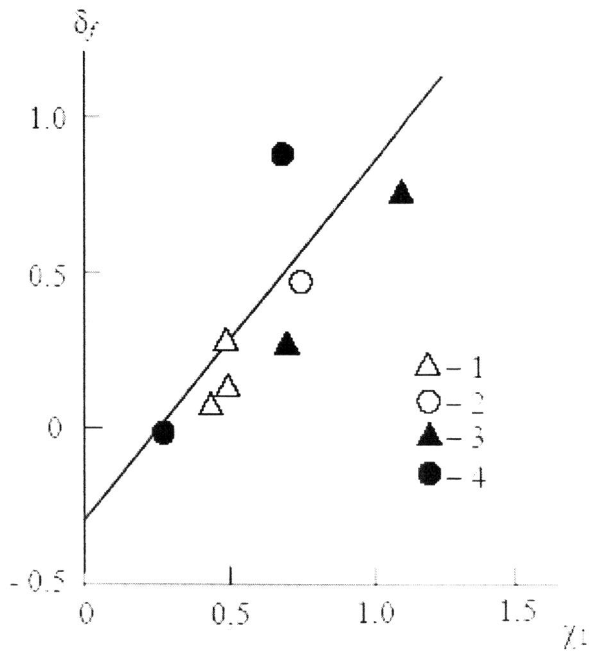

Figure 11. The relationship between the fractal dimension δ_f of "swarm" of solvent molecules and Flory-Huggins interaction parameter χ_1 for polymethylmethacrylate (1), polystyrene (2), polyvynilacetate (3) and polysulfone (4) [51].

For the purposes of the present is discussion is important, that in case of the transparent coils an exponent in the right part of the relationship (44) becomes negative. This allows to suppose, that the dimension δ_f characterizes structure (distribution in space) of the low-molecular solvent molecules and that each contact of the coil and the solvent molecules should be considered as an intersection point of two fractals: coil and "swarm". It is quite obvious, that the solvent molecules must occupy the same space region, that the macromolecular coil with a gyration radius R_g and that's why they cannot form a dense Euclidean object, i.e., $\delta_f<d$. As follows from the equation (29), the maximal value δ_f, at which a compact globule is formed ($D_f=d$) [12], is equal to ~ 2,667. Consequently, the dimension δ_f characterizes the number of the polymer-solvent interactions or the number of the low-molecular solvent molecules n_s in "swarm" of radius R_g according to the general fractal relationship [3]:

$$n_s \sim R_g^{\delta_f} . \tag{46}$$

It is easy to see, that the macromolecular coil will be opaque for the solvent molecules (accounting for the equation (29)) at condition $D_f \geq 2$, $\delta_f \geq 1$. Accounting for the condition of the approximate equality of "swarm" radius and R_g and the known fractal relationship $R_g \sim N^{1/D_f}$ [2], we can obtain the following relationship for n_s [51]:

$$n_s \sim N^{\delta_f / D_f}. \tag{47}$$

From the relationship (47) it follows, that the δ_f decrease, resulting to weaker D_f decrease according to the equation (29), means the reduction n_s at N=const, i.e., the indicated relationship describes the well known effect of the solvent "squeezing" from the macromolecular coil [53].

Using the equations (29), (43) and the literary values χ_1 [13], the limiting magnitudes δ_f can be evaluated. From the equation (29) it follows, that for a coil in a good solvent ($D_f \approx$ 1,667 [2]) the value δ_f=0. It means that the solvent with such a dimension fully screens the interactions of the attraction of macromolecular coil elements. For the permeable coil (D_f=1,50 [2]) realization the value δ_f= - 0,645 is already required, i.e., in this case the solvent must not only screen the noted above interactions, but introduce the repulsive interactions of polymer-solvent. Thus, the value δ_f<0 means the existence of the repulsive interactions of polymer-solvent, δ_f>0 – the attraction interactions and δ_f=0 – the absence of any interactions of polymer-solvent [51]. The cited in [13] values χ_1 for 74 pairs of polymer-solvent vary within limits - 0,30-1,55. According to the equation (43) it means δ_f the variation within limits -0,645-1,483, that in its turn, according to the equation (29) means D_f variation within limits 1,50-2,21. Such a variation includes the full interval of the possible D_f change of real macromolecular coils: from the permeable (D_f=1,50 [20]) to the so-called compensated coil state (D_f=2,28 [12]).

As it is assumed, that δ_f is a measure of polymer-solvent interactions, then it is natural to expect the certain interrelation δ_f with the parameters of the solubility of polymer δ_p and solvent δ_s, characterizing the cohesion energy of these substances [11, 13]. This interrelation is given by the equations (28) and (42) and also by the following relationship [51]:

$$\delta_f = \left(\delta_s^{1/2} - 27/\delta_p\right), \tag{48}$$

where δ_s and δ_p are expressed in $(cal/cm^3)^{1/2}$.

The equation (48) differs from the classical view on polymer dissolution problem. It is assumed [50] now, that a good solvent is realized at the condition δ_s=δ_p, that corresponds to D_f=1,667 or, according to the equation (29), to δ_f=0. However, according to the equation (48), this criterion will have the other form [51]:

$$\delta_s^{1/2} = \frac{27}{\delta_p}. \tag{49}$$

In paper [11] the great number of polymers and solvents for them are cited and the latter were conditionally divided in 4 groups: good, intermediate, poor (where the polymer is partially dissolved or swollen) and non-solvent. In Table 2 the comparison of the evaluation of a solvent type according to the criteria δ_s=δ_p and (49) in case of polycarbonate, for which the quantitative measures of deviation $|\delta_p-\delta_s|$ and $|\delta_s^{1/2}-27/\delta_p|$ are used, respectively. As one can see from the data of Table 2, the solvent quality is much better described by the criterion (49), then the solvent-non-solvent transition is fully defined by the value $|\delta_p-\delta_s|$. We should note, that the variation of constant 27 in the equation (48) for the various polymers as a function of their characteristics is possible [51].

It was shown before [16], that for the series of polyarylates (PAr), produced by the high-temperature (equilibrium) and interfacial polycondensation, the different values of exponent b_η in the Mark-Kuhn-Houwink equation for PAr of the same chemical constitution, but produced by the different methods (for the second method the value b_η is higher) are observed. It means the different structure of a macromolecular coil for PAr, produced by the different methods of polycondensation according to the equation (4).

The evaluations according to the equation (31) showed, that in case of the interfacial polycondensation δ_f=0 and in case of the high-temperature polycondensation - $\delta_f > 0$ [54]. This means that the solvent does not take part in the macromolecular coil formation in the first case, but it defines its structure in the second case. Such treatment is assumed by the difference of mechanisms of the indicated methods polycondensation: if the high-temperature polycondensation is carried out in solution, then the interfacial polycondensation – on the phase boundary. Therefore, received in the presence of solvent with $\delta_f > 0$ the macromolecular coil structure is more compact than without its influence (δ_f=0). This effect of the structural memory is preserved at the dissolution of PAr in the same solvent, and it defines the different values of exponent b_η for PAr of the same chemical constitution, but produced by the indicated above methods of polycondensation [54].

Table 2. Characteristic of the solvent quality according to two criteria [51]

Solvent quality	Criterion	
	$\lvert\delta_p-\delta_s\rvert$, $(cal/cm^3)^{1/2}$	$\lvert\delta_s^{1/2}-27/\delta_p\rvert$
Good	0,46-1,82	0,02-0,22
Intermediate	0-3,30	0,28-0,41
Poor	0,10-0,78	0,11-0,79
Non-solvent	1,43-2,35	0,05-0,11

6. Application of the Theory of the Fractional Derivatives for Description of Polymer Solutions

The fractality of macromolecular coil structure allows to use for the description of its characteristics the mathematical theory of the fractional derivation [55-57]. Within the framework of this formalism the possibility of the precise description of such non-linear phenomena as, for example, the spatial correlations, is presented [57]. The authors of papers the [58, 59] used this approach for the calculation of the average end-to-end distance for a chain of polycarbonate (PC) in two different solvents.

There is a number of methods for the calculation of the mean-square end-to-end distance of a polymeric chain $\left\langle \bar{r}^2 \right\rangle^{1/2}$, which is an important parameter in the theory of polymeric solutions [13]. So, the following empirical relationships for PC in a solution in methylene chloride (MC) and tetrahydrofuran (THF) were obtained [60]:

$$\left\langle \bar{r}^2 \right\rangle^{1/2} = 0{,}66 M_\eta^{0{,}58}, \text{ for MC,} \tag{50}$$

and

$$\left\langle \bar{r}^2 \right\rangle^{1/2} = 1{,}04 M_\eta^{0{,}53}, \text{ for THF.} \tag{51}$$

Another method is the usage of the following equation [13]:

$$[\eta] = \Phi(\alpha)\frac{\left\langle \bar{r}^2 \right\rangle^{1/2}}{M_\eta}. \tag{52}$$

Besides, the equation for the estimation of value $\left\langle \bar{r}^2 \right\rangle^{1/2}$ can be received within the framework of the fractional derivation as follows [61]. Let $x=x(t)$ be the law of the change of some physical property due time t. The rate of change $x(t)$ has the form:

$$\frac{dx}{dt} = \vartheta(t)\tau_0, \tag{53}$$

where t is dimensionless time, τ_0 is characteristic time of the given process.

The equation (53) can be presented as:

$$D_{0_t}^{\nu} D_{0_t}^{1-\nu} x(t) = \vartheta(t)\tau_0, \tag{54}$$

where

$$D_{0_t}^{\nu} f(t) = \frac{1}{\Gamma(1-\nu)} \frac{d}{dt} \int_0^t \frac{f(\tau)d\tau}{(t-\tau)^{\nu}}, \tag{55}$$

is a fractional derivative of Rimman – Liouville of the order ν; $0 < \nu < 1$.

If we enter the notation $D_{O_t}^{1-\nu}x(t)=r(t)$, the equation (54) becomes:

$$D_{O_t}^{\nu}r(t)=\vartheta(t)\tau_0. \tag{56}$$

The solution of the equation (56) has the form:

$$r(t)=\frac{\tau_0}{\Gamma(\nu)}\int_0^t\frac{\vartheta(\tau)d\tau}{(t-\tau)^{\nu}}. \tag{57}$$

The integral in the right part (57) is easily calculated at $\vartheta(t)=\vartheta$ =const and, returning to the dimensional t, we receive [61]:

$$r(t)=\frac{\vartheta\tau_0^{\nu}}{(1-\nu)\Gamma(\nu)}, \tag{58}$$

where $\Gamma(\nu)$ is Euler's gamma function.

Comparing the expression (58) at $\nu=1/2$ with the known Einstein's formula for the mean-square displacement of a particle making Brownian motion, the authors [61] have drawn the conclusion, that the value $r(t)$ can be considered as $r=\langle x^2\rangle^{1/2}$.

As it is known [13], the polymeric macromolecule can be divided in the statistical segments of length l_{st} and one may simulate it (in the simplest case) as Brownian motion of a segment. Then the equation (58) can be used for the description of a polymeric chain. In this case the rate ϑ can be treated as the rate of a segment jump and τ_0 as the time of one jump and supposing $l_{st}=\vartheta\tau_0$, $t=\tau_0N_{st}$ (N_{st} is the number of the statistical segments in a chain), we receive [61]:

$$\left\langle \overline{r}^2\right\rangle^{1/2}=\frac{l_{st}N_{st}^{1-\nu}}{(1-\nu)\Gamma(\nu)}. \tag{59}$$

The authors [58, 59] made the calculation $\left\langle \overline{r}^2\right\rangle^{1/2}$ according to the equations (50) - (52) and (59) with the following comparison of the results on an example of PC solutions in two solvents (MC and THF). For this purpose 5 molecular weights of M for PC were arbitrary chosen: 2,5; 5,0; 7,5; 10,0 and 12,5×10^4. Then, according to the equations (50) and (51) the empirical values $\left\langle \overline{r}^2\right\rangle^{1/2}$ were calculated for the indicated M. In case of the application of the equation (52) for the determination of values $[\eta]$, corresponding to the indicated M, the Mark–Kuhn–Houwink equations for PC and MC, THF [60] were used. For the application of the equation (59) one should define the parameters, included in it, l_{st}, N_{st}, ν and $\Gamma(\nu)$. For the determination l_{st}, N_{st} and $\Gamma(\nu)$ the usual techniques, in detail described in [58, 59] were used, and we are going to consider the ν determination more in detail.

As it was shown in paper [55], a fractional exponent ν coincides with the fractal dimension of Cantor's set and indicates a fraction of the system, the status kept for all time of the evolution t. Let's remind that the Cantor's set is considered in one-dimensional Euclidean space (d=1) and consequently its fractal dimension d_f <1 by virtue of the fractal definition. For the fractal objects in Euclidean spaces with the higher dimensions (d>1) as ν one should accept a fractional part d_f or [62, 63]:

$$\nu = d_f - (d-1), \tag{60}$$

Let's consider the physical sense and the definition of a fractional exponent value ν in the given context. As it is known [21], the transition to the condensed polymeric state occurs at D_f=2,5. It means that the limiting value ν is reached at this value D_f, being equivalent to d, and then we receive [64]:

$$\nu = D_f - (2.5-1), \tag{61}$$

or

$$\nu = D_f - 1.5, \tag{62}$$

In Fig. 12 the comparison of the dependences, calculated by three indicated methods, $\langle \bar{r}^2 \rangle^{1/2}$ on M for the solutions of PC in MC is shown. As one can see, the good correspondence (within the limits of 8 %) of values $\langle \bar{r}^2 \rangle^{1/2}$ calculated according to the equations (52) and (59) with the usage of a dynamic variant of the estimation C_∞, i.e., the equation (14), is obtained. The application of a static variant C_∞=const=2,4 [65] increases an error of the calculated values up to ~ 12 %. As to the empirical equation (50), it gives the values $\langle \bar{r}^2 \rangle^{1/2}$ much lower, than the estimation according to the equations (52) and (59). In essence, the similar picture is received for the solutions PC in THF [59]. It is necessary to mark the important feature of the dependences $\langle \bar{r}^2 \rangle^{1/2}$ on M, calculated according to the equation (59) - at large M they grow faster than the similar dependences calculated according to the equation (52). As it is noted above, at large M the macromolecular coil becomes more compact, that results in the decrease of an exponent b_η in the Mark–Kuhn–Houwink equation and, according to the equation (4), to the increase D_f. The estimations have shown, that in case of PC solutions in MC increase D_f from 1,648 up to 1,681, i.e., on 2 % (or decrease b_η

from 0,820 down to 0,785) results in decrease $\left\langle \bar{r}^{2} \right\rangle^{1/2}$ from 107,4 nm down to 99,6 nm, i.e., eliminates the indicated difference.

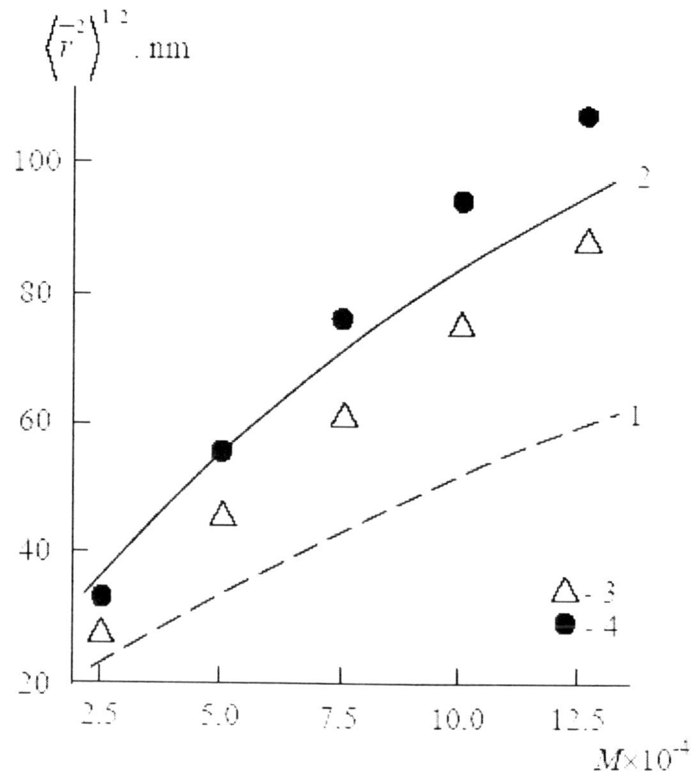

Figure 12. The dependences of mean-square end-to-end distance of polymeric chain $\left\langle \bar{r}^{2} \right\rangle^{1/2}$ on a molecular weight M for solution of PC in methylene chloride. Calculation according to the equations: (50) (1), (52) (2), (59) at C_∞=const (3) and C_∞, estimated according to the equation (14) (4) [58].

The results of the present chapter allow to make two main conclusions. First, the methods the theory of fractional derivatives (the equation (59)) allows the calculation of the mean-square end-to-end distance of the polymeric chain nor less precisely as the other computational techniques which exist now. Second, the account for the change of the chain molecular characteristics of polymeric is required for the correct calculation of the indicated parameters, i.e., one should take into consideration their dynamics when the structure of macromolecular coil varies [58, 59].

7. Fractal Analysis of the Film Formation from the Polymer Solutions

At first, let's consider the dissolution process of solid polymers, which is essentially opposite in respect to the film formation from a solution. The studies of the heats of dissolution of the amorphous polymers were made rather often. It is supposed that the thermal effect of the system transition from the methastabile (nonequilibrium) glassy state in the quasiequilibrium solution makes the dominant contribution in the value ΔH_d of the heat of dissolution. At the same time the essential contribution can be made by component, determined by the polymer structure, particularly, by the existence ordered regions. The authors [66] made the estimation of the ΔH_d value in terms of a cluster model of the structure of polymer amorphous state [67, 68]. This model assumes the existence in the amorphous polymer structure the regions of a local order (clusters), consisting of some densely packed collinear segments of the different macromolecules (the amorphous analogue of crystallite with the extended chains). These clusters are connected between themselves by "tie" chains, forming by virtue of this the network of the physical entanglements with the density ν_{cl} and surrounded by loosely packed matrix, in which all fluctuation free volume of polymer [68] is concentrated.

Some common features of ΔH_d behaviour attract attention. First, above glass transition temperature of polymer T_g the value ΔH_d does not depend on the dissolution temperature T. In terms of a cluster model the thermofluctuational decay of clusters at T_g is postulated, i.e., we should expect, that the change of the ΔH_d behaviour at T_g is namely due to this effect. Second, the T_g rise results to the increase ΔH_d at the fixed T and in terms of a cluster model, the polymers with the highest T_g have higher values ν_{cl} at the fixed of the tests temperature. Third, the rise of the dissolution temperature results to the ΔH_d reduction and the cluster model assumes the ν_{cl} decrease at the temperature rise. But the linear dependence ΔH_d on the difference of temperatures (T_g-T) the greatest interest represents. Such dependence assumes that ΔH_d does not depend on the features of the amorphous polymer constitution, but it is determined only by the degree of approaching to T_g. The dependences ν_{cl} on the value (T_g-T) are fould similar in form, but different by the absolute values ν_{cl}. Some more general characteristic of the degree of local ordering of the amorphous polymer structure is a relative fraction of clusters φ_{cl} [68, 69]. For three polymers (PC, PAr, PMMA) all data in coordinates φ_{cl}-(T_g-T) lie on one curve. Sequently, as ΔH_d, the degree of local ordering in polymers is defined by approaching T to T_g and this allows to assume the possibility of the correlation ΔH_d and ν_{cl} or φ_{cl}. Let's note that the similar in form dependences of polymer properties on (T_g-T) are often offered in literature [69].

Treating the segments entering in clusters as linear defects (the analogue of dislocations), the mathematical methods of the dislocation theory for the description of the amorphous polymer structure and properties [68] can be used. Within the framework of this treatment the energy U_{dis} of the clusters dissociation was calculated and the comparison of the values U_{dis} and ΔH_d as a function (T_g-T) for three indicated polymers showed their close quantitative agreement, it allows to affirm that the value ΔH_d represents itself the energy which is necessary for the dissociation (decay) of clusters in the process of polymer dissolution. The last phenomenon means the transition of polymer from the methastabile nonequilibrium state in the quasiequilibrium solution [66, 68].

Now it is well known [40], that between the structures of a macromolecular coil in solution and the condensed state of polymers the certain interrelation, expressed by the relationship of the fractal dimensions of these states, exists. The value of fractal dimension of the structure of the condensed state can be determined so [40]:

$$d_f = \frac{d_s(d+2)}{2}. \tag{63}$$

In its turn, the value D_f of a macromolecular coil in the diluted solution is defined according to the equation (27). For the linear polymers d_s=1,0 [41] and the combination of the equations (27) and (63) allows to receive the simple relationship between D_f and d_f for the indicated case (d_s=1,0, d=3) [70-73]:

$$d_f = 1{,}5D_f. \tag{64}$$

The equation (64) clearly demonstrates the genetic interrelation between the structures of a macromolecular coil in solution and the condensed state of polymers and it is basic at the determination of the structure of polymeric films. On using it, the authors [74] gave the quantitative description of the structure formation of polymeric films, obtained from the various solvents, within the framework of the fractal analysis and Witten-Sander model of the irreversible aggregation on the example of the amorphous glassy polyarylatesulfone (PASF).

Let's consider the estimation of dimension d_f within the framework of Witten-Sander model [75]. As it was shown in papers [76, 77], the structure of the amorphous glassy polymers can be modelled as the totality of a large number of Witten-Sander clusters (clusters WS), having the radius R_{cl}. The value R_{cl} is determined so [78]:

$$R_{cl} \sim c_0^{-d}, \tag{65}$$

where c_0 is "seeds" number, around which the clusters WS grow.

The nodes of macromolecular entanglements ("hookings") with the density ν_e play the role of "seeds" at the structure formation of amorphous polymers are played. Then at the high concentration of "seeds" it can be written [78]:

$$R_{cl}^{d_f} \sim c_r / c_0, \tag{66}$$

where c_r is the concentration of particles, forming the cluster WS.

In the considered case under such a particle the statistical segment – "rigidity sector" of a macromolecule with the interindependent orientation of a position in the space [76] is accepted. The length l_{st} of a statistical segment is determined as follows [65]:

$$l_{st} = l_0 C_{\infty}, \quad (67)$$

where l_0 is skeletal bond length of polymer main chain.

The common length of macromolecules L per unit of polymer volume can be determined so [68]:

$$L = S^{-1}. \quad (68)$$

Thus, the number of the statistical segments per unit of polymer volume is equal to [74]:

$$c_r = \frac{L}{l_{st}} = \frac{1}{S l_0 C_{\infty}}. \quad (69)$$

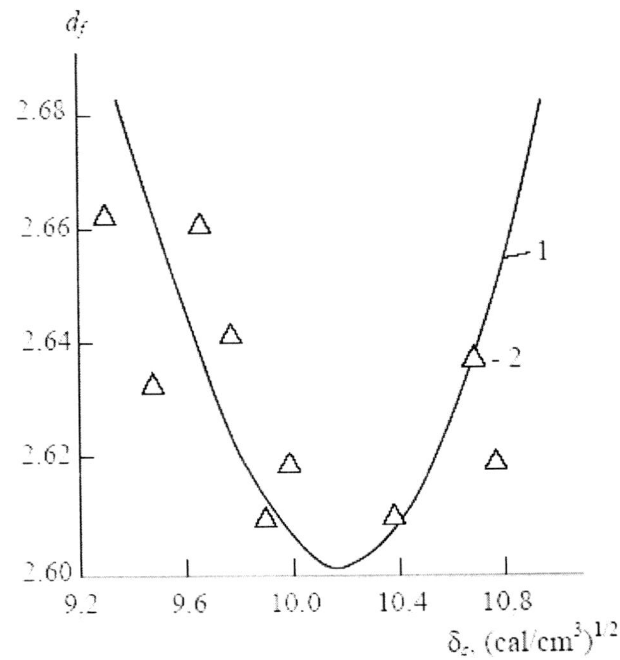

Figure 13. The dependences of the fractal dimension d_f of polymeric films structure on solubility parameter δ_s of solvent for PASF. 1 – the calculation according to the equation (64); 2 – the calculation according to the equation (66) [74].

In Fig. 13 the comparison of the fractal dimensions d_f, calculated according to the equations (64) and (66) (at condition c_0=ν_e) is adduced, from which their good correspondence follows. This confirms the correctness of the description of the amorphous polymers structure as the totality of clusters WS and indicates the factors which control it. So, the molecular characteristics of a polymeric chain (l_0, C_{∞}, S) and the node density of macromolecular hookings network (c_0=ν_e) have the strong influence on the polymer structure. That's why, let's consider the factors defining the value ν_e or c_0. As it is known [40], the number of the intersections of fractals (in our case – a macromolecular coil) N_{is} is determined according to the equation (44) and relationship between R_g and M is given by the formula (39). The combination of the relationships (39) and (44) allows to obtain [74]:

$$N_{is} \sim M^{(2D_f - d)/D_f}. \tag{70}$$

It was shown [74], that at M=const the dependence ν_e on M is linear, i.e., the value ν_e is also determined by the fractal dimension D_f of a macromolecular coil and the polymer molecular weigth (the latter is well known fact [79]).

The authors [80-82] used this approach for the quantitative prediction of the mechanical properties of polymer film samples, obtained from the different solvents. It should be noted that the prediction of the properties on the full extent of stress-strain diagram is carried out within the framework of one approach and with the exactness, that is sufficient for the practical applications. This approach is based on the strict analytical ground of the interrelation between the structures of a macromolecular coil in solution and the condensed state of polymers [73].

8. Some other Problems of Polymer Solutions

The study of the dependences of self-diffusion coefficient D_{sd} of the chain Gaussian macromolecules on the different factors has the great significance both for the development of the ideas about the macromolecule mobility in solution and at the decision of the various problems of the polymer physics and chemistry [13]. However, up to now the main attention was given to D_{sd} dependence on the solution concentration c and the macromolecule molecular weigth M [83]. Nevertheless, another very important factor exists – a macromolecular coil structure [84]. Budtov proposes the following relationship for the evaluation of the value D_{sd} [83]:

$$D_{sd} \approx A_1 \left(\frac{c^*}{c} \right)^{\beta} D_R, \tag{71}$$

where A_1 is a numerical coefficient, c^* is a threshold value of concentration c, D_R is a macromolecule friction coefficient, for which for the intramolecular hydrodynamical interaction between the chain elements is not accounted, β is an exponent, determined as follows [83]:

$$\beta = \frac{2 - \nu_F}{3\nu_F - 1}, \tag{72}$$

where ν_F is Flory exponent in the relationship R_g-N [2, 13].

The value c^* can be determined according to the equation [83]:

$$c^* = 0{,}35c[\eta] = 0{,}35\left[0{,}64\ln^2\left(2\sqrt{N}\right)\right]. \qquad (73)$$

The value c^* for polydimethyldiallyl ammonium chloride (PDMDAACh) can be determined at $[\eta]$=0,80 dl/g and N=315 [84]. Besides, c is determined as c_0 $[\eta]$, where c_0 is monomer concentration. From these estimations the authors [84] were obtained the ratio value $c^*/c \approx 1{,}32$.

As it is known [2], between ν_F and D_f the following relationship exists:

$$\nu_F = D_f^{-1}. \qquad (74)$$

The combination of the equations (72) and (74) allows to express the exponent β as a function D_f [84]:

$$\beta = \frac{2D_f - 1}{3 - D_f}. \qquad (75)$$

Now the value D_{sd} in the relative units can be estimated, as a function D_f assuming A_1=const and D_R=const and using the equations (71) and (75). In Fig. 14 the dependence of the polymerization rate k_p on D_{sd} for PDMDAACh is shown. As it can be seen, the correlation $k_p(D_{sd})$ is linear and passes through the coordinate origin. Such dependence was expected, as the existing theories of polymer synthesis foresee proportional relationship between k_p and D_{sd}. So, in paper [85] two relationships obtained according to the approximation of the chaotic phases, are cited:

$$k_p = 4\pi D_{sd} R_g \left(\frac{9}{5} + \frac{R_g}{aN}\right)^{-1}, \qquad (76)$$

and according to the average density approximation:

$$k_p = 4\pi D_{sd} R_g \left[1 - \left(\frac{R_g}{4\pi a N}\right)^{1/3}\right], \qquad (77)$$

where a is a reactive radius of the reacting particles.

For PDMDAACh radical polymerization we can write down [85]:

$$a = 2R_g. \tag{78}$$

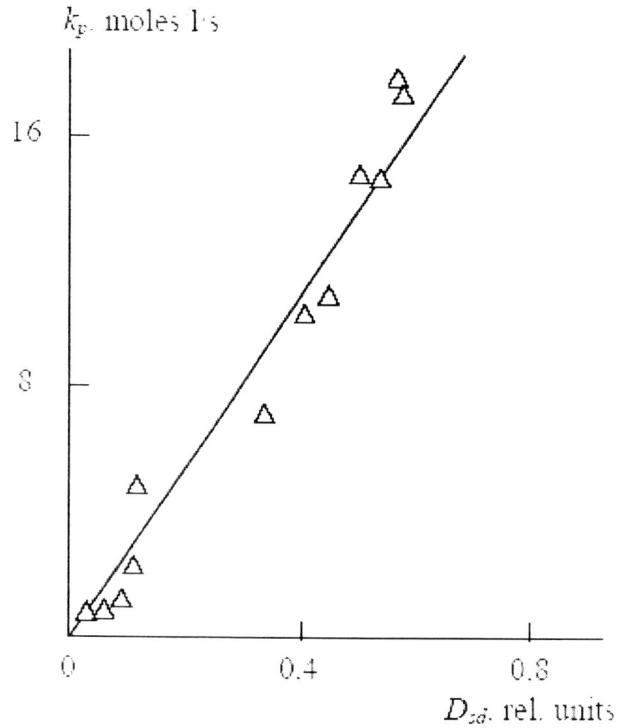

Figure 14. The dependence of reaction rate k_p on self-diffusion coefficient of a macromolecular coils D_{sd} for PDMDAACh [84].

In this case the members in brackets of the equations (76) and (77) give very weak correction to the directly proportional dependence k_p on D_{sd}, especially at rather large N [84].

The fractal reactions are admitted to call either the reactions of fractal objects or the reactions in fractal spaces [86]. The typical indication of these reactions is autodeceleration, i.e., the decrease of reaction rate k_p with the time of its duration t [87]. Let's note, that for Euclidean reaction is typical the linear kinetics and, correspondingly, the condition k_p=const [88]. The fractal reactions in wide sense of this term are met very often in the practice (reactions of the synthesis, sorption curves, stress-strain diagrams and so on) [57]. The simplest and visual relationship for the description of this effect is following [87]:

$$k_p \sim t^{-h}, \tag{79}$$

where h is a heterogeneity exponent ($0 \le h \le 1$), converted to zero in case of the classical behaviour (reactions in the homogeneous or Euclidean mediums) and then k_p=const.

The relationship (79) allows to give the following treatment of the physical sense of the reactive medium heterogeneity: the higher degree of this heterogeneity (fractality) is, the faster decay k_p at the reaction elapsion is. Within the framework of the fractal kinetics of reactions the authors [89] obtain the following interrelation between h and D_f:

$$h = \frac{D_f - 1}{2}. \tag{80}$$

Let's estimate the limiting values of the fractal dimension of a macromolecular coil in solution for two cases: h=0 (D_f^0) and h=1 (D_f^1). From the equation (80) it follows: D_f^0=1,0 and D_f^1=3,0 [89]. The physical sense of the obtained limiting values D_f in this case is obvious. For the homogeneous reactive medium (h=0) k_p is maximal for all $t > 1$ and D_f^0=1,0 means, that the macromolecule represents itself a fully stretched chain, but not a macromolecular coil. If the latter is a fractal object, the inner regions of which are screened by the surface and inaccessible for the reaction [90], then for the stretched chain all reactive centres are accessible and the steric hindrances for the passing of reaction are absent. Therefore, the value k_p is maximal and constant. The value D_f^1=3,0 means, that the macromolecule is coiled up in a compact globule, only small part of surface of which is accessible to the reaction. That's why, the value k_p is minimal and decreases fastly to zero [89].

And in conclusion let's consider a fractal model of low-molecular admixtures by polymeric flocculator (PDMDAACh) [91]. As it is known [92], the value D_f characterizes the degree of "oppeness" ("looseness") of a fractal object structure. This degree can be more precisely expressed by the object density ρ determined as follows [92]:

$$\rho = \rho_0 R_g^{D_f - d}, \tag{81}$$

where ρ_0 is the density of a three-dimensional Euclidean object.

For a macromolecular coil accounting for the equation (39) we can write down [91]:

$$\rho \sim \left(\frac{M}{m_0}\right)^{-(d-D_f)/D_f}. \tag{82}$$

By the application of the equations (1) and (4) the following results for PDMDAACh were obtained: in aqueous solution D_f=1,44 and in NaCl solution D_f=1,65. So, one of the effects of medium, in which the flocculation takes place, on a macromolecule of flocculator is the change of its conformation (and therefore, D_f) with the variation of the solvent quality [91].

As follows from the relationship (82), for a compact object (D_f=d) it is obtained that ρ=1 (in relative units). One of the most important properties of fractal objects is the reduction of their density (loosening) with the increase R_g or M even at D_f=const. It is obvious that the flocculation degree will be the function not only of the number of active centers, but of the degree of their accessibility. Within the framework of the fractal analysis the last factor can be characterized by the value ρ - the lower ρ is, the easier the trapping of adsorbed substance is (in the considered case – phosphatides [94]) in all the coil volume. In essence, the similar explanation of the observed effect is given in [94], where the decrease of the flocculant (PDMDAACh) concentration c_f with its increase [η] is also connected to the geometrical features of a macromolecular coil, though only on the qualitative level.

In Fig. 15 the relationship $c_f(M^{-1})$ in double log-log coordinates, plotted according to the data [94] is shown. As it can be seen, this relationship can be approximated by the following scaling expression [94]:

$$c_f \sim M^{-n}, \tag{83}$$

where the exponent n is equal about to 0,80, that is very close on its absolute value to the exponent $(d-D_f)/D_f$ in (82), which for D_f=1,65 is equal to 0,818.

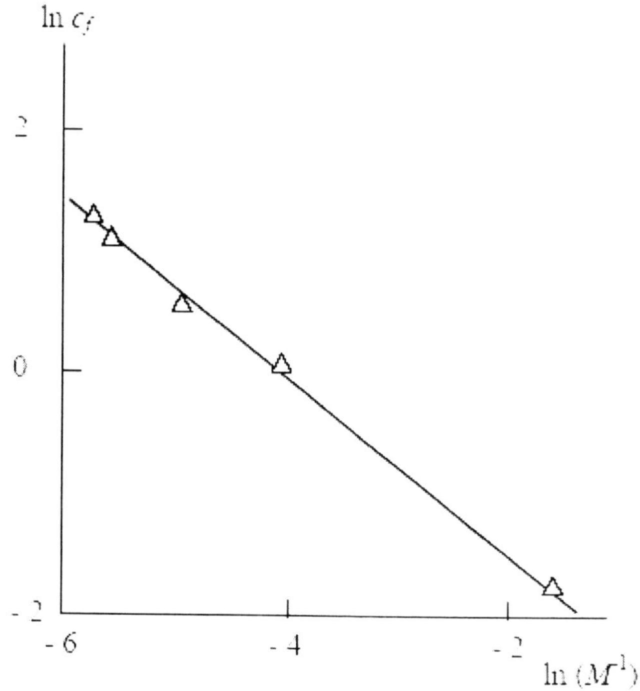

Figure 15. The scaling relationship between a concentration of PDMDAACh c_f and its average viscosity molecular weight M in double log-log coordinates [91].

The physical sense of the equation (83) can be easily understood within the modern ideas about the fractal clusters [86, 95]. The depth of the penetration of a particle in cluster Δr is determined as follows [95]:

$$\Delta r \sim N^{q}. \tag{84}$$

The exponent ratio q/D_f for three-dimensional Euclidean space is equal to ~0,8 [95]. For D_f=1,65 with the appreciation of the condition $q \approx n^{-1}$ we shall obtain $n\approx0,76$ that is close to the value n evaluated from the plot of Fig. 15. Thus, the bigger the depth of the penetration of phosphatides is in a PDMDAACh macromolecular coil, the smaller the optimal concentration of flocculator is [91].

Apparently, one more factor influencing on the efficiency of flocculation process will be the fractal dimension D_f of a flocculator macromolecular coil. So, according to the relationship (83) at the change of D_f it is possible to preserve the value of c_f on previous level by M variation. The authors [93] compared this possibility for PDMDAACh in two solvents: water and NaCl aqueous solution (D_f=1,44 and 1,65, respectively) and they obtained the coefficient k_c which shows how many times it is necessary to decrease M of polymer at the transition from D_f=1,65 to D_f=1,44 in order to preserve the optimal value of c_f. It proves, that at the indicated D_f and initial M=2,99×10^5 it is possible to decrease M almost in one order of the value [93].

Thus, the cited above results show, that between the factors influencing on the efficiency of the flocculation process by polymeric flocculator PDMDAACh there are the molecular weight, the fractal dimension of a macromolecular coil and the medium in which the flocculation takes place. The effect of the medium on the flocculation process can be realized by two ways – by the change of the fractal dimension of a macromolecular coil and the viscosity variation. The last factor can influence on the intensity of diffusive processes. The only factor which will influence in equal degree on the properties of fractal and compact objects is the variation of the medium viscosity and the influence of three remaining factors is defined only by the fractal nature of macromolecular coil of the polymeric flocculator [91, 93].

Let's mark another interesting feature, cited in paper [94], namely, the extreme change of the degree of the removal of phosphatides as a function of PDMDAACh concentration for each molecular weight. Because of its applied and theoretical importance this problem requires the special examination. Therefore, in paper [91] the theoretical description of this effect for PDMDAACh within the framework of the fractal analysis was given.

The increase of the degree of the removal of phosphatides Q up to some polymer concentration c_f (c_{max}), at which the maximal value Q (Q_{max}) is achieved, is due to the simple increase of "active centres" (trapping sites [94]) for the flocculation owing to the increase of a number of macromolecular coils (polymer concentration) in solution. At the concentration c_{max} the touching of macromolecular coils takes place, that corresponds to Q_{max}. At c_f increase the interpenetration of coils is realized and the scale of the mentioned transition r_c is defined by the criterion [78]:

$$r_c \sim c_f^{-1/(d-D_f)}. \tag{85}$$

The value r_c at the condition of coil touching is accepted to be $2R_g$ [91]. The comparison of the calculated according to the relationship (85) theoretical values c_{max} (c^T_{max}) and the experimental magnitudes of this parameter (c^e_{max}) showed the good correspondence of the theory and the experiment for all M, except the smallest out of the used ([η]=0,1 dl/g or $M \approx 4\times10^3$), that proves the made above assumption about the physical sense of the value c_{max}. As for PDMDAACh with $M \approx 4\times10^3$, then the value c^T_{max} is found about 8 times more c^e_{max}, i.e., the efficiency of low-molecular flocculator is found much higher than the expected one. This important question deserves the special consideration.

For its molecular weight, PDMDAACh with $M \approx 4\times10^3$ is closer to olygomer than to polymer. Within the framework of the models of irreversible aggregation it was shown [95], that at low N the small rod-like aggregates are formed, assuming smaller value D_f than the obtained one according to the equation (4) at b_η=0,82 for the high-molecular polymer [96]. Besides, it is known [17], that the value D_f is a monotonously increasing function of M. Thus, for the low-molecular ($M \approx 4\times10^3$) PDMDAACh the value D_f will be much lower than 1,65, obtained for the high-molecular polymers. From the condition $c^T_{max} = c^e_{max}$ and using the relationships (4) and (85), the magnitude D_f for the low-molecular PDMDAACh was estimated, which was found equal to ~ 1,26, that completely agrees with the made above assumptions and results of papers [7, 96]. This example demonstrates very strong effect of the spatial geometric structure of a macromolecule, characterized by dimension D_f, which controls the access of impurities (in our case-phosphatides) into internal regions of flocculator during the flocculation process.

The power dependence of ρ on D_f defines the strong dependence Q on D_f. So, in order to increase Q twofold for PDMDAACh with M=3×10^5 it is necessary to reduce D_f from 1,65 to 1,50 at the constant flocculator concentration. As it is known [45], the value of the exponent b_η in the Mark-Kuhn-Houwink equation depends on the type of solvent used in measurement. Therefore, by the selection of the latter the macromolecular coil conformation can be changed and by this way it is possible to control its ability to flocculate the impurities. The control of this ability can be made by the variation and the measurement of the value b_η accounting for its connection with D_f.

Now let's consider the reasons of the extreme dependence $Q(c)$, experimentally obtained in paper [94], for each value of [η]. As follows from the mentioned above considerations, the value Q should depend, as minimum, on two parameters [91]:

$$Q = k_0\left(\frac{c}{\rho}\right), \tag{86}$$

where k_0 is a constant, ρ is the density determined according to the equation (82).

For $c < c_{max}$ the coils do not touch each other, the value ρ for them will be constant (at M=const) and, in essence, Q is a function only of c. For $c > c_{max}$ the interpenetration of macromolecular coils on their external regions is realized, i.e., as if they flocculated each other that reduced their ability to flocculate the impurities from the solvent. Let's remind, that the fractal aggregates have one common feature – for rather large N the addition of particles (or the small clusters of particles) to this aggregate can be realized only on narrow enough external "active zone" and their internal regions are screened by the indicated zone and can not add the particles [90]. Therefore, between the effective (non-screened) radius of a macromolecular coil R_{ef} and the polymer concentration c there is a relationship [78]:

$$c \sim R_{ef}^{D_f - d} \tag{87}$$

from which it follows the R_{ef} reduction at $c > c_{max}$. Using the values obtained by that way, the effective density of a coil ρ_{ef} can be estimated according to the relationship (82) and then after calculating the constant k_0 in the equation (86) from the condition of the equality of the theoretical and experimental values Q in the maximum point for PDMDAACh with different M it is possible to estimate theoretically the dependence $Q(c)$. In Fig.16 the comparison of the theoretical (curves) and experimental (points) dependences $Q(c)$ for PDMDAACh with viscosity $[\eta]$=0,9; 1,8 and 3,45 dl/g is shown. As it can be seen, the proposed method expresses exactly the qualitative change Q with c, though the quantitative correspondence is worse, especially at $c < c_{max}$. The authors [91] assumed that this discrepancy is not only due to the imperfection of the theoretical calculation though its simplicity gives the certain possibilities for the improvement. So, the obvious extrapolation Q to the zero at c=0 should be expected though the experimental data assume this not always (for example, for $[\eta]$=1,8 dl/g [94]). Nevertheless, one from the possible improvements of the proposed methods of calculation can be indicated [91]. All cited up to now equations assume that the aggregate (a macromolecular coil) consists of zero-dimensional objects (points). Apparently, the real polymeric coil consists of the monomer units with finite sizes (for example, of length a_m) and in this case it is necessary to incorporate the dimensional characteristics (scale) in the corresponding relationships. For example, the relationship (39) has the form [97]:

$$\left(\frac{R_g}{a_m}\right)^{D_f} \sim N\ . \tag{88}$$

It is also apparently, that the incorporation of a linear scale is especially important at the comparison of the flocculating ability of the various polymers. However, the authors [91] did not attempt to achieve the full quantitative agreement of the theory and the experiment, but they wanted to demonstrate the principal possibility of the description of such complicated phenomenon as the flocculation within the framework of the models of the irreversible aggregation and the fractal analysis.

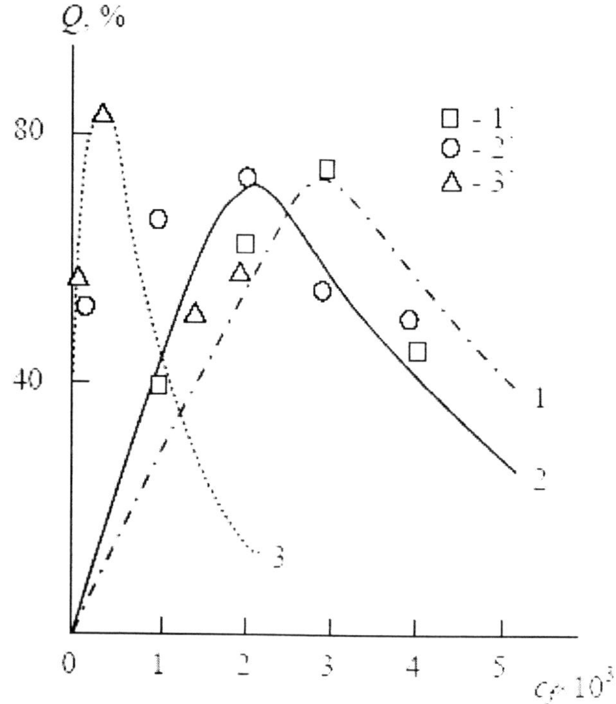

Figure 16. The dependence of the degree of phosphatides removal Q on flocculator concentration c_f for PDMDAACh with molecular weight: $5{,}8\times10^4$(1, 1'), $13{,}5\times10^4$ (2, 2') and 30×10^4 (3, 3') calculated according to the equation (86) (1, 2, 3) and experimentally obtained (1', 2', 3') [91].

9. Conclusions

Thus, in the present review the main aspects of the application of the fractal analysis for the description of the behaviour of macromolecular coils in the diluted solutions are considered. The coil structure is quantitatively described with the help of its fractal (Hausdorff) dimension, characterizing the distribution of coil elements in space. A number of the experimental methods of the determination of this dimension is offered. The interrelation of the classical and fractal (structural) characteristics of a macromolecular coil is shown. The fractal model is used for the description of such phenomena as film formation from polymer solutions, flocculation and self-diffusion of macromolecular coils. The example of the application of the theory of fractional derivatives for the description of the main parameters of a macromolecular coil in solution is given.

References

[1] Tsallis C. In book: *Fractals in Physics*. Ed. Pietronero L., Tosatti E. Amsterdam, Oxford, New York, Tokyo, North-Holland, 1986, p. 98-105.

[2] Baranov V.G., Frenkel S.Ya., Brestkin Yu.V. *Dokl. Akad. Nauk SSSR,* 1986, v. 290, № 2, p. 369-372.

[3] Mandelbrot B.B. The Fractal Geometry of Nature. San-Francisco, W.H. *Freeman and Comp.,* 1982, 459 p.

[4] Karmanov A.P., Monakov Yu.B. *Vysokomol. Soedin. B,* 1995, v. 37, № 2, p. 328-331.

[5] Pavlov G.M., Korneeva E.V., Mikhailova N.A., Anan'eva E.P. *Biofizika,* 1992, v. 37, № 6, p. 1035-1040.

[6] Pavlov G.M., Korneeva E.V. *Biofizika,* 1995, v. 40, № 6, p. 1227-1233.

[7] Kozlov G.V., Dolbin I.V. *Biofizika,* 2001, v. 46, № 2, p. 216-219.

[8] Kozlov G.V., Dolbin I.V., Zaikov G.E. In book: *Perspectives on Chemical and Biochemical Physics.* Ed. Zaikov G. New York, Nova Science Publishers, Inc., 2002, p. 217-223.

[9] Ptitsyn O.B., Eizner Yu.E. Zh. *Tekh. Fiz.,* 1959, v. 29, № 9, p. 1117-1134.

[10] Kozlov G.V., Dolbin I.V., Mashukov N.I., Burmistr M.V., Korenyako V.A. *Voprosy Khimii i Khim. Technol.,* 2001, № 6, p. 71-77.

[11] Wiehe I.A. *Ind. Engng. Chem. Res.,* 1995, v. 34, № 2, p. 661-673.

[12] Family F. *J. Stat. Phys.,* 1984, v. 36, № 5/6, p. 881-896.

[13] Budtov V.P. *Physical Chemistry of Polymer Solutions* (in Russian). Sankt-Peterburg, Khimiya, 1992, 384 p.

[14] Temiraev K.B., Kozlov G.V., Sozaev V.A. *Vestnik of Kabardino-Balkarian State University,* 1999, № 3, p. 24-27.

[15] Kozlov G.V., Temiraev K.B., Sozaev V.A. Zh. *Fizich. Khimii,* 1999, v. 73, № 4, p. 766-768.

[16] Askadskii A.A. *Physical Chemistry of Polyarylates* (in Russian). Moscow, Khimiya, 1968, 216 p.

[17] Dubrovina L.V., Pavlova S.S.-A., Bragina T.P. *Vysokomol. Soedin.* A, 1988, v. 30, № 5, p. 995-1000.

[18] Kozlov G.V., Temiraev K.B., Kaloev N.I. *Dokl. Russian Akad. Nauk,* 1998, v. 362, № 4, p. 489-492.

[19] Kozlov G.V., Burya A.I., Shustov G.B., Temiraev K.B., Shogenov V.N. *Vestnik of Dniepropetrovskogo University,* 2000, № 5, p. 96-102.

[20] Kozlov G.V., Afaunova Z.I., Temiraev K.B. In book: *Fractals and Local Order in Polymeric Materials.* Ed. Kozlov G., Zaikov G. New York, Nova Science Publishers, Inc., 2001, p. 21-28.

[21] Novikov V.U., Kozlov G.V. *Russian Chemical Reviews,* 2000, v. 69, № 4, p. 378-399.

[22] Kozlov G.V., Shustov G.B., Zaikov G.E. J. *Balkan Tribol. Assoc.,* 2003, v. 9, № 4, p. 467-514.

[23] Novikov V.U., Kozlov G.V. In book: *Prikl. Sinergetika, Fraktaly i Komp'yut. Modelir. Structur.* Ed. Oksogoev A.A. Tomsk, TGU, 2002, p. 268-302.

[24] Dolbin I.V., Kozlov G.V. Mater. Of All-Russian conf. *"Perspectiva-2003",* v. 4, Nal'chik, 2003, p. 108-111.

[25] Dondos A. *Polymer,* 2001, v. 42, № 4, p. 897-901.
[26] Gans C., Schnee J., Scherf U., Staikos G., Pierri E., Dondos A. *Polymer,* 1998, v. 39, № 17, p. 4155-4158.
[27] Papkov S.P. *Vysokomol. Soedin.* B, 1982, v. 24, № 11, p. 869-873.
[28] Kozlov G.V., Temiraev K.B., Mikitaev A.K. *Izvestiya VUZov, Khimiya,* 2002, v. 45, № 2, p. 30-33.
[29] Kozlov G.V., Shustov G.B., Dolbin I.V. Mater. *I Intern. Conf. "Modern Problems of Organic Chemistry, Ecology and Biotechnology".* Luga, 2001, p. 17-18.
[30] Kozlov G.V., Temiraev K.B., Lipatov Yu.S. In book: *Fractals and Local Order in Polymeric Materials.* Ed. Kozlov G., Zaikov G. New York, Nova Science Publishers, Inc., 2001, p. 1-9.
[31] Okatova O.V., Lavrenko P.N. *Vysokomol. Soedin.* B, 1992, v. 34, № 7, p. 9-18.
[32] Tsvetkov V.N. *Rigidchain Polymer Macromolecules* (in Russian), Leningrad, Khimiya, 1986, 328 p.
[33] Ryskina I.I., Zhiganova I.Yu. *Vysokomol. Soedin.* B, 1994, v. 36, № 3, p. 503-506.
[34] Khamrakulov G., Musaev Kh.N., Budtov V.P., Kuleznev V.N. *Vysokomol. Soedin.* A, 1993, v. 35, № 6, p. 705-709.
[35] Korshak V.V., Pavlova S.S.-A., Timofeeva G.I., Kroyan S.A., Krongauz Ye.S., Travnikova A.P., Raubach Ch., Schulz G., Gnauk R. *Vysokomol. Soedin.* A, 1984, v. 26, № 9, p. 1868-1876.
[36] Temiraev K.B., Shustov G.B., Mikitaev A.K. *Vysokomol. Soedin.* B, 1993, v. 35, № 12, p. 2057-2059.
[37] Burya A.I., Kozlov G.V., Temiraev K.B., Malamatov A.Kh. *Voprosy Khimii i Khim. Technol.,* 1999, № 3, p. 26-28.
[38] Shustov G.B., Temiraev K.B., Afaunova Z.I., Kozlov G.V. *Izvestiya KBSC RAS,* 2000, № 2(5), p. 92-94.
[39] Kozlov G.V., Dolbin I.V. *Central Eur. J. Chem.,* 2004 (in press).
[40] Vilgis T.A. *Physica* A, 1988, v. 153, № 2, p. 341-354.
[41] Alexander S., Orbach R. *J. Phys. Lett.* (Paris), 1982, v. 43, № 17, p. L625-L631.
[42] Dolbin I.V., Kozlov G.V. In book: *Book of Young Scientifics Works* (in Russian), Nal'chik, KBSU, 2002, p. 84-89.
[43] Kozlov G.V., Dolbin I.V. Mater. All-Russian Conf. *"Chemistry in Technology and Medicine".* Makhachkala, DSU, 2002, p. 45-48.
[44] Frenkel S.Ya. *Introduction to the Statistical Theory of Polymerization* (in Russian). Moscow, Nauka, 1965, 268 p.
[45] Kozlov G.V., Dolbin I.V. *Vysokomol. Soedin.* B, 2002, v. 44, № 1, p. 115-118.
[46] Kozlov G.V., Dolbin I.V., Zaikov G.E. In Book: *New Perspectives in Chemistry and Biochemistry.* Ed. Zaikov G. New York, Nova Science Publishers, Inc., 2002, p. 41-48.
[47] Kozlov G.V., Dolbin I.V., Zaikov G.E. In book: *Polymer Yearbook* 18. Ed. Pethrick R., Zaikov G. Shawbyry, Rapra Technology Limited, 2003, p. 393-400.
[48] Kozlov G.V., Malkanduev Yu.A., Ulybina A.S. *Vestnik KBSU, Khimich. Nauki,* Nal'chik, KBSU, 2003, p. 175.
[49] Kozlov G.V., Dolbin I.V., Shustov G.B. *Proceeding of XVII Mendeleev Conf. On General and Applied Chemistry.* Kazan, 2003, v. 1, p. 279.
[50] Askadskii A.A. *Structure and Properties of Thermo-resistant Polymers* (in Russian). Moscow, Khimia, 1981, 320 p.

[51] Kozlov G.V., Dolbin I.V. *Izvestiya VUZov, Severo-Kavkazs. Region, Estestv. Nauki,* 2004, № 3, p. 69-71.
[52] Feder E. *Fractals.* New York, Plenum Press, 1988, 256 p.
[53] Andrianov K.A., Pavlova S.A., Tverdochlebova I.I., Pertsova N.V., Temnikovskii V.A. *Vysokomol. Soedin., Ser.* A, 1972, v. 14, № 8, p. 1816-1821.
[54] Kozlov G.V., Shustov G.B., Dolbin I.V. Proceeding of XVII Mendeleev *Conf. On General and Applied Chemistry. Kazan,* 2003, v. 2, p. 442.
[55] Nigmatullin R.R. *Theoret. i Matemat. Fizika,* 1992, v. 90, № 3, p. 354-367.
[56] Bolotov V.N. *Pis'ma v ZhTF,* 1995, v. 21, № 10, p. 82-84.
[57] Meilanov R.P., Sveshnikova D.A., Shabanov O.M. Izvestiya VUZov, Severo-Kavkazs. Region, *Estestv. Nauki,* 2001, № 1, p. 63-66.
[58] Kozlov G.V., Dolbin I.V., Shogenov V.Kh., Zaikov G.E. In book: *Fractal Analysis of Polymers: From Synthesis to Composites.* Ed. Kozlov G., Zaikov G., Novikov V. New York, Nova Science Publishers, Inc., 2003, p. 123-130.
[59] Kozlov G.V., Dolbin I.V., Shogenov V.Kh., Zaikov G.E. *J. of the Balkan Tribological Association,* 2003, v. 9, № 3, p. 428-434.
[60] Schnell H. *Chemistry and Physics of Polycarbonates.* New York, London, Sidney, Interdcience Publishers, 1965, 229 p.
[61] Shogenov V.Kh., Shkhanukov-Lafishev M.Kh., Beshtoev Kh. M. *Fractional Derivatives: Interpretation and some Applications in Physics.* (Preprint). Dubna, OIYaI, 1997, 14 p.
[62] Kozlov G.V., Batyrova H.M., Zaikov G.E. *J. Appl. Polymer Sci.,* 2003, v. 89, № 7, p. 1764-1767.
[63] Kozlov G.V., Shustov G.V., Zaikov G.E. *J. Appl. Polymer Sci.,* 2003, v. 89, № 9, p. 2378-2381.
[64] Kozlov G.V., Shustov G.V. *Proceeding Intern. Seminar "Fractals and Applied Synergetics".* Moscow, MSOU, 2001, p. 155-157.
[65] Wu S. J. *Polymer Sci.: Part B: Polymer Phys.,* 1989, v. 27, № 4, p. 723-741.
[66] Kozlov G.V., Dolbin I.V., Zaikov G.E. Mater. V All-Russian Seminar *"Modelling of nonequilibrium systems".* Krasnoyarsk, KSU, 2002, p. 96-97.
[67] Kozlov G.V., Beloshenko V.A., Varyukhin V.N., Lipatov Yu.S. *Polymer,* 1999, v. 40, № 4, p. 1045-1051.
[68] Kozlov G.V., Zaikov G.E. *Structure of the Polymer Amorphous State.* Leiden, Brill Academic Publishers, 2004, 465 p.
[69] DiBenedetto A.T., Trachte K.V. *J. Appl. Polymer Sci.,* 1970, v. 14, № 11, p. 2249-2262.
[70] Mashukov N.I., Temiraev K.B., Shustov G.B., Kozlov G.V. *Papers of the* 6th *Int. Workshop of Polymer Reaction Engng.* Berlin, 1998, v. 134, p. 429-438.
[71] Kozlov G.V., Temiraev K.B., Malamatov A.Kh. *Khimich. Promyshl.,* 1998, № 4, p. 230-232.
[72] Kozlov G.V., Temiraev K.B., Shustov G.B. *Izvestiya VUZov,* Severo-Kavkazs. Region, Estestv. Nauki, 1999, № 3, p. 77-81.
[73] Kozlov G.V., Temiraev K.B., Shustov G.B., Mashukov N.I. *J. Appl. Polymer Sci.,* 2002, v. 85, № 6, p. 1137-1140.
[74] Dolbin I.V., Kozlov G.V. *Izvestiya KBSC RAS,* 2004 (in press).
[75] Witten T.A., Sander L.M. *Phys. Rev. Lett.,* 1981, v. 47, № 19, p. 1400-1403.

[76] Kozlov G.V., Beloshenko V.A., Varyukhin V.N. *Ukrainsk. Fizich. Zhurn.,* 1998, v. 43, № 3, p. 322-323.
[77] Kozlov G.V., Shogenov V.N., Mikitaev A.K. *Inzhenerno-fizich. Zhurn.,* 1998, v. 71, № 6, p. 1012-1015.
[78] Witten T.A., Meakin P. *Phys. Rev.* B, 1983, v. 28, № 10, p. 5632-5642.
[79] Mandelkern L. *Polymer J.,* 1985, v. 17, № 1, p. 337-350.
[80] Novikov V.U., Kozlov G.E., Zaikov G.E. *Russian Polymer News,* 1998, v. 3, № 2, p. 29-34.
[81] Shogenov V.N., Belosshenko V.A., Kozlov G.V., Varyukhin V.N. *Fizika i Technika Vysok. Davl.,* 1999, v. 9, № 3, p. 30-36.
[82] Kozlov G.V., Shogenov V.N., Ozden S., Zaikov G.E. In book: *Perspectives on Chemical and Biochemical Physics.* Ed. Zaikov G. New York, Nova Science Publishers, Inc., 2002, p. 159-168.
[83] Budtov V.P. *Vysokomol. Soedin.* A, 1986, v. 28, № 12, p. 2575-2581.
[84] Kozlov G.V., Malkanduev Yu.A., Burya A.I., Burmistr E.M. *Voprosy Khimii i Khim. Technol.,* 2003, № 2, p. 69-72.
[85] Burlatskii S.F., Oshanin G.S., Likhachev V.N. *Khimichesk. Fizika,* 1988, v. 7, № 7, p. 970-978.
[86] Shogenov V.N., Kozlov G.V. *Fractal Clusters in Physics and Chemistry of Polymers* (in Russian). Nal'chik, Polygraphservice and T, 2002, 268.
[87] Klymko P.W., Kopelman R. *J. Phys. Chem.,* 1983, v. 87, № 23, p. 4565-4567.
[88] Kozlov G.V., Zaikov G/E. *Teoret. Osnovy Khimich. Technol.,* 2003, v. 37, № 5, p. 555-557.
[89] Dolbin I.V., Kozlov G.E. *Dokl. Adygsk. Mezdunar. Akad. Nauk,* 2004, v. 7, № 1, p. 134-137.
[90] Meakin P., Stanley H.E., Coniglio A., Witten T.A. *Phys. Rev.* A, 1985, v. 32, № 4, p. 2364-2369.
[91] Kozlov G.E., Malkanduev Yu.A., Zaikov G.E. In book: *Homolytic and Heterolytic Reactions. Problems and Solytions.* Ed. Zaikov G., Monakov Yu., Jimenez AA. New York, Nova Science Publishers, Inc., 2004, p. 91-120.
[92] Brady R.M., Ball R.C. *Nature,* 1984, v. 309, № 5965, p. 225-229.
[93] Esmursiev A.M., Malkanduev Yu.A., Kozlov G.E. Vestnik KBSU, *Khimich. Nauki,* Nal'chik, KBSU, 2001, № 4, p. 121-123.
[94] Shnaider M.A., Kolganova I.V., Ter-Minasyan R.I., Topchiev D.A. *Maslozhirov. Promyshl.,* 1990, № 10, p. 17-21.
[95] Smirnov B.M. *Physics of Fractal Cluster* (in Russian). Moscow, Nauka, 1991, 136 p.
[96] Kolb M., Botet R., Jullien R. *Phys. Rev. Lett.,* 1983, v. 51, № 13, p. 1123-1126.
[97] Hentschel H.G.E., Deutch J.M., Meakin P. *J. Chem. Phys.,* 1984, v. 81, № 5, p. 2496-2502.

In: Synthesis and Properties of Low- and High-Molecular Compounds ISBN 1-59454-716-5
Editor: Gennady E. Zaikov et al., pp. 183-196

Chapter 10

FUNCTIONALISING OF LOW-MOLECULAR, OLIGOMER DIENES AND OLEFINS WITH S, O-CONTAINING COMPOUNDS

R. Z. Biglova*[1], *A. U. Galimzjanova*[1], *V. A. Docichev*[2], *G. V. Konesev*[3], *G. E. Zaikov*[4] *and R. F. Talipov*[1]
[1]Bashkir State University, Ufa, Russia
[2]Institute of Organic Chemistry Ufa Branch of Russian Academy of Sciences, Ufa, Russia
[3]Ufa State Oil Technical University, Ufa, Russia
[4]N.M.Emanuel Institute of Biochemical Physics Russian Academy of Sciences, Moscow, Russia

More and more wide application is found with multipurpose additives to polymers, and also packages of additives to various oils with a complex of necessary properties [1,2]. In this connection reactions of element sulfur with dienes, oligodienes and oligoolefins are investigated. As initial hydrocarbons are involved cheap and accessible piperylene fraction (a large-tonnage waste at reception isoprene in manufacture of rubber), its oligomerization product, and also oligomerization products of fulfilled buten-isobutane fractions of various molecular weight.

As antistriking, antiwear properties of additives depend on the maintenance in them of the covalent-connected sulfur, selection of optimum conditions of realization of sulfiding processes is begun from introduction of the greatest possible quantity covalent sulfur. For this purpose functionalizing of dienes and olefins hydrocarbons conducted in a wide time-temperature mode. Taking into account that fact, that temperature of boiling piperylene fractions low (42-44°C), sulfiding carried out in constant temperature-controlled autoclave at the presence of the catalyst cobalt phthalocyanine [3], in the environment of not polar solvents (for example, heptane). Under conditions of realization of synthesis: 130°C, 3 h, >C=C<: S, mole = 1:4 - the product is received, the maintenance of sulfur in which achieved 54.95 mass.%, and yield – 10mass.%. Low value of yield of a target product is caused by realization of experiment with the static conditions, therefore the following series of experiences was carried out in dynamic conditions. At realization of sulfiding process in constantly rotating autoclave at the same parameters of synthesis, but in the environment of aromatic hydrocarbons (toluene), yield has made 49,5 mass.% and the maintenance of sulfur has increased till 70.35 mass. %.

Table 1. Sulfiding of piperylene fractions with element sulfur in constantly rotating autoclave (V=17 ml), *t*=130°C, τ= 3 h

Conditions of realization of reaction	1	2	3	4	5	6
> C=C <: S, mole	1: 2	1: 1	1: 2	1: 1	1: 2	1: 1
Solvent	toluene	toluene	kerosene	kerosene	*p*-xelene	*p*-xelene
Yield of a product,mass. %	48.0	24.9	43.0	19.5	100.0	78.6
The maintenance of sulfur in a product,mass. %	69.86	48.23	66.11	47.01	68.24	50.71

Interactions piperylene fractions with element sulfur in absence of the catalyst has improved results (tabl.1). At mole ratio > C=C <: S, mole = 1 : 2 in *p*-xelene environment sulfur has reacted quantitatively.

The structure of the synthesized compounds is established by set of methods: NMR-H[1], NMR-C[13]-spectroscopy and the element analysis. At the spectra NMR-H[1] is observed an intensive signal at 5.43 м.д., characteristic for olefins protons. A signal at 1.10 м.д. concerns to protons of methyl groups. Intensive multiplet with the centre at 2.13 м.д. belongs to methine and methylene protons. In NMR-C[13] spectrum at 52.1 м.д. takes place singlet, responsible for presence of groups of atoms C-S.

According to results of analyses, reaction of piperylene with element sulfur proceeds under the following scheme with obtaine piperylene *bis*- tetrasulfide:

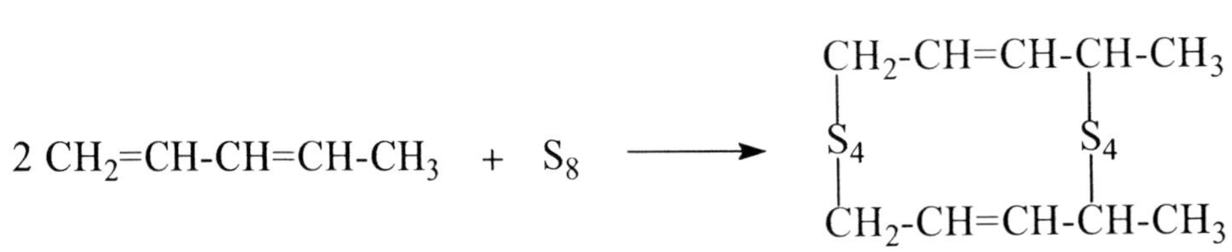

The given scheme will be coordinated to the data received by authors [3,4] at sulfiding of low-molecular dienes, in particular, divinyl.

For studying interaction of oligomerization product of piperylene fractions with element sulfur applied oligopiperylene (OPP) with molecular weight $\overline{M}_n$=910. NMR-H[1], NMR-C[13]-spectra of a trial sample compared to the spectra given in [5]. The analysis of sizes of chemical shifts and multiplicity signals testifies that the sample of oligomer marks SROP (synthetic rubber oligopiperylene) is mainly *1,4-trans*-oligomer. General nonsaturation of a sample makes 30 %, that corresponds to presence in a molecule of four active double bonds.

Results by definition of quantity >C=C< bonds (on bromic number) correlate with the spectral data.

The data on interaction of oligopiperylene (OPP) and oligoisobuttylens (OIB, $\overline{M}_n$= 390; 880) with element sulfur are given in tab. 2, 3. According to results of the element analysis, the contents of sulfur in the received products is increased both with rise in temperature of synthesis, and with increase of duration of process. The increase of a ratio of initial substances more equivalent mole ratio of oligomers and sulfur does not result to appreciable improvement of values of a mass content of sulfur in a product. Modification of oligopiperylene at temperature is higher 140°C results in sewing together of macromolecule. Reaction with element sulfur in the environment of nonpolar solvents (octane, kerosene) does not reduce percentage of sulfur in a product and reduces an opportunityof cross-linking, and in aromatic hydrocarbons results to the low contents of sulfur.

Table 2. Functionalization of oligopiperylene with element sulfur at a) * *t* = 120°C; б) * t = 130°C; в) *t* =130°C, τ=8 h. A parameter - the contents of sulfur in a product, mass. %.

	Conditions of realization functionalization	τ, ч		
	> C=C <: S, mole	4	6	8
a	1.00: 0.50	0.67	1.11	1.69
	1.00 : 1.00	1.15	2.99	3.40
	1.00 : 2.00	0.95	2.87	3.29
	1.00 : 3.00	0.92	2.11	3.16
b	1.00: 0.40	2.23	2.68	3.39
	1.00 : 0.50	3.57	4.02	4.48
	1.00 : 0.75	3.67	4.24	4.77
	1.00 : 1.00	4.19	5.97	6.57
	1.00 : 2.00	3.46	5.67	6.55
c		Solvent		
		octane	*p*-xelene	kerosene
	1.00: 0.05	1.93	1.17	2.57
	1.00 : 0.75	2.21	1.58	2.76
	1.00 : 1.00	3.59	2.21	6.10

*-Without solvent

Table 3. Functionalization of oligoisobutylene with element sulfur. A parameter - the contents of sulfur in a product, mass. %.

Conditions of realization functionalization	1	2	3	4	5	6	7	8
	Solvent (*t*, °C)							
	octane 120°C	decane 160°C		*p*-xelene 140°C		- 140°C	- 160°C	- 180°C
	τ, ч							
> C=C <: S, mole	6	6	8	3	6	6	6	6
1.0: 0.8	1.00	2.77	2.81	2.45	2.51	4.14	4.98	6.77
1.0 : 1.0	2.61	3.38	3.42	3.06	3.12	6.16	7.00	7.35

1-5 - $\overline{M}$ п = 880; 6-8 - $\overline{M}$ п = 390.

Depending on sizes of molecular weight of products and the contents of sulfur in them, presence mono- and disulfide bridges in macromolecule is possible. It will be coordinated to the data of work [4] in which interaction of sulfur with isobutylene in an interval of 100 up to 140°C was studied. On an example of isobutylene oligomers and a linkof oligopiperylene, containing double > C=C < bond it is possible to present the scheme of processes as:

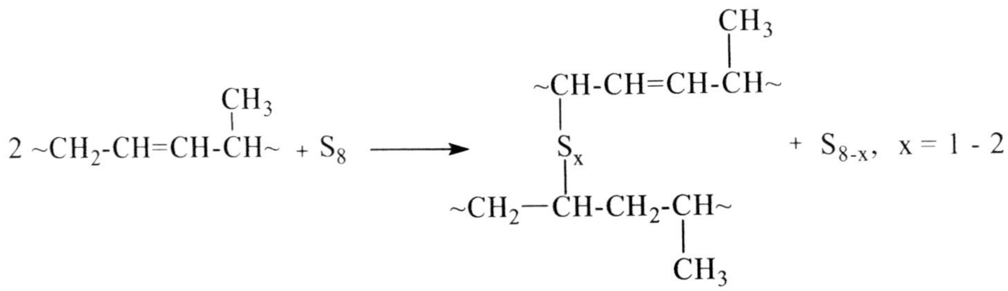

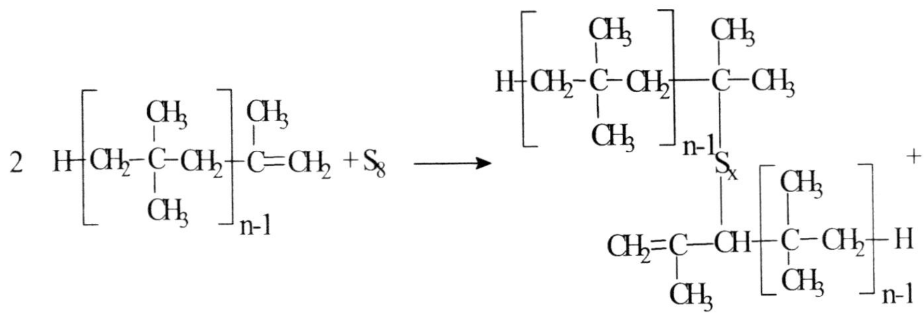

n = 7; 16.
x = 1-2.

Sulfur-containing compounds can get antioxidizing and anticorrosive properties at introduction in their molecules of the appropriate functional groupings (a fragment of the shielded phenol). Therefore the following stage of work became modification of oligomers with oxygen-containing compounds (phenol, 2,6-di-*tret*-butylphenol). The sequence of modification should be following: 1)alkylation; 2)sulfiding. Change of a sequence is undesirable, as sulphidic bridges have no sufficient durability and at the subsequent alkylation their break is possible. Whereas in macromolecules of oligoolefins there are only trailer double bonds investigated compositions sulfiding and alkyl-oligomers as multipurpose additives. Alkylation carried out in nonpolar solvents (octane) at presence catalytic systems with lowered relative acidity $Na[AlCl_4]$ within 8 hours at temperature 100-120°C at mole ratio >C=C<: phenol: the catalyst, mole= 1:1 : 0.2 according to the mentioned below scheme on an example of isobutylene oligomers and a link of oligopiperylene, containing >C=C< [6]. The contents of sulfur in modified oligopiperylene makes 4.92 mass. %, oxygen 1.58 mass. %.

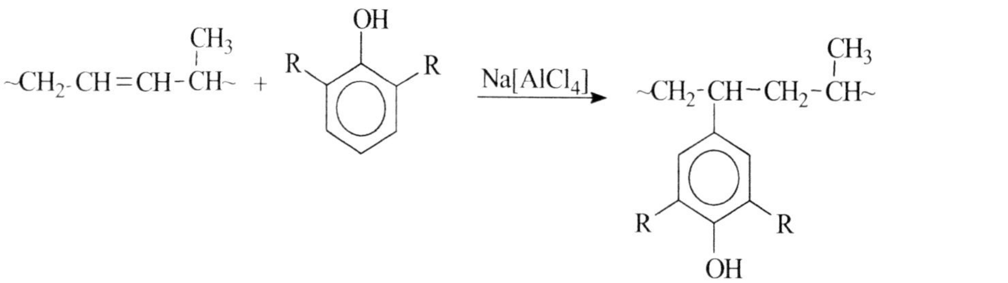

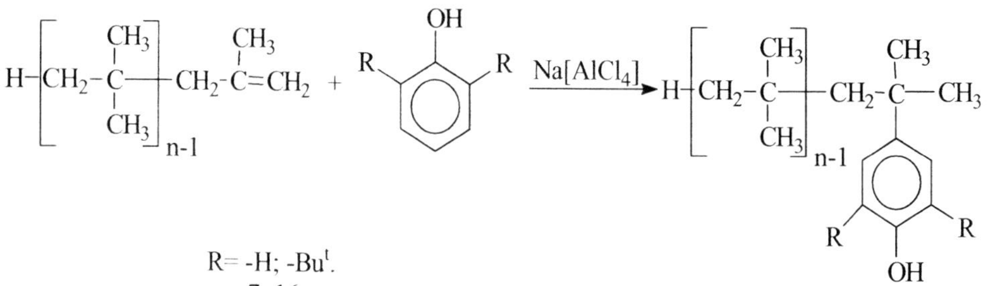

R= -H; -Bu^t.
n = 7; 16.

Functionalization of oligoisobutylenes with phenols carried out also by an alternative technique in the environment of polar solvents (DMF, DMSO) in which conducted reaction of sulfur with low-molecular phenols [5]. As initial substances were used earlier alkylating phenols (4-oligoisobutenylphenols) and element sulfur. Interaction carried out in a current of inert nitrogen (removal from a zone of reaction of hydrogen sulphide allocated at it) at 140-150°C. Results of experiements are given in tab.4. For the best solubility in a reactionary mix added *p*-xelene, THF. A ratio of solvents in relation to weight of initial phenol phenol: DMF(DMSO): *p*-xelene (THF),mass. = 1:4:1.

Table 4. Interaction of sulfur with 4-oligoisobutenylphenols in the environment of polar solvents. t = 145-150°C, τ =6 h.

Conditions of realization of interaction	1	2	3	4	5	6
Phenol: S_8, mole	1.0: 1.5	1.0: 1.0	1.0: 0.5	1.0: 0.5	1.0: 0.5	1.0: 0.3
Solvent	DMF	DMF+ *p*-xelene	DMF + *p*-xelene	DMF+ THF	DMSO+ *p*-xelene	DMSO+ *p*-xelene
Initial oligoisobutylene ($\overline{M}_n$ = 390)						
Yield of a product,mass. %	21.0	18.0	42.0	34.0	28.0	46.0
The contents of sulfur in a product,mass. %	8.39	6.09	6.46	6.15	3.92	3.50
Initial oligoisobutylene ($\overline{M}_n$ = 880)						
Yield of a product,mass. %	29.0	30.7	96.0	41.0	65.0	72.6
The contents of sulfur in a product,mass. %	1.24	1.86	3.76	0.63	1.40	0.73

It is experimentally established, that in DMF environment reaction proceeds with the big yield, rather than in DMSO. With reduction of a ratio of initial substances the yield of a product is increased, however at ratio smaller, than 1.0:0.5, the contents of sulfur in final compounds appears less.

Relative viscosity of modified oligomers, determined by the viscosimetry method, is a little bit higher than values appropriate initial oligomers (tab. 5). Notice gives the basis to believe, that during interaction of oligomers with phenols and element sulfur there is an increase of molecular weight in view of formation functionalised product.

Table 5. Viscosity characteristics of initial and of functionalized oligomers

Oligomer	c, g/dl	η_{rel}
Oligoisobutylene ($\overline{M}_n$ = 390)	4.2 1.0	1.14 1.03
Sulfiding 4-oligoisobutenylphenol	4.2 1.0	1.41 1.32
Oligoisobutylene ($\overline{M}_n$ = 880)	4.2 1.0	1.33 1.19
Sulfiding 4-oligoisobutenylphenol	4.2 1.0	1.92 1.48
Oligopiperylene ($\overline{M}_n$ = 910)	4.2 1.0	1.42 1.26
Sulfiding oligopiperylene	4.2 1.0	2.29 1.67

According to results of the element analysis, definition of relative viscosity modified oligomers, to the spectral data and references [7], the scheme of interaction alkylated with oligoisobutylenes phenols with element sulfur in our case can be submitted in the following kind:

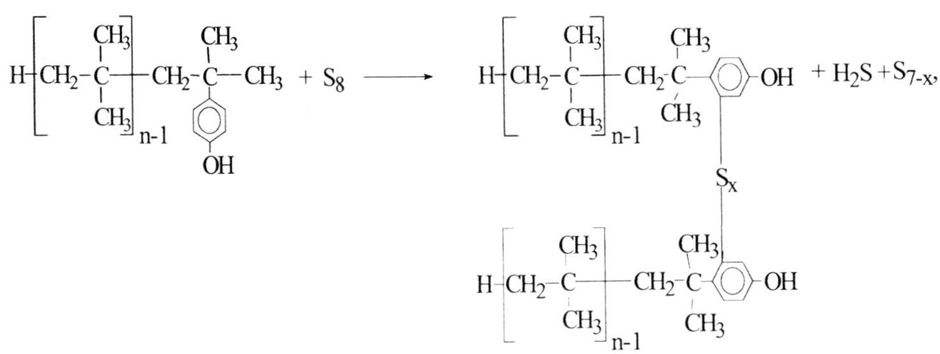

n = 7; 16.
x = 1-2.

Functionalizated S-,O-containing oligomers were investigated as additives. For long-term operation of oils in them enter up to 10 % of the additives distinguished on the functional influence. They should protect surfaces greased with oil to improve properties of oils and to protect an oil composition. According to the listed parameters apply the certain classes of the chemical compounds providing necessary properties.

Are investigated antiwear, antistriking properties S-containing compounds on a basis piperylene fractions. For the characteristic of the designated properties of additives used the following important parameters: speed of wear process (a_m) and factor of friction (k_{fr}). Tests of sulfurcontaining substances to scouring liquids (a clay solution) and greasings carried out on experimental installation MT3 according to a technique described in [8]. Depending on applied loading speeds of wear process of cores from chisel steel in compositions were determined on the basis of cylinder oil of mark 52 at the presence of the synthesized substances. In comparison with additive ВНИИНП-354 traditionally used in the industry (o-,o- *di*(octylphenyl)-dithiophospate zinc), received piperylene *bis*- tetrasulfide and modified by sulfur oligopiperylene high results (rice 1) have shown.

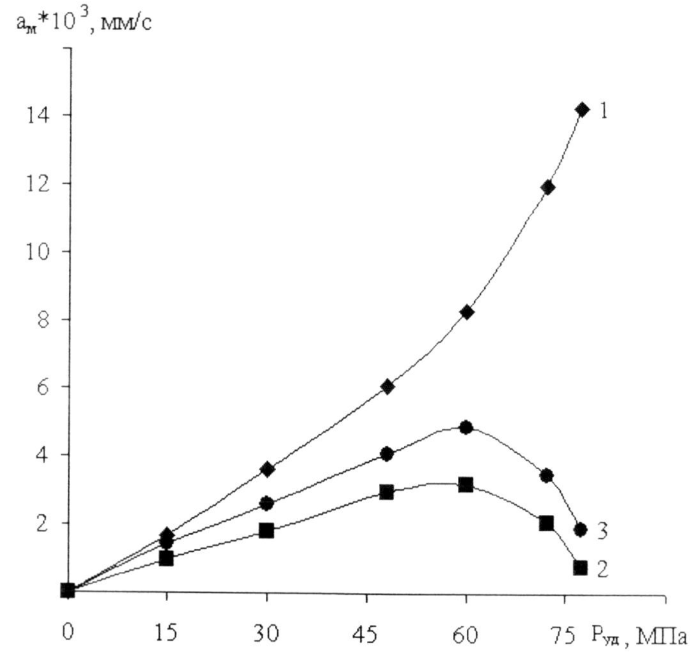

Figure 1. Dependence of speed of wear process on applied loading; 1-industrial oil of mark 52 - ВНИИНП-354; 2- industrial oil of mark 52 - piperilene *bis*- tetrasulfide; 3- industrial oil of mark 52 - sulfiding oligopiperylene;

Studying antiwear properties of clay solutions at the presence of insignificant amounts (up to 1 mass.%) sulfurcontaining product and up to 3 mass.% of SAS (SDBUR) has shown, that with increase of pressure in contact decrease of values of factor of friction and speed of wear process of cores from chisel steel on 30-35 % in comparison with the appropriate parameters for a clay solution without additives (rice 2,3) takes place. To increase of values of axial loading there is a formation films on a surface of friction owing to what serviceability of chisel solutions grows at the raised loadings. It is revealed, that operational parameters are influenced with the order of mixture of components. Compositions of a clay solution with xelene solution of sulfiding piperylene fractions overestimate values of speed of wear process and factor of friction, than a product in absence of solvent a little.

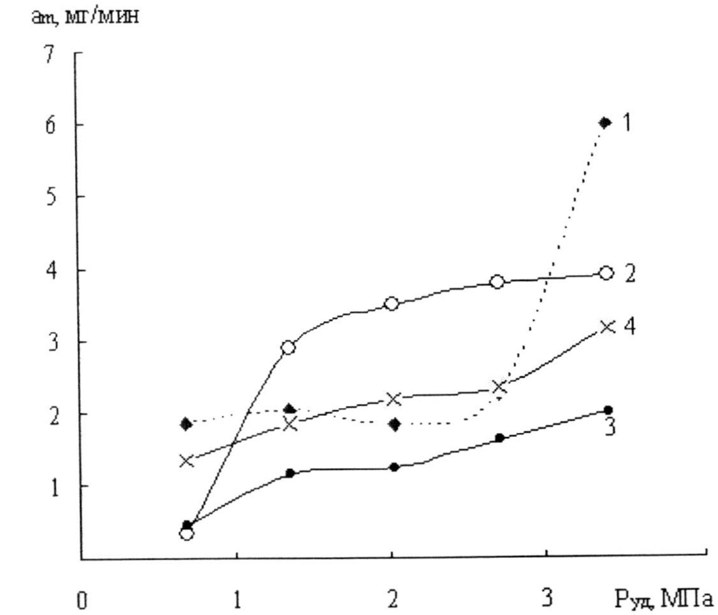

Figure 2. Dependence of speed of wear process on applied loading; 1 - a clay solution; 2 - a clay solution – SDBUR (1.0 mass.%); 3 - a clay solution – SDBUR (1.0 mass.%) - piperilene *bis*- tetrasulfide (0.1 mass.%); 4 - a clay solution – SDBUR (1.0 mass.%) - piperilene *bis*- tetrasulfide in solvent (0.1 mass.%).

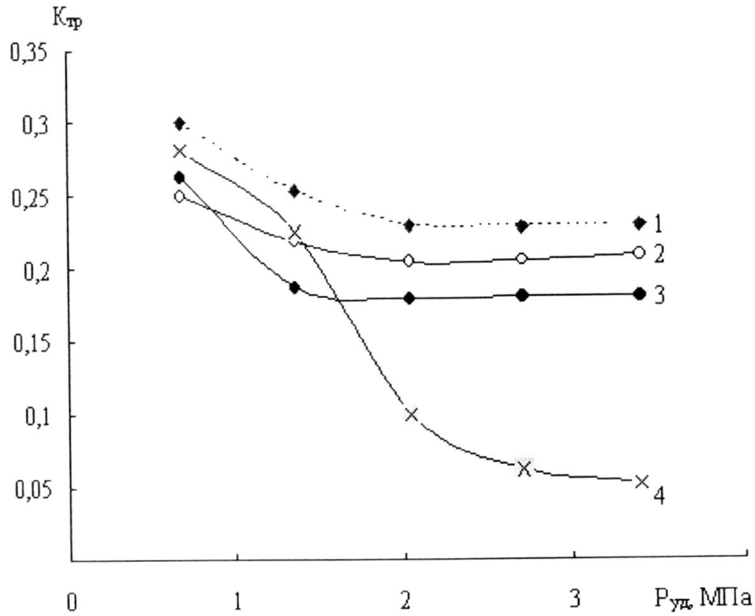

Figure 3. Dependence of factor of friction on applied loading; 1 - a clay solution; 2 - a clay solution – SDBUR (1.0 mass.%); 3 - a clay solution – SDBUR (1.0 mass.%) - piperilene *bis*- tetrasulfide (0.1 mass.%); 4 - a clay solution – SDBUR (1.0 mass.%) - piperilene *bis*- tetrasulfide in solvent (0.1 mass.%).

Tests of an oil composition at the presence of synthesized piperylene *bis*- tetrasulfide carried out on twenty chisels of chisel installations in conditions of Far North.

Antioxidizing properties of oil with additives on a basis of oligopiperylene determined by method of measurement of stability on the induction period of deposition (IPD). Thermostabilized ability of sulfiding oligopiperylenylphenol at introduction in industrial oil of mark I-20 is in the limits satisfying ГОСТу (the contents of deposit X_0 no more than 0.5 mass.%). The specified compositions also were tested on viscosity properties. For thichening action the index of viscosity should make not less than 9, to what the given tab. 6 coordinated.

Detergent-dispersion additives are obligatory components of batch additives. More often in this quality use imides of amber acid, which washing action consider in aspect of their solubilzing abilities, i.e. transfer in a solution of products by SAS micelle, insoluble in the given environment. With the purpose of optimization of concentration of the compounds present in a package influence of oxidations inhibitors (oligoolefynylphenol, oligodienylphenol), antiwear additives (sulfiding oligomers of isobutylene and piperylene), chemicals-additives of multifunctional action (alkylation products of phenol by olgoolefins and oligodienes and products of subsequent sulfiding of the received compounds both in not polar, and in polar solvents) on efficiency detergent-dispersion actions of cuczinimid is investigated.

According to the literary data [9], concentration dependences of antiwear efficiency of sulfurcontaining compounds have complex extreme character that speaks by micelle formation in oil solution of additive. From this point of view it is interesting to investigate concentration dependences of compositions antiwear and detergent-dispersion additives.

Table 6. Characteristics of oil I- 20 at the presence of additives

Additive	Additives concentration in oil, mass. %	Viscosity, cCт at		IV	Deposit, mass. % (IPD)
		40°C	100°C		
Oligopiperylene ($\overline{M}_n$=910)	2 5	74.2 84.7	9.1 10.3	95 98	-
Sulfiding 2,6-di-Bu^t-4-oligopiperylenyl phenol	2 5	81.0 103.3	10.1 11.4	96 100	0.22
Oil I-20	-	66.7	8.3	91	0.85

Necessary for studying solubilisation process cuczinimid is synthesized on a basis of oligoisobutylene ($\overline{M}_n$ = 880) by known technique [10] and the contents of nitrogen in it has made 3.98 mass.% (is agrees TU- 38101146-77 the maintenance should not less than 1.4 mass.%). Research of solubilizing abilities of additives carried out by a technique described in [11]. In relation to dye solubilizing action was to a greater or lesser extent shown with all types of investigated compounds. Curve dependences of solubilization effect (ES) compositions from concentration of additives have complex extreme character; also variously their arrangement in relation to axes of coordinates. For the majority of substances curve dependences have three strongly pronounced areas. The first - covers an interval of concentration at which the solubilization effect is absent, the second - promotes growth of solubilizing ability at change of the maintenance of an additive, and the third - area of the raised concentration - answers the maximal values of effect. It is connected by that in each of the specified areas solutions of additives have various colloid properties.

In experiences with родамином C received mainly two types of curves (fig. 4a, b,c,d): for the first - typically fast colloid dissolution of dye and stability of a solution (for example, curves 2b, 3b); for the second - more long stabilization of solutions (curves 2a, 3a), but with sharp growth of solubilization effect for compositions in the field of the increased concentration (a curve 9a). For compositions of the specified additives with cuczinimid the increase of solubilization effect and displacement of values of critical micelle concentration (CMC) in area of their reduction takes place at comparison with individual substances in isooctane (tab. 7). If for sulfiding piperylene fractions interval CMC 0.05-0.45 mass.% is characteristic, at the presence of cuczinimid 0.5 and 1.0 mass.% to areas CMC there correspond the following values: 0.02-0.50 and 0.01-0.50 mass.%.

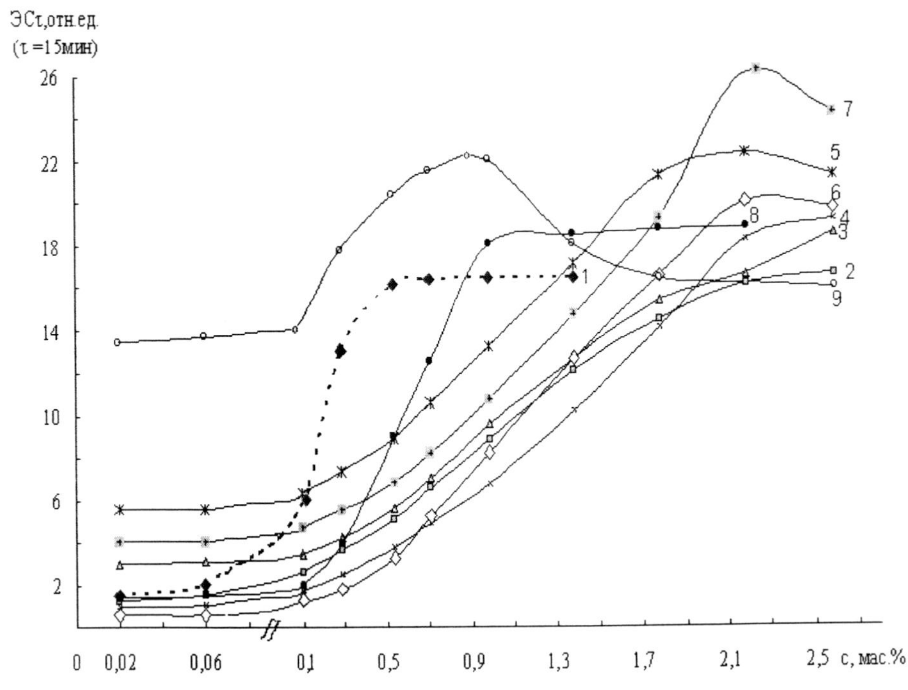

Figure 4. Dependence solubilizing abilities from concentration of an additive in a solution. a) Modified oligoisobutylene ($\overline{M}_n$= 880); 1 - cuczinimid; 2- sulfiding oligoisobutylene; 3- sulfiding oligoisobutylene - cuczinimid (0.3 mass.%); 4- 2,6-d i-Bu^t-4-oligoisobutenylphenol; 5- 2,6-d i-Bu^t-4-oligoisobutenylphenol - cuczinimid (0.3 mass.%); 6- 2,6-di-Bu^t-4-oligoisobutenylphenol: sulfiding oligoisobutylene, mass. = 1 : 1; 7- 2,6-d i-Bu^t-4-oligoisobutenylphenol: sulfiding oligoisobutylene, mass. = 1 : 1 - cuczinimid (0.3 mass.%); 8- Sulfurcontaining *bis*- 4,4 `-oligoisobutenylphenol; 9- Sulfurcontaining *bis*- 4,4 `-oligoisobutenylphenol - cuczinimid (0.3 mass.%);

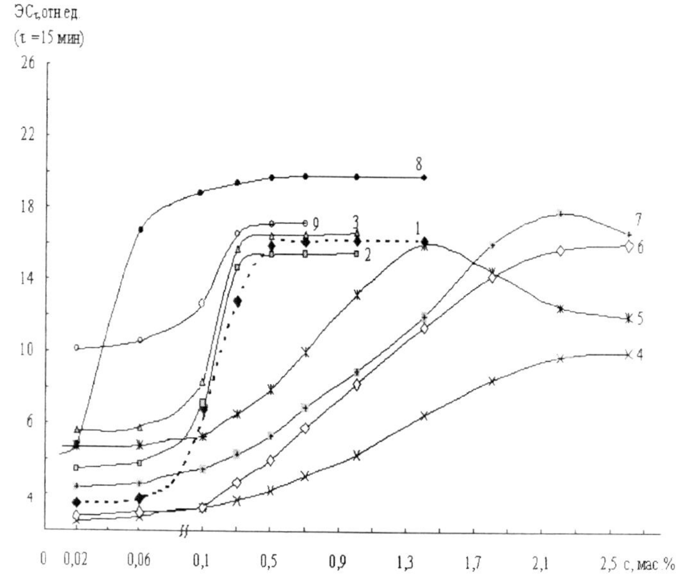

Figure 4b) Modified oligoisobutylene ($\overline{M}_n$= 390); 1 - cuczinimid; 2- sulfiding oligoisobutylene; 3- sulfiding oligoisobutylene - cuczinimid (0.3 mass.%); 4- 2,6-d i-Bu^t-4-oligoisobutenylphenol; 5- 2,6-d i-Bu^t-4-oligoisobutenylphenol - cuczinimid (0.3 mass.%); 6- 2,6-di-Bu^t-4-oligoisobutenylphenol: sulfiding oligoisobutylene, mass. = 1 : 1; 7- 2,6-d i-Bu^t-4-oligoisobutenylphenol: sulfiding oligoisobutylene, mass. = 1 : 1 - cuczinimid (0.3 mass.%); 8- Sulfurcontaining *bis*- 4,4 `-oligoisobutenylphenol; 9- Sulfurcontaining *bis*- 4,4 `-oligoisobutenylphenol - cuczinimid (0.3 mass.%);

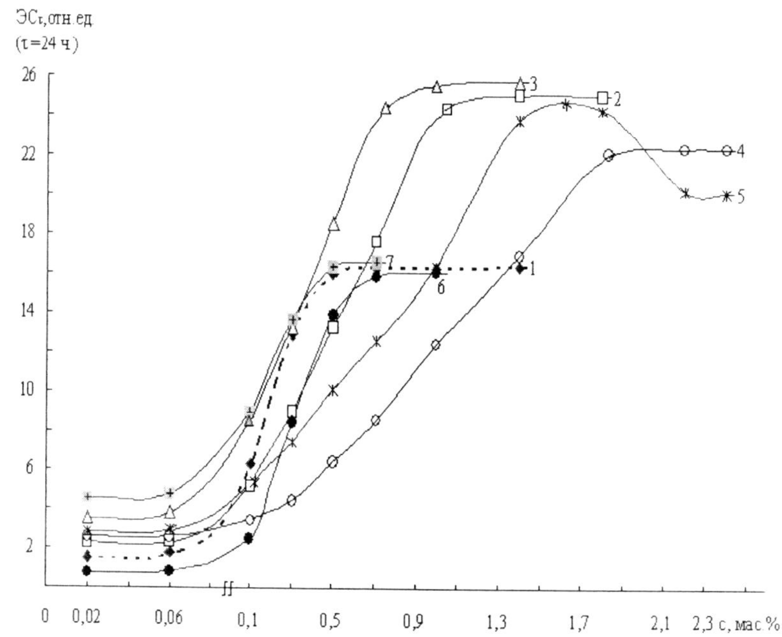

Figure 4c) Modified oligopiperylene; 1-cuczinimid; 2-sulfiding oligopiperylene; 3-sulfiding oligopiperylene - cuczinimid (0.3mass.%); 4- 2,6-di -Bu^t-4-oligopiperylenylphenol; 5-2,6-di -Bu^t-4-oligopiperylenylphenol - cuczinimid (0.3mass.%); 6-sulfiding 2,6-di -Bu^t-4-oligopiperylenylphenol; 7- sulfiding 2,6-di -Bu^t-4-oligopiperylenylphenol - cuczinimid (0.3mass.%);

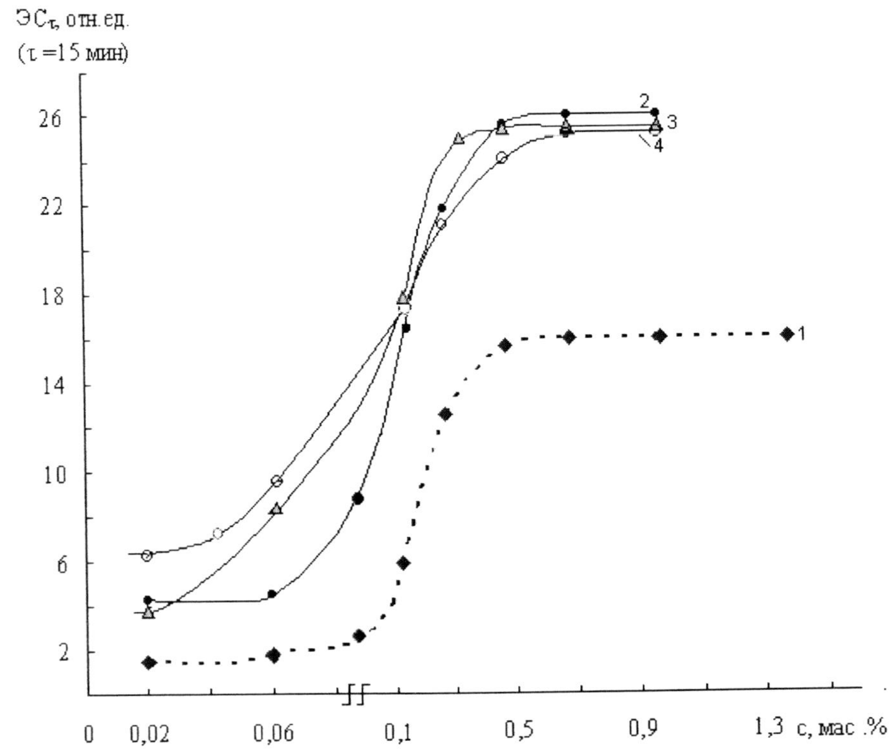

Figure 4d) sulfiding piperylene fraction; 1- cuczinimid; 2- piperilene *bis*-tetrasulfide; 3- piperilene *bis*-tetrasulfide - cuczinimid (0.5 mass.%); 4- piperilene *bis*-tetrasulfide - cuczinimid (1.0 mass.%);

Influence on cuczinimid detergent-dispersion action of size and structure of a hydrocarbonic radical of antioxidizing and antiwear additives entered into an oil composition Is traced. The maximal solubilisation effect takes place for the ramified and smaller radicals on the size. Such effect the substances synthesized on a basis of oligopiperylene ($\overline{M}_n$=910) and oligoisobutylene ($\overline{M}_n$=390) have. Apparently, notice speaks that in the opposites emulsion such as «water in oil» with increase of length of the hydrocarbonic assistant at one-CH_2-group in given homologous line critical micelle concentration is shifted in area of the big values.

The Increase of the contents of sulfur in functionalized samples promotes narrowing of interval CMC and its displacement in area of smaller values (rice 4d: sulfiding piperylene fraction containing 47.01 mass. % of sulfur).

Experimental data (tab. 7) testify that introduction of the synthesized substances in an oil composition with cuczinimid substantially allows to lower a dosage of the last for maintenance of operational characteristics on enough high level.

Table 7. Critical micelle concentration of functionalized products, mass. %.

Additive	OPP ($\overline{M}_n$=910)	OIB ($\overline{M}_n$=880)	OIB ($\overline{M}_n$=390)
Cuczinimid	0.08 - 0.42	0.08 - 0.42	0.08 - 0.42
Sulfiding oligomer	0.09 - 1.30	0.10 - 1.90	0.09 - 0.30
Sulfiding oligomer - cuczinimid (0.3 mass. %)	0.08 - 0.70	0.08 - 1.70	0.08 - 0.20
Alkylated 2,6-di -Bu^t-phenol	0.20 - 1.80	0.30 - 3.00	0.20 - 2.20
Alkylated 2,6-di -Bu^t-phenol - cuczinimid (0.3 mass. %)	0.08 - 1.60	0.10 - 2.40	0.10 - 1.40
Product of consecutive alkylation and sulfiding in nonpolar solvents	0.09 - 0.56	0.10 - 2.40	0.16 - 2.20
Product of consecutive alkylation and sulfiding in nonpolar solvents - cuczinimid (0.3 mass. %)	0.09 - 0.30	0.10 - 2.20	0.08 - 2.10
Product of consecutive alkylation and sulfiding in polar solvents	-	0.15 - 0.95	0.07 - 1.00
Product of consecutive alkylation and sulfiding in polar solvents - cuczinimid (0.3 mass. %)	-	0.03 - 0.09	0.04 - 0.09

CONCLUSIONS

It Is carried out functionalization of piperylene fractions, oligodienes andoligoolefins, and also alkylated listed by oligomers phenols by element sulfur, optimum conditions of realization of their interaction with introduction of the greatest possible quantity of sulfur are picked up.

The opportunity of use functionalized compounds Is shown as the multipurpose additives showing highantiwear, antistriking and simultaneously antioxidizing and viscosity properties.

Influence received sulfurcontaining substances and the shielded phenols on detergent-dispersion action of cuczinimid Is investigated. It is established, that joint presence antiwear and antioxidizing additives in an oil composition with cuczinimid appreciably allows to lower the maintenance of the last for maintenance enough high operational characteristics of lubricants.

REFERENCES

[1] B.A.Sobolev. Manufacture and consumption of additives in Russia.// *Mir nefteproductov*. – 2000. - №2. – p.1-2.

[2] I.E.Selezneva, A.J.Levin, S.V.Monin. Detergent-dispersion additives to motor oils. // *Khim. i tekhnol. topl. i mas*. - 1999. - № 6. - p.39-43.

[3] M.G.Voronkov, N.A.Vjazankin, E.N.Derjagina etc. *Reactions of sulfur with organic compounds*./under red. M.G.Voronkova. - Novosibirsk: science. - 1979. - p. 368

[4] S.Oae. *Chemistry of organic compounds of sulfur:* пер. С яп./под ред. E.N.Prilezhaevoj.- M.: Chemistry. - 1975.

[5] S.A.Egoricheva, V.A.Rozentsvet, B.I.Pantuh, M.V.Eskina, A.S.Hachaturov, R.M.Livshits. Molecular characteristics of oligopiperylene, received by cationic polymerization. // *Neftekhim.prom.* - 1982. - №8. - p.12-13.

[6] R.Z.Biglova, V.P.Malinskaja, K.S.Minsker. Polymeranalogues reactions of polyolefins with phenols and aminophenols. // *Vysokomol. Soedin.*-1994. - vol.36A.- № 8. - p.1276-1280.

[7] S.V.Buharov, L.V.Konoshenko, S.E.Solov'eva etc. Interaction of sulfur with *2,6*-di - *tret*-butylphenol in dipolar aprotic solvents. // *Zh. Obshch. Khim.*- 1999. - vol.69. - вып.1. - p.130-133.

[8] G.V.Konesev, M.R.Mavljutov, A.I.Spivak, R.A.Ismagilov. Lubricant action of environments in chisel technology. - M.: Bowels. - 1993. – p.46-50.

[9] N.N.Loznetsova, K.A.Pavlov, J.P.Toporov, G.G.ShChegolev. A role micelle formation in display antiwear properties lubricant oils. // *short notes to II Internat. Conf. "Colloid*-2003." - 2003. – p.184.

[10] Glavati, T.D.Popovich, V.T.Borislavsky, A.S.Zhurba, A.N.Lukashevich. Improvement of quality cuczinimid additives. // *Khim. i tekhnol. topl. i mas.* - 1989. - № 3. - p.22-24.

[11] A.B.Vipper, S.E.Krejn, V.V.Sher, P.I.Sanin. Solubilizing action of additives of a various structure and its influence on properties lubricant oils. //*Neftekhim.* - 1968. - vol.5. - № 5. – p.798-806.

In: Synthesis and Properties of Low- and High-Molecular Compounds ISBN 1-59454-716-5
Editor: Gennady E. Zaikov et al., pp. 197-206

Chapter 11

ON THE NANOMETRIC PARTICLE-LIKE LOCAL STRUCTURES AND THEIR IMPLICATIONS IN POLYMER BEHAVIOUR

N. Guarrotxena

Dpto. Química y Propiedades de Materiales Polímeros, Instituto de Ciencia y Tecnología de Polímeros (ICTP), Consejo Superior de Investigaciones Científicas (CSIC), Juan de la Cierva, 3, 28006, Madrid (Spain).

ABSTRACT

Some samples of poly(vinylchloride) (PVC) of different stereochemical microstructure have been prepared by stereoselective substitution reaction with sodium benzenethiolate at various conversions. A full characterization of the samples has been made by 13C-NMR spectroscopy so as to determine the content of the most important nanometric structures especially the mmr termini of isotactic sequences. They have been considered as the microstructure shaping factor in earlier work. The dielectric behaviour and the relaxation processes have been studied for all samples. Novel correlations between these behaviours and the nanometric structures have been obtained. They provide relevant information as to the mechanisms of the physical processes properties determining thereby contributing to some progress in the nanostructured materials.

INTRODUCTION

The prominent role of a number of stereochemical microstructures in governing the behaviour of some industrial polymers like PVC and PP has been the objective of a considerable amount of work in our laboratory. We denote by stereochemical microstructures those tetrads located at the end of any tactic sequence as well as some short isolated triads or tetrads. In fact we classified them into three different groups: 1) the mmr triads termini of isotactic sequences equal to or longer than one heptad; 2) the same triads terminal of isotactic sequences shorter than one heptad, and 3) some short sequences including the pure heterotactic, and the mmrr pentads which may occur whenever a short isotactic or syndiotactic sequence breaks off. The mmrm pentad and the rrrm pentad relate preferably to long isotactic and syndiotactic sequences respectively. Out of these groups, the former is specially important. Actually, the mmr tetrad when relating to long isotactic sequences, is able to adopt either the GTTG^{-}TT or the GTGTTT conformation, the former one being much lesser probable than the latter. As will be seen later the GTTG^{-}TT conformation proves to be of great importance because it exhibits great free volume and low coupling in rotational mobility, relative to the other microstructures. The latter characteristics are the fundamental reason for the observed microstructure-property relationships. As a result, the stereochemical microstructures which are reckoned in our work as local disruptions along the rather regular chain structure are crucial for explaining and controlling the polymer physical and technological behaviour.

On the other hand, the so-called nanoscience is attracting an enormous interest for the last years. This particular chapter of the material science arises from the observed evidence that the presence of nanoparticles or structures of size as small as a few nanometers, produces profound changes in both inter- and intramolecular interaction, and, as a consequence, in properties. Most of the reasons for such behaviour remain still to be explained, despite of the abundant attempts that have been made. Be that as it may, this promising matter should give rise to great progresses in the utilisation of polymeric materials in the most advanced technology.

Now, the above mentioned stereochemical microstructures, as studied in our laboratory, happen to be nanometric in size and occur incidentally along the chain without changing a polymer structure other than the local stereochemistry. In addition, the amount of those microstructures may be planned, to a certain extent, through the polymerization process or by means of chemical or physical treatments. Moreover such microstructures are inherent to any vinyl polymer, even if their effect on properties has never been studied until our own contributions.

Taking this into account we endeavoured recently first to re-interpret the microstructure/property relationships, as accurately obtained in our laboratory, on the basis of the nanometric character of the microstructures, and, secondly, to take profit from our prior and present results to shed light on some nanoscience fundamentals.

The present article complies a few contributions as inferred from our recent work on the mechanisms of the physical processes involved in the relaxation behaviour of PVC.

Results and Discussion

A Brief Overview of the Stereochemistry-Based Nanostructures in PVC and PP

For purposes of clarity we think it interesting to survey in this section some recent results which allow one to state and to measure the above quoted microstructures[1]. ^{13}C-NMR spectroscopy was used to investigate the sorts of mmr- and rrm- based stereochemical sequences and their surroundings for one series of PVC samples and one series of PP samples, of distinct tacticities. The reason for this choice was that PVC exhibits Bernoullian isotactic, irrespective of the overall tacticity value in both polymers. As extensively argued[2, 3] ^{13}C-NMR measurements provide, through the relative peak intensities, the isotactic (mm), heterotactic (rm or mr), and the syndiotactic (rr) triad probabilities. From them it is possible to calculate the values of P_{rr} and P_{mr} which denote that a r placement follows a r placement and a m placement, respectively. Similarly P_{mm} and P_{rm} stand for the probability that a m placement follows a m placement and a r placement, respectively. Obviously, if Bernoullian statistics apply, it follows by definition that $P_{rr}=P_{mr}$, so that P_{mr}-P_{rr} value (or P_{rm}-P_{mm}) is a measure of the degree of departure from Bernoullian condition. Starting from the experimental triad contents P_{mm} and P_{mr}, like P_{rr} and P_{rm}, can be easily calculated by applying universal equations which make no assumptions above the type of statistics which apply[3, 4].

On these grounds one series of PVC samples of isotactic triad probabilities ranging from 0.12 to 0.21 was shown to be quite Bernoullian, what maked it possible to calculate the probability of occurrence of each repeating stereochemical sequence[3, 4]. The evolution with increasing isotactic content of some sequences of great potential interest, especially the mmr and rrm tetrads and the mmmr and rrrm pentads, is depicted in Figure 1.

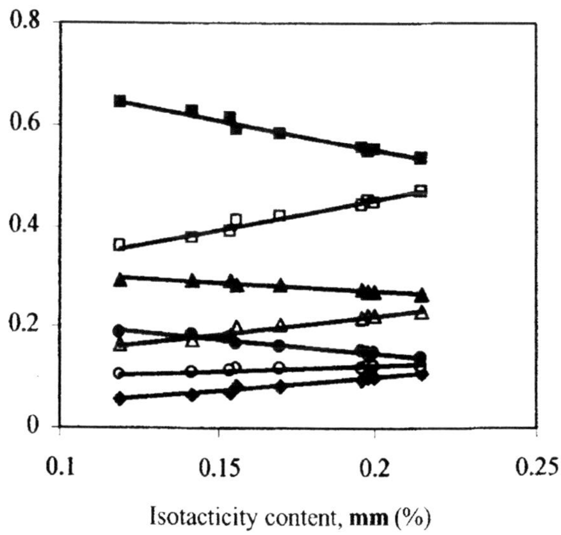

Figure 1. Evolution with isotactic triads content, mm of: (■) probability of isotactic placement; m, (▪) probability of syndiotactic placement, r, (△) isotactic tetrads, mmr, (▲) syndiotactic tetrads, rrm; isotactic pentads (♦) mmrm and (O) mmrr; (•) syndiotactic pentads, rrrm.

The mmr- and rrm- based repeating sequences occur necessarily whenever an isotactic or syndiotactic sequence breaks off respectively.

In accordance with Bernoullian statistics, the stereochemical sequences all vary linearly with increasing isotactic content. Interestingly, on one hand the slopes for mmr and mmmr, and on the other hand for rrm and rrrm sequences are similar in magnitude but reverse in sign. Thus, the number of interruptions of regular sequences, whether isotactic or syndiotactic, will change with a well-known factor as the isotactic content increases, which makes it easy to compare the stereochemical composition of the samples.

As discussed elsewhere[1] the repeating stereosequences mmrm and rrmr change with increasing isotacticity in a similar way to mmr and rrm. Conversely, mmrr, a pentad that may relate either to an isotactic or a syndiotactic sequence, hardly changes, certainly because the decrease of rr triads sets off the increase of mm triad as the overall isotacticity increases. In consistant with these variations P_{rr} and P_{mm} values were found to be lower as the isotactic content increases. Besides, as a consequence of the Bernoullian statistics, they are very close for each sample.

It could be therefore inferred that the stereochemical composition of all samples will consist of: (1) pure isotactic and syndiotactic sequences with average length decreasing and increasing, respectively as the isotactic content decreases; (2) a number of mmrm-based interruptions of isotactic sequences, which decreases linearly as the isotactic content increases; (3) a number of rrmr-based interruptions of syndiotactic sequences, which increases linearly as the isotactic content increases at a similar rate to that of mmrm decrease; (4) a content of mmrr-based interruptions of either isotactic or syndiotactic sequences and of pure rmrm heterotactic pentads, which shuld both remain practically changed for all samples.

It must be emphasised first, that the above structures are all present in the samples, and second, that their relative contents, except for mmrr and rmrm, change linearly with the overall isotactic content.

Polypropylene a polymer highly non Bernoullian isotactic, was found to behave in a quite different way to PVC. Actually, when plotting the same repeating stereosequences as a function of overall isotacticity, the linear behaviours are maintained only up to an isotacticity of around 0.91 and then there is a levelling off. The degree of departure from Bernoullian condition (P_{mr}-$P_{rr}\approx 0$) changes abruptly at isotacticity of 0.91. As a result, the stereochemical composition appears to be different from that of PVC especially because some of the microstructures considered may be absent in PP. A detailed discussion about this matter is given in reference 1 to which the reader is referred.

It must be also indicated that, according to these results, what is important to highlight in the fact that the microstructures that have been viewed as the very identification of PVC and PP samples are nanometric in size and, as already mentioned, are of prominent importance in determining the physical properties.

This has been also argued, on the ground of first, the fact that mmr repeating sequence is shorter and of greater volume than the remaining nanostructures, especially when mmr is adopting the $GTTG^{-}TT$ conformation; secondly, the rotational motions are favoured and are less dependent on the adjacent isotactic section in $GTTG^{-}TT$ conformation. What means that the motion of this conformation is less coupled in nature than the GTGTTT conformation.

The Role of the Stereochemical Nanostructures in the Dielectric Behaviour of PVC by Dielectric Relaxation Spectroscopy (DRS)

The dielectric properties have been recently studied for a PVC prepared at 70°C by bulk polymerisation and for the same polymer after modification through substitution reaction with sodium benzenethiolate (NaBT) at various conversions up to 15%. The reaction conditions and the characterisation of the samples by ^{13}C-NMR have been published[5].

The samples were all studied by DRS[6-10], which allows to measure simultaneously the real (ε') and the imaginary (ε'') parts of the complex dielectric constant (ε* =ε' – iε'') under a controlled atmosphere of helium in a frequency range between 1 and 10^6 Hz, and a temperature range between 100 and 600 K in isothermal conditions.

The isothermal ε'' curves obtained in the temperature region where α-relaxation of PVC appears, after being substracted from the DC conductivity and β-relaxation contributions, were used to built master curves for each sample. As it is obtained over all the glassy polymers, these master curves were fitted to the phenomenological Havriliak-Negami (HN) function[11] (depicting the relaxation in the frequency domain) that, as it has been demonstrated in the last decade[12], can be considered in good approximation as the Fourier transform of the well known Kohlrausch-Williams-Watts (KWW) function[13] (that describes the relaxation in the time domain). This fact allows to calculate easily the non-exponential parameter b of the KWW function form the shape parameters of the HN function obtained from the fits of the experimental curves. Note that KWW function and Ngai's relaxation function[14, 15] are formally the same. The results have been discussed in detail elsewhere[6-10]. We shall give herein some of the most attractive and novel conclusions.

Although α-relaxation as analysed by DRS, and the calorimetric Tg are the less influenced, a small change was observed for the 0.7% substituted PVC. Taking into account the stereoselective mechanism of substitution[5, 16-18], the above changes might be explained by the specific removal of mmr (GTTG¯TT) by exchanging them for a TTTTTT conformation which takes place during this substitution period[5, 16-18].

More marked changes were shown for the β-relaxation as studied by DRS. Figure 2 depicts the corresponding variation of tgδ with temperature for all the PVC samples. Interestingly, the substituted samples at low percentages present b-relaxation intensity higher than the one of pure PVC. In contrast, the higher substituted samples exhibit lower loss values. In addition, the maxima of characteristic β-relaxation curves for all substituted samples are shifted towards lower temperatures with respect to the unmodified PVC.

Such an important effect of the nanostructures is still enhanced for the coupling degree of the local motions, according to Ngai's theory. As illustrated by Figure 3, β clearly decreases up to 0.7% and then it increases rather rapidly up to 7% and slowly afterward. For purposes of advancing the novelty of the results obtained herein the evolution of Nagi's β-parameter with substitution has been published recently[19, 20].

Comparing this behaviour and the corresponding evolution of microstructure as well stated in earlier work[5, 16], it is evident that: (a) the lowest values of b agrees with the highest content of the long isotactic-based mmr structures taking GTGTTT conformation, which thus appears to experience the most coupled motions; (b) the mmr taking GTTG¯TT also associated with long isotactic sequences, which vanish from the unmodified sample to the 0.7-substituted sample, is drastically less sensitive to coupling; and (c) the coupling is anyway associated with the mmr termini of long isotactic sequences, and is less significant after the removal of them (substitution degrees higher than 7%).

These correlations are quite novel in the literature and open new prospects in the nanostructure science in that a few and well defined nanostructures are able to determine important properties like those considered above.

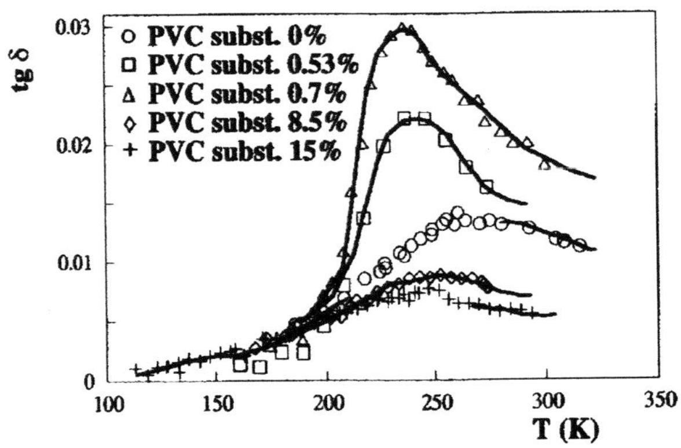

Figure 2. Raw isochronal loss curves obtained at 316 Hz corresponding to the β-relaxation for the studied simples.

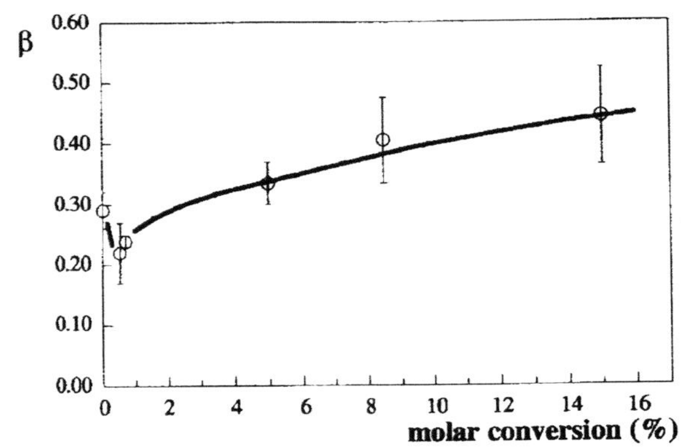

Figure 3. Variation of the coupling parameter β versus the percentage of conversion.

The Role of the Stereochemical Nanostructures in the Relaxation Processes due to Electrical Charges of PVC by Thermally Stimulated Depolarization Current (TSDC) Method

Although TSDC has a relatively short history, it has already evolved into a basic tool for the identification and evolution of dipole reorientation processes and of trapping and recombination levels.

The sample is metallized on both sides, and charged by application of a DC field at a high temperature. This field is maintained, and the sample cooled to room temperature or below. Next, it is short-circuited and reheated at a linear rate of, say, 2°C min^{-1} (this being low enough to prevent temperature lags and to guarantee a good resolution of peaks) in the temperature range from 25 to 150°C, the discharge current generated being measured with an electrometer and recorded as a function of temperature by an *x-y* plotter. As will be explained later, the peak labelled α is mainly due to dipoles, whereas the ρ peaks are due to trapped space charge.

This technique is a useful tool to investigate relaxation processes in polymers. The depolarization current, when raising the temperature at constant rate exhibits a series of maxima which correspond to the different thermal transitions. The most important is α relaxation which agrees with the glass transition temperature (Tg). At temperature above Tg another relaxation happens frequently to occur. This is denoted by ρ relaxation and, unlike α relaxation, which is intrinsic to the material, is generally believed to obey the release of space charge trapped in the material. Thence, it is an extrinsic phenomenon and it is observable only through TSDC technique. The conventional dynamic methods cannot detect it. Neither the very origin of ρ relaxation is not well known nor has the nature of the charge trapping sites been stated as yet. Nevertheless, ρ relaxation is more and more thought to be associated with space charge arising from electrode injection. This circumstance led us to compare the ρ relaxation, as measured by TSDC, of the samples of Table 1. Indeed, it appeared of great interest to know whether or not the evolution of the polymer microstructure, as accurately performed by nucleophilic substitution, is accompanied by gradual changes in intensity of ρ relaxation. If it proved so, then the correlation between **mmr** and the space charge distribution, as drawn from Thermal step (TS) studies[21], would have given further evidence.

Table 1. Tacticity Characteristics of the PVC-Substituted Samples

Conversion (%)	mm	mr	rr	mmmr	rmmr	mmr
0	20,1	49,6	30,3	9,6	6,3	22,2
0,53	19,6	49,55	30,85	9,3	6,1	21,5
0,7	19,4	49,1	31,5	9,4	6,1	21,6
5	16,41	47,98	35,6	7,3	4,9	17,1
8,5	13,52	46,54	40,02	5,6	3,9	13,4
15	10	42,35	47,65	3,7	2,8	9,3

The TSDC spectra of PVC samples (Table 1) are presented in Figure 4 (a). The spectra always consist of two well differentiated peaks. One peak is the α transition and relates to the glass transition temperature.

It is generally assumed to obey segmental cooperative motions along the chain, which occur whenever the frozen-in chain alignment is released. Despite the abundant publications on this phenomenon the very nature of the chain segments that are involved in it remain to be satisfactorily known.

The other peak, as already mentioned, is believed to be related to the release of space charges probably produced by electrode injection. Therefore they are, unlike the chain segments engaged in α relaxation, extrinsic in nature. As can be seen the intensity of α relaxation is very high relative to that of ρ relaxation. This makes it difficult to compare the ρ relaxations of the samples, unlike the α ones, unless the spectra are sufficiently amplified. The ρ peak at a larger scale are shown in Figure 4 (b).

From Figure 4 (a) and 4 (b) it may be straightforwardly inferred that α and ρ relaxations decrease both with degree of substitution. This is quantitatively illustrated in Figures 5 and 6. Interestingly the α and ρ intensities decrease rather abruptly up to conversion of 1.1%; then the decrease continues at lower rate up to about 7% and 10% respectively, after which the trend, within the experimental uncertainties, is towards levelling off.

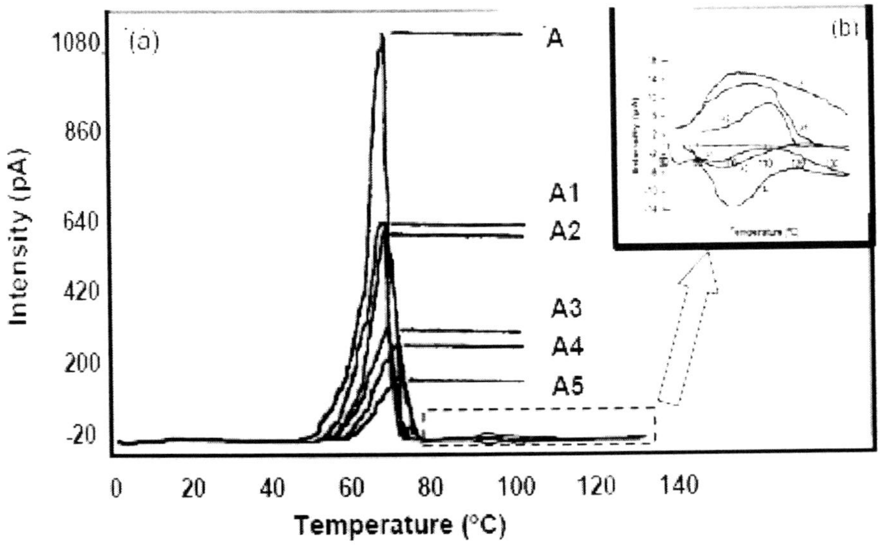

Figure 4. TSDC spectra in polarized PVC modified to different degrees: (A) 0%; (A1) 1.1%; (A2) 2.7%; (A3) 5%; (A4) 10%; (A5) 13% (10 kV/mm, 50°C, 2h). (a) whole spectra; (b) ρ relaxation region.

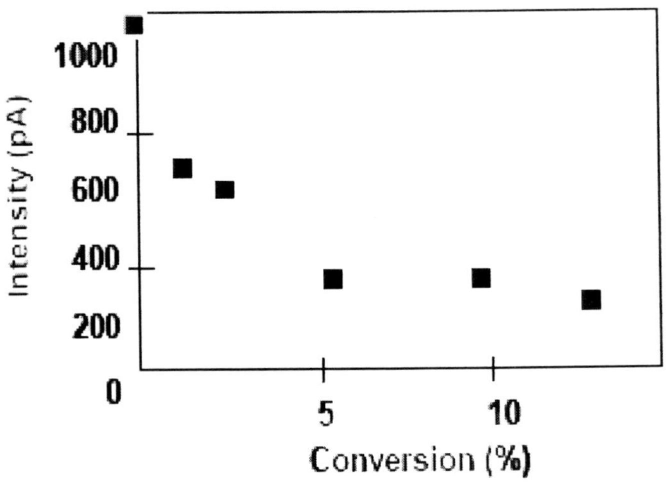

Figure 5. Evolution of the polarization peak intensity (α) of PVC samples with substitution degree.

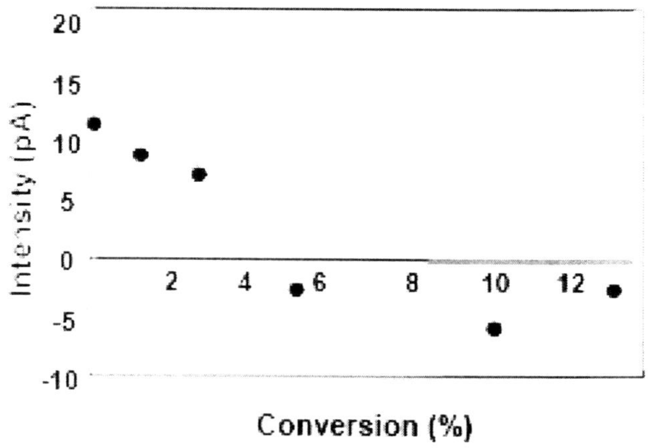

Figure 6. Evolution of the space charge peak intensity (ρ) of PVC samples with substitution degree.

Taking into account the stereochemical mechanisms of substitution[16-18], the above results provide undeniable arguments in favour of the important role of the nanostructures, as considered in our work, in the origin of both relaxations. The following relationships may be inferred: 1) the strong drop of α intensity agrees with the disappearance of permanent mmr (GTTG⁻TT) structures attached to isotactic sequences of at least one heptad in length, by exchanging them for all trans sequences. On the other hand, the adjacent isotactic sequence is shortened. In addition, and this is particularly important, the motion of the involved chain segment is much more coupled[19, 20] with that of its surroundings than it was for the same segment prior to chemical substitution. This clearly suggests that α relaxation should be due to the cooperative motions of chain regular segments bearing local structures such as mmr (GTTG⁻TT) tetrad, which are able to rotate without any or with little coupling with the remaining parts of the segment. If this conclusion holds true, then the molecular motions which are responsible for Tg should require an initiation process namely the occurrence of non coupled local rotational motion. Whether or not the cooperative motions of Tg involving segments of chain originate from initiating local motions, has been extensively controverted in the literature, but there is no a well stated conclusion about; 2) The second step in Figure 5, within the 1.1-5% conversion range, agrees with the disappearance of mmr (GTGTTT) structures attached to isotactic sequences equal to or longer than one heptad[16-18]. This behaviour is in accordance with the fact that the conformation GTGTTT exhibits an appreciable degree of coupling compared to GTTG⁻TT conformation. Thence the coupling enhancement stemmed from its replacement for an all trans conformation as the result of the substitution reaction[16, 19, 20] proves not to be so important as it was during the first step (Figure 5); and 3) the main decrease of ρ relaxation occurs, during the second reaction period up to conversion around 5%. Prior to this period the decrease is, unlike α relaxation, little significant. This agrees with our prior finding that mmr (GTGTTT) which disappear during this period, are the more salient traps of injection space charge[21]. As already mentioned the coupling of that structure with surrounding sequences ranges between that of the mmr (GTTG'TT) and either the adjacent isotactic sequences or the syndiotactic sequences which might exist in the polymer. Now since there is a dynamic equilibrium between both mmr structures we think it reasonable that the local motion of mmr should be the causal phenomenum of both the cooperative motion of the adjacent isotactic sequences, i.e. α relaxation, and the release of trapped charges (ρ relaxation). Such a hypothesis would give support to the occurrence of an initiation of a relaxation. Besides, it corroborates the relationship between mmr (GTGTTT) and trapping of injected space charges, as proposed previously[21]. The research work now under way is expected to shed light on this matter.

As a consequence β, α and ρ relaxations are to be viewed as processes connected with well defined nanostructures and their adjacent regular sequences respectively. The great free volume together with the degree of coupling associated with the former structures would be explain satisfactorily the occurrence of local motions in them (ρ relaxation) and the extension of these motions to the cooperative motions of the latter sort of structures (relaxation α).

REFERENCES

[1] N. Guarrotxena, F. Schue, A. Collet and J.L. Millán, *Polym. Int.*, 52, 420 (2003)
[2] J. Millán, G. Martínez, M.L. Jimeno, *Eur. Polym J.* 27, 483 (1991)
[3] J. King, D.I. Bower, W.F. Maddams and H.K. Pyszora, *Makromol. Chem.* 184, 879 (1983)
[4] F.A. Bovey, *High Resolution NMR of Macromolecules*, chapters 3 and 8, Academic Press, New York, 1972.
[5] N. Guarrotxena, G. Martínez, J. Millán, *J. Polym. Sci. Polym. Chem.*, 34, 2387 (1996)
[6] A.Elícegui, J.J. del Val, J. Colmenero, G. Martínez, J.L. Millán, *J. Non-Cryst. Solids* 172/174, 955 (1994)
[7] Elícegui, J.J. del Val, J. Colmenero, G. Martínez, J. Millán, V. Bellenger, J. Verdu, *Macromol. Chem. Phys.*, 197, 991 (1996)
[8] Elícegui, J.J. del Val, V. Bellenger, J. Verdu, *Polymer* 38, 1647 (1997)
[9] Elícegui, J.J. del Val, J. Millán, C. Mijangos, *J. Non-Cryst. Solids* 235/237, 623 (1998)
[10] Elícegui, F. Alvarez, J.J. del Val, *J. Polym. Sci. Polym. Phys.*, 38, 234 (2000)
[11] S. Havriliak, S. Segami, *Polymer* 8, 161(1967)
[12] F. Alvarez, A. Alegría, J. Colmenero, *Phys. Rev.* B., 47, 125 (1993)
[13] G. Williams, D.C Watts, *Trans. Faraday Soc.*, 66, 80 (1970)
[14] K.L. Ngai, *Comments of Solid State Physics* 9, 127 (1979)
[15] K.L. Ngai, *Comments of Solid State Physics* 9, 141 (1980)
[16] N. Guarrotxena, G. Martínez, J. Millán, *J. Polym. Sci. Polym. Chem.*, 34, 2563 (1996)
[17] N. Guarrotxena, G. Martínez, J. Millán, *Eur. Polym. J.*, 33, 1473 (1997)
[18] N. Guarrotxena, G. Martínez, J. Millán, *Acta Polymerica* 50, 180 (1999)
[19] N. Guarrotxena, J.J. del Val, J. Millán, *Polymer Bulletin* 47, 105 (2001)
[20] N. Guarrotxena, J.J. del Val, A. Elícegui, J. Millán, *J. Polym. Sci. Polym. Physics* 42, 2337 (2004)
[21] N. Guarrotxena, N. Vella, A. Toureille, J. Millán, *Macromol. Chem Phys.*, 198, 457 (1997).

In: Synthesis and Properties of Low- and High-Molecular Compounds ISBN 1-59454-716-5
Editor: Gennady E. Zaikov et al., pp. 207-212

Chapter 12

STABILITY TO THE CRACKING IN ACTIVE ENVIRONMENT OF MODIFIED POLYETHYLENE

***G. V. Kozlov*[1] *and G. E. Zaikov*[2]**
[1]Kabardino-Balkarian State University,
Nal'chik – 360004, Chernyshevski st. 173, Russian Federation
[2]Institute of Biochemical Physical of Russian Academy of Science
Moscow – 119991, Kosygin st., 4, Russian Federation

ABSTRACT

It is shown, that the criterion of polyethylenes samples fracture in tests on cracking under stress in active environments is reaching by polar liquid of sample median plane. Stability to cracking is correctly described within the framework of fractal model of transport processes in polymers. The cause of extreme raising of stability to cracking are structural changes, which are due to introduction of high disperse mixture Fe/FeO and characterizing by the dimension of excess energy localization regions.

Key words: polyethylene, modification, diffusion, voids, brittle fracture.

INTRODUCTION

The term "cracking at simultaneous action of stress and environment" was introduced for the description of polymers (mainly polyethylenes) brittle fracture, which are present in a stressed state in the presence of mobile polar liquids. It was shown [1], that, what all is said and done, for material strength at this fracture mode is responsible the weakest amorphous part of semi-crystalline polymer. This allows to connect occurring at cracking phenomenon with polar liquid diffusion into amorphous regions.

The authors [2] found, that in case of high density polyethylene (HDPE), modified by high disperse mixture Fe/FeO (Z), is observed strong extreme rise of stability to cracking expressed by the time up to fracture τ_{50}. So, if for the initial HDPE normative value τ_{50}.is equal to 10 hours, then for composition HDPE+Z with content Z C_Z=0.05 mass.% the value τ_{50} reaches 250 hours. The purpose of the present paper is the explanation of this important effect both from theoretical and practical points of view within the framework of fractal conception of transport processed.

EXPERIMENTAL

The gasphase HDPE of industrial production mark 276 with average weight molecular weight $\overline{M}_w \approx 1,5\times10^5$ and crystallinity degree 0,68, determined by samples density, is used. The method of processing of compositions HDPE+Z samples in paper [3] was expounded. The initial HDPE and its compositions with contents Z within the interval 0,01÷1,0 mass.% were used. The figures in conditional designation of compositions HDPE+Z mean content of Z in mass%.

The tension tests were made on film samples with thichness 0,06÷0,08 mm, width 5 mm and base length 40 mm. The samples were made by hot pressing at temperature 463 K and pressure ~5MPa. The testing is made at temperature 323 K and strain rate $2,7\times10^{-3}s^{-1}$.

The test on stability to cracking under stress was made accoring to the standard (GOST 13 518-68) on samples, cutting out from plates, which were made by hot pressing. The sample sizes corresponded to the mentioned above standard. Before testing sample was placed in conductor socket and by handle pressure on it the notch of length 0,1 mm was made. Then each sample was bent in special arranging so that, the notch was placed on the outside and put in the holder. One holder maintains 10 samples [2].

Then holder with samples was placed in the bath with active environment (20%-th aquatic solution of OP-7, GOST 8433-57), which were placed in thermostat with temperature 323÷0,5 K. Samples examining was made visually during first two days every each hour and further two times in one day.

As stability of polyetylenes to cracking is adopted the time in hours from testing beginning up to appearance of cracks of 50% samples (τ_{50}) [2].

RESULTS AND DISCUSSION

For theoretical prediction of value τ_{50}, characterizing stability to cracking, two main assumptions will be made. Firstly, it is assumed, that the samples fracture occurs, when active environment in diffusion process reaches their median plate. This assumption is based on the analysis of cracking under stress process [1]. Then theoretical value τ_{50} (τ_{50}^T) is expressed by the basic equation of stationary diffusion [4]:

$$\tau_{50}^T = \frac{l^2}{GD}, \qquad (1)$$

where l is one half of sample thichness, which is equal in our case to 2 mm, D is diffusivity of active environment in HDPE.

The second assumption consists in the fact, that the diffusion of water molecules clusters without consideration of the molecules OP-7 sizes is considered. As a matter of fact, this means, that in cluster of molecules H_2O is assumed the replacement of one of these molecules on molecule OP-7. The clusterization of water molecules at interaction with polymer is a well known fact [5, 6]. The estimations show, that in this case the cluster consists of three molecules H_2O [6]. The schematic representation of water cluster according to the data of paper [5] is shown in Fig. 1. This scheme allows to calculate the largest size of cluster $d_m \approx 7{,}8$ Å allowing, that water molecule diameter is equal to 3,08 Å [5].

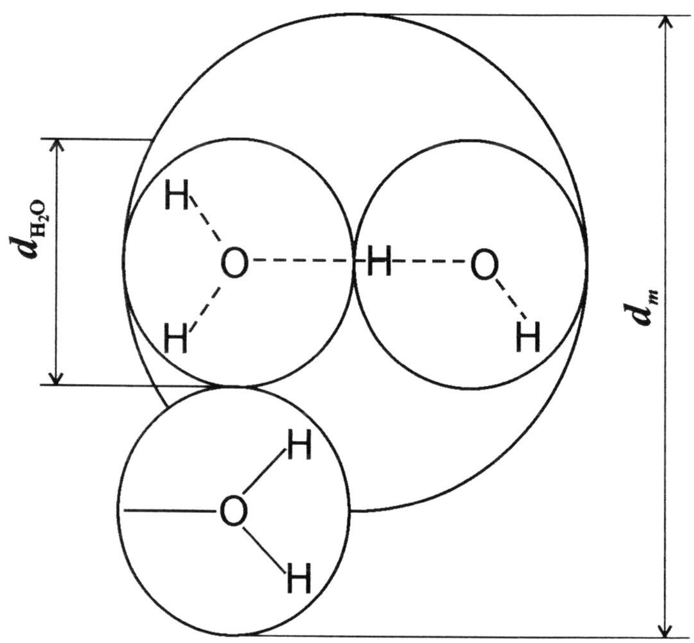

Figure 1. The model of adsorbed by polymer water molecules cluster [5]. d_{H_2O} is diameter of water molecule, d_m is calculated diameter of water cluster.

For a calculation of the diffusivity D the fractal model of transport processes [7] will be use, according to which the value D is equal to:

$$D = D'_0 f_g (d_h / d_m)^{2(D_t - d_s)/d_s}, \qquad (2)$$

where D'_0 is a universal constant, which is equal to $3{,}7\times10^{-7}$ cm^2/s, f_g is relative free volume, d_h is diameter of this volume microvoid, D_t is polymer structure dimension, controlling the transport processes, d_s is spectral dimension, adopted for linear HDPE equal to 1,0 [8].

The choice of dimension D_t depends on the value of relation d_h/d_m [9]. At $d_m < 0{,}6 d_h$ interaction of diffusant molecules with walls of free volume microvoid is small and transport process is controlled by fractal dimension of structure d_f (structural transport). At $d_m \leq 0,6d_h$ on transport processes has strong influence interaction of diffusant molecules with walls of free volume microvoid, which are polymeric macromolecules surface with dimension D_f (D_f is the dimension of excess energy localization regions) [10]. In this case $D_t = D_f$ (molecular transport) [9] is adopted.

Let's consider the methods of parameters estimation which enter the equation (2). The value f_g can be determined according to the equation [10]:

$$f_g = 0{,}017\left(\frac{1+\nu}{1-2\nu}\right), \tag{3}$$

where ν is Poisson's ratio, defined according to the results of mechanic testing with the aid of the relationship [11]:

$$\frac{\sigma_Y}{E} = \frac{(1-2\nu)}{\sigma(1+\nu)}, \tag{4}$$

where σ_Y is yielding stress, E is elasticity modulus.

The dimension D_f is calculated according to the following equation [12]:

$$D_f = \frac{2(1-\nu)}{1-2\nu}. \tag{5}$$

The volume of free volume microvoid v_h within the framework of fractal model [10] can be calculated according to the equation:

$$v_h = \frac{D_f(1-2\nu)kT_m}{f_g E}, \tag{6}$$

where k is Boltzmann constant, T_m is polymer's melting temperature (for HDPE T_m=403 K [13]), and then to estimate the diameter of this microvoid d_h from geometric opinions.

The values of D_f and d_h for studied compositions HDPE+Z in table 1 are cited. The value d_h can be compared with corresponding experimental data obtained by positrons annihilation method. For HDPE at T=323 K experimental value is $d_h \approx 6{,}8$ Å [14]. This value d_h corresponds well enough with corresponding calculated values d_h cited in table 1.

Now we can calculate the value D according to the equation (2) (table 1) and then theoretical value of stability to cracking τ_{50}^T according to the equation (1). The comparison of experimental values τ_{50}^l and τ_{50}^T in table 1 is cited. As can be seen, the good correspondence of theory and experiment is obtained – the average discrepancy τ_{50}^l and τ_{50}^T

is equal to ~9%. Allowing for statistical character of testing on cracking in active environments, it can be said, that this discrepancy is not exceeded the experimental error. It is important to note, that at calculation τ_{50}^{T} the fitted empirical constants were not used and extreme change τ_{50} is fully explained by structural changes, due to introduction Z and characterized by dimension D_f. Besides, the correspondence of theory and experiment confirms the correctness of the made above assumptions.

Let's consider structural aspect of τ_{50} change due to introduction Z. As it is known [3, 15], for compositions HDPE+Z is observed the extreme rise of relative fraction of local order regions (clusters) φ_{cl}, that results to decrease of fractal dimension of structure d_f according to the equation [15]:

$$d_f = 3 - 6\left(\frac{\varphi_{cl}}{SC_\infty}\right)^{1/2}, \tag{7}$$

were S is cross-sectional area of macromolecule, C_∞ is characteristic ratio, which is an indicator of polymeric chain statistical flexibility [16].

In its turn, dimensions d_f and D_f are connected by the relationship [12]:

$$D_f = 1 + \frac{1}{3 - d_f}. \tag{8}$$

Hence, the reduction d_f results to decrease D_f that is the main factor defining the diffusivity D reduction (the equations (2) and (6)) and, as consequence, τ_{50} rise (the equation (1)). It will be noted also, that comparatively small variation D_f (about 20%) determines strong (eightfold) change D and, as consequence, τ_{50} in virtue of power-type dependence of the equation (2) typical for fractal relationships.

Table 1. The characteristics of diffusion process of active environment for compositions HDPE+Z

The composition	D_f	d_h, Å	$D\times10^8$, cm²/s	τ_{50}^{l}, hours	τ_{50}^{T}, hours
HDPE	5,17	8,65	4,76	10 (normative)	38,6
HDPE+0,01Z	5,0	8,56	4,11	36	44,1
HDPE+0,05Z	4,33	6,65	0,69	250	268
HDPE+0,10Z	5,0	8,56	4,11	38	44,1
HDPE+0,15Z	5,17	8,65	4,76	37	38,6
HDPE+1,0Z	5,17	8,65	4,76	39	38,6

CONCLUSIONS

Therefore, the results of the present paper have shown, that the criterion of polyethylenes samples fracture in tests on cracking under stress in active environments is reaching by polar liquid of sample median plane. Stability to cracking is correctly described within the framework of fractal model of transport processes in polymers. The cause of extreme raising of stability to cracking are structural changes, which are due to introduction of high disperse mixture Fe/FeO and characterized by the dimension of excess energy localization regions.

REFERENCES

[1] Howard J.B. In book: *Engineering Design for Plastics*. Ed. Baer E. London, Chapman and Hall, LTD., 1966, p. 331.

[2] Mashukov N.I., Krupin V.A., Mikitaev A.K., Malamatov A.Kh. *Plast. Massy,* 1990, No 11, p. 31.

[3] Mashukov N.I., Sedyuk V.D., Kozlov G.V., Ovcharenko E.N., Gladyshev G.P., Vodachov A.B. *Stabilization and Modification of Polyethylene by Oxygen Acceptos.* (Preprint). Moscow, IchF AN SSSR, 1990, 64 p.

[4] Rogers G.E. In book: *Engineering Design for Plastics*. Ed. Baer E. London, Chapman and Hall, LTD., 1966, p. 193.

[5] Belford G., Sinai N. In book: *Water in Polymers,* Ed. Rowland S.P. Washington, D.C., 1980, p. 314.

[6] Brown G.L. In book: *Water in Polymers,* Ed. Rowland S.P. Washington, D.C., 1980, p. 419.

[7] Kozlov G.V., Zaikov G.E. *Vysokomolek. Soed.* B, 2003, v. 45, No 7, p. 1197.

[8] Alexander S., Orbach R. *J. Phys. Lett.* (Paris), 1982, v. 42, No 17, p. L625.

[9] Kozlov G.V., Afaunov V.V., Mashukov N.I., Lipatov Yu.S. *Doklady AN Ukraine,* 2000, No 10, p. 140.

[10] Kozlov G.V., Sanditov D.S., Lipatov Yu.S. In book: *Uspekhi v Oblasti Fiziko-Khimii Polimerov.* Ed. Zaikov G.E. a. a. Moscow, Khimiya, 2004, p. 412.

[11] Kozlov G.V., Sanditov D.S. *Anharmonic Effects and Physical-Mechanical Properties of Polymers* (in Russian). Novosibirsk, Nauka, 1994, 261 p.

[12] Balankin A.S. *Synergetics of Deformable Body (in Russian).* Moscow, Publishers of Ministry of Defence SSSR, 1991, 404 p.

[13] Kalinchev E.L., Sakovtseva M.B. *Properties and Processing of Thermoplasts* (in Russian). Leningrad, Khimiya, 1983, 288 p.

[14] Lin D., Wang S.J. J. Phys.: Condens. Matter, 1992, v. 4, No 12, p. 3331.

[15] Kozlov G.V., Zaikov G.E. *Structure of the Polymer Amorphous State.* Utrecht-Boston, Brill Academic Publishers, 2004, 465 p.

[16] Budtov V.P. *Physical Chemistry of Polymer Solutions.* Sankt-Peterburg, Khimiya, 1992, 384 p.

In: Synthesis and Properties of Low- and High-Molecular Compounds ISBN 1-59454-716-5
Editor: Gennady E. Zaikov et al., pp. 213-219

Chapter 13

INITIATION OF METHYL METHACRILATE POLYMERIZATION WITH BENZOYL PEROXIDE - QUATERNARY SALTS AND BENZOYL PEROXIDE - 4-[4-(DIMETHYLAMINO)STYRIL] PYRIDINE AND ITS N-OXIDE

M. A. Turovskyj [1]***, I. O. Opeida*** [1]***, O. V. Kusch*** [1]***,***
E. L. Baranovskyj [1] ***and G. E. Zaikov*** [2]
[1]Institute of Physico-Organic and Coal Chemistry of the National Academy of Sciences of Ukraine, R. Luxemburg, 70, 83114 Donetsk, Ukraine,
E-mail: turov@dongu.donetsk.ua
[2]Institute of Biochemical Physics, Russian Academy of Sciences, 4ul. Kosygina, 117334 Moscow, Russian Federation, e-mail:chembio@sky.chph.ras.ru

ABSTRACT

Polymerization of methyl methacrilate (MMA) using a benzoyl peroxide (BPO) with quaternary salts (tetraethyl ammonium bromide (**1**), tetraethyl ammonium chloride (**2**), tetraethyl ammonium benzoate (**3**), triphenylbenzyl phosphonium bromide (**4**), triphenylbenzyl phosphonium chloride (**5**)) in acetonitrile and benzoyl peroxide with tertiary amines (4-[4-(dimethylamino)styril]pyridine (**6**) and its N-oxide (**7**)) in benzene chloride at temperature 303 have been studied. The rates of decomposition of BPO in the presence of amines and quaternary salts, the initiation rates, the initial rates of polymerization and the efficiencies of radical production at 303 K have been determined.

1. INTRODUCTION

The decompositions of peroxides both in termally promoted conditions [1] and induced by electron donor compounds [2] includes the homolytic cleavage of the OO bond with formation of free radicals as crucial step. The binary systems of diacyl peroxides with tertiary amines [3, 4] and diacyl peroxides with quaternary salts [5] have been widely known as initiators of radical polymerization of vinyl monomers.

In this work, we studied the efficiencies of radical production of binary systems in the polymerization of methyl methacrilate using a benzoyl peroxide with quaternary salts (tetraethyl ammonium bromide, tetraethyl ammonium chloride, tetraethyl ammonium benzoate, triphenylbenzyl phosphonium bromide, triphenylbenzyl phosphonium chloride) in acetonitrile and benzoyl peroxide with tertiary amines (4-[4-(dimethylamino)styril]pyridine and its N-oxide) in benzene chloride at temperature 303 K.

2. Experimental

2.1. Materials

BPO was recrystallized twice from ethanol. The peroxide was 99.4% pure (iodometric titration). 6 and 7 were prepared by the procedure [7]. The solvents were purified using standard methods. 1 and 2 were commercially, 4 and 5 were prepared from triphenylphosphate and corresponding benzylgalohenide. Quaternary salts were recrystallized twice from an acetonitrile into dry diethyl ether; then the salt was dried under reduced pressure at 333 K and stored in a glove box over phosphorus pentoxide. Methyl methacrylate was freed from inhibitor by washing with 5 % aqueous sodium hidroxide, dried over calcium chloride for 24 h and distilled under reduced pressure. 2,2,6,6-tetramethyl-1-piperidinyloxy was purified by sublimation.

2.2. Kinetic Measurements

Polymerization of Methyl Methacrilat Using a Benzoyl Peroxide with Quaternary Salts and Benzoyl Peroxide with Tertiary Amines as Initiators

Methyl methacrylate polymerization in the presence of the inhibitor has been used to determine radical yields in the binary systems. The polymerization was studied dilatometrically at (30 ± 0.05) ^{0}C to a monomer conversion of 3 % in the absence of air. The dilatometers were cooled in ice bath, filled with cooled solution of monomer containing known amounts of initiator and inhibitor and was deaerated by bubbling nitrogen gas. The dilatometers were placed in a thermostat and the contractions recorded at time intervals. The values of polymerization rates calculated from the initial linear parts of the conversion - time curves.

The initial concentrations of reagents were as follows:

For the reactions of polymerization of MMA in acetonitrile at 303 K in the presence of system BPO and tetraethyl ammonium bromide, BPO and tetraethyl ammonium chloride: $[1]_0 = [2] = 5\times10^{-3}$ M, [BPO] = 2.5×10^{-2} M, $[In]_0 = (0\text{-}1)\times10^{-3}$ M, [MMA] = 25 vol. %.

For the reactions of polymerization of MMA in acetonitrile at 303 K in the presence of system BPO and tetraethyl ammonium benzoate, triphenylbenzyl phosphonium bromide, triphenylbenzyl phosphonium chloride: $[3]_0 = [4]_0 = [5]_0 = 2.5\times10^{-2}$ M, [BPO] = 5×10^{-3} M, $[In]_0 = (0\text{-}4)\times10^{-4}$ M, [MMA] = 25 vol. %.

For the reactions of polymerization of MMA in chlorobenzene at 303 K in the presence of system BPO and amines - $[6]_0 = 2.5\times10^{-4}$ M, $[7]_0 = 2.2\times10^{-4}$ M, [BPO] = 7.5×10^{-3} M, $[In]_0 = (0\text{-}5)\times10^{-5}$ M, [MMA] = 25 vol. %.

The measurement of the rate of initiation of polymer chain in initiated polymerization of MMA by binary systems involves the use of the inhibitor 2,2,6,6-tetramethyl-1-piperidinyloxy. In the presence of this substance, there is an induction period in the polymerization during which the inhibitor is consumed.

Decomposition of Benzoyl Peroxide by 4-[4-(Dimethylamino)Styril]Pyridine and its N-Oxide

Pseudo-first-order rate constants (k_{obsd}) were determined by amines absorbance decrease at λ_{max}=375 nm for 6 (ε = 30000±400 $M^{-1}\cdot cm^{-1}$) and the consumption of 7 at λ_{max}=395 nm (ε = 32000±500 $M^{-1}\cdot cm^{-1}$) at 303 K. A dried and freshly distilled benzene chloride was used as a solvent. The initial amine concentration of $[6]_0 = [7]_0 = 2.5\times10^{-5}$ M. Reactions were carried out under peroxide excess (0.01-0.4 M) over the amine.

Decomposition of Benzoyl Peroxide by Quaternary Salts

The reactions were carried out under pseudo-monomolecular conditions at 303 K under salts excess. The rate constants (k_{obsd}) for the induced decomposition of BPO by quaternary salts were obtained by following the disappearance of the C=O absorption band (ν = 1764 sm^{-1}). A dried and freshly distilled acetonitrile was used as a solvent. The initial concentration of BPO 1.5×10^{-2} M The salt concentrations of 1 - $(2.6\text{-}10.34)\cdot10^{-2}$ M; 2 - $(1.7\text{-}13)\cdot10^{-2}$ M; 5 - $9\cdot10^{-3}$ M. Rate constants were produced by the method of least squares from ln $(C_0/C_t) = k_{obsd}\, t$. C_0 and C_t are concentrations of BPO at time 0 and t, respectively. Most of the plots of ln (C_0/C_t) vs t showed excellent linear relations ($r \geq 0.98$).

3. Results

It has been established that the period of induction of MMA polymerization linearly depends on concentration of the inhibitor. The rate of polymerization after complete consumption of the inhibitor is equal to the rate of polymerization in the absence of inhibitor. It has been assumed that one molecule of inhibitor stops one radical chain. Figure 1 illustrates the results of a typical run.

The induction period (τ) is taken to be a time obtained using extrapolation of the conversion - time curve at zero conversion.

The initiation rate is described by the equations 1 and 2

$$W_{in} = [In]/\tau \qquad (1)$$

$$W_{in} = nfW_d \qquad (2)$$

By combining this equations we find that

$$f = W_{in}/nW_{d,} \tag{3}$$

Where W_{in} is the initiation rate, τ is the induction period, [In] is the initial concentration of inhibitor, W_d is the rate of induced decomposition of peroxide by tertiary amines and quaternary salts, f is the efficiencie of radical production of binary systems in the polymerization of methyl methacrilate, n =2 – number of initiating radicals.

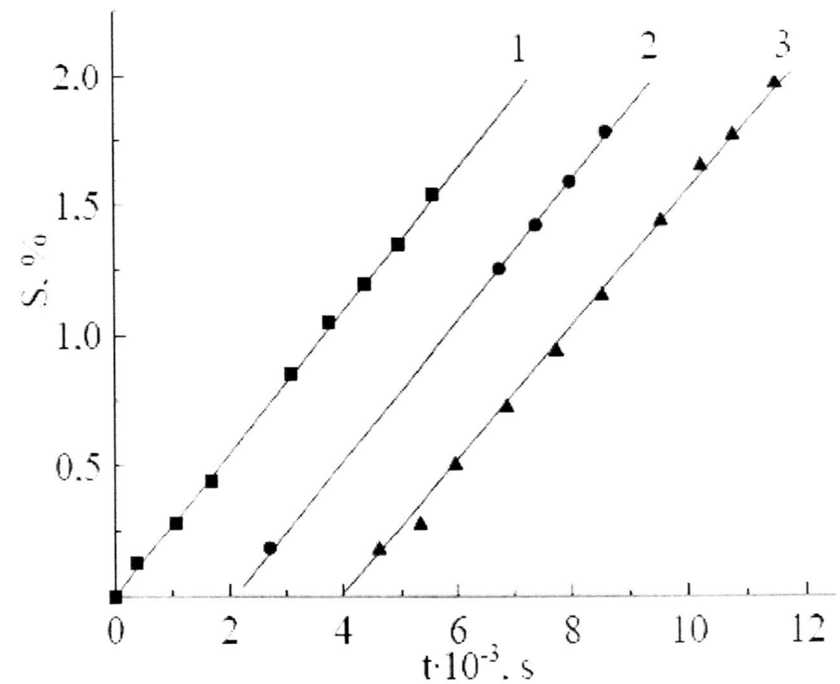

Figure 1. Polymerizations of MMA in acetonitrile at 303 K in the presence of system 3 -BPO and inhibited by 2,2,6,6-tetramethyl-1-piperidinyloxy. 1- polymerization in the absence of inhibitor; 2-[In] = $1\cdot10^{-4}$; 3 - $2\cdot10^{-4}$ M. $[3]_0 = 5\times10^{-3}$M, [BPO] = 2.5×10^{-2}M, [MMA] = 25 vol. %

Walling and Indictor [8] have noted that each reaction of - N,N-dimethylaniline and PBO leads to the production of two radicals. Nitrogen is found in the polymers which were obtained using binary initiating system - N,N-dimethylaniline and PBO. To characterize the intermediate radicals produced in the initiation of vinyl polymerization with binary systems of diacyl peroxides and tertiary amines, spin trapping technique was applied by using 2-methyl-2-nitrosopropane as a spin trapping reagent [9]. There were concluded that in the reactions of - N,N-dimethylaniline and - N,N-diethylaniline with benzoyl peroxide, benzoyloxy, N-methylanilinomethyl and N-ethylanilino-1-ethyl radicals are initiating radicals. Thus, cation-radical of amine was suggested to induce the radical polymerization of methyl methacrilate. From this, the radical generation process may be considered to include the following steps:

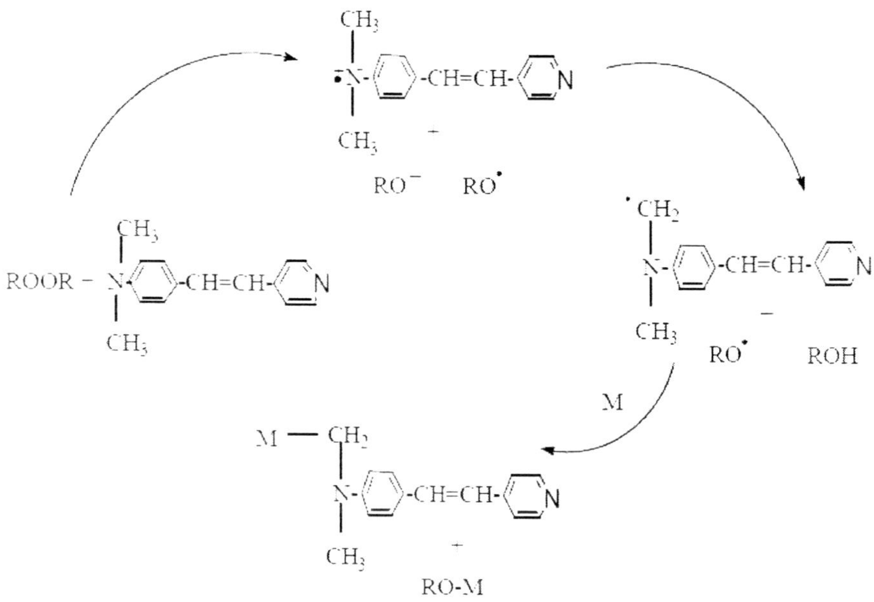

Scheme I.

The polymerization of MMA with cetyl trimethyl ammonium bromide and BPO at 40 ^{0}C was studied in a paper by P.Ghosh and S.N.Maity. End-group analysis for amino end-groups by the dye technique [5] clearly indicated the incorporation of basic (amino) end-groups. Each reaction of quaternary salt and PBO leads to the production of two radicals. Benzoyl peroxide decomposes in the presence of quaternary salt by two possible paths:

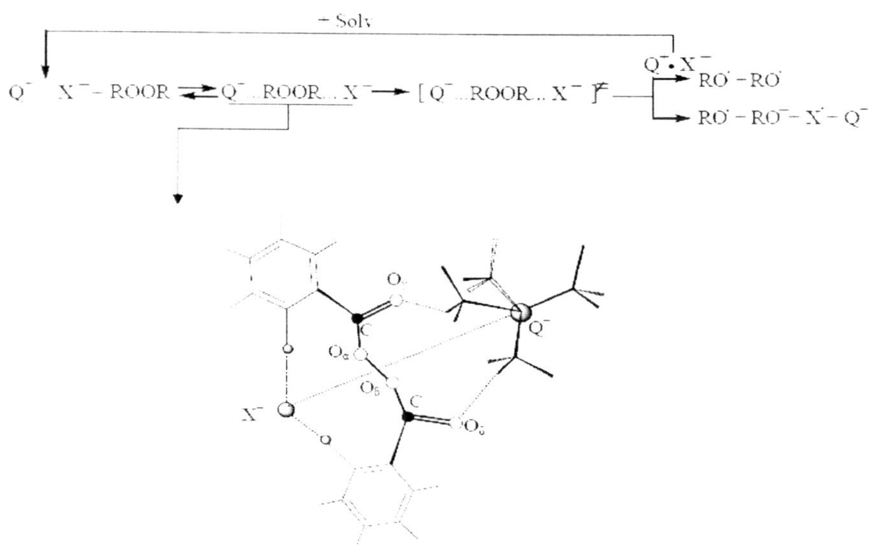

Scheme II.

For both cases the decompose reaction of BPO leads to the formation of two radicals.

Rates of decomposition were determined as described in Experimental section and calculated from:

$$W_d = k_d[\text{BPO}][\text{Inductor}]$$

Values of *f* calculated from eq. 3 for systems amines – BPO and quaternary salts – BPO are collected in Table.

Table. The rates of decomposition of BPO in the presence of amines and quaternary salts (W_d), - the initiation rates (W_{in}), the initial rates of polymerization (W_{pol}) and the efficiencies of radical production (*f*) at 303 K

Inductor	$W_{pol}\times10^6$ (Ms^{-1})	$W_{in}\times10^8$ (Ms^{-1})	$W_d\times10^8$ (Ms^{-1})	f
1	9.11 ± 0.05	13.9 ± 0.3	1400 ± 40	< 0.01
2	6.18 ± 0.03	14.5 ± 0.5	38 ± 8	0.19
3	6.30 ± 0.07	4.9 ± 0.2	6.2 ± 0.2	0.40
4	6.39 ± 0.05	5.1 ± 0.7	840 ± 16	< 0.01
5	8.2 ± 0.1	16 ± 0.8	39 ± 2	0.21
6	13.2 ± 0.01	1.32 ± 0.30	0.9 ± 0.1	0.70
7	14.1 ± 0.01	1.29 ± 0.06	1.05 ± 0.2	0.60

The data obtained show that the inition rate in the polymerization of methyl methacrilate in the presence of the benzoyl peroxide and quaternary salts decreases in following sequence (the initial concentrations and other conditions being equal) :

$$Ph_3(PhCH_2)P^+Cl^- > Et_4N^+Br^- > Et_4N^+Cl^- > Ph_3(PhCH_2)P^+Br^- > Et_4N^+Benz^-.$$

And the efficiencie of radical production of binary systems (the benzoyl peroxide and quaternary salts) in the polymerization of methyl methacrilate decreases in following sequence:

$$Et_4N^+Benz^- > Ph_3(PhCH_2)P^+Cl^- > Et_4N^+Cl^- > Ph_3(PhCH_2)P^+Br^- > Et_4N^+Br^-.$$

Formation of radicals in the decomposition reaction of BPO in the presence quaternary salts is low-yield process. A comparison of the data of Table shows that the systems BPO with dialkylaminostyrilpyridine and its N-oxide are more effective in the polymerization reaction of MMA than the systems BPO – quaternary salts. As Schemes I and II illustrate N-methylamino-methylstyrilpyridine radical larger than radicals $Br^\bullet$, $I^\bullet$, $PhC(O)O^\bullet$ and very inefficient in cage recombination, and this is beacause the rate of recombination reaction depends on the size of radical, steric retardation and radical stability [3]. For example, the yield of free radicals from the decomposition of *tert*-butyl peroxybenzoate in the presence of the dimethyl sulfide is only 2 % results from the efficient recombination reaction of benzoyloxyl radical with the radical cation of dimethyl sulfide [10]. Thus, the most lager radicals are the most effective in the reaction of polymerization.

REFERENCES

[1] S.S.Kim, I.S.Baek, A.Tuchkin, K.M.Go. *J.Org.Chem.*, 66, 4006 (2001).

[2] J.J.Zupancic, K.A.Horn. *J. Am. Chem. Soc.*, 102, 5279 (1980).

[3] S. Srinivas, K.G. Taylor. *J. Org. Chem.*, 55, 1779 (1990).

[4] N. Nishimura, T.Nakamura, Y.Sueishi, S. Yamamoto. *Bull. Chem. Soc. Jpn.*, 67, 165 (1994).

[5] P.Ghosh, S.N.Maity. *Eur. Polym.* J., 14., 855 (1978).

[6] M.Imoto, T.Otsu, K. Kimura. *J. Polym. Sci.*, 15, 475 (1955).

[7] E.D. Parker, A.Furst. *J. Org. Chem.*, 23, 201 (1958).

[8] C. Walling, N. J. Indictor. *J. Amer. Chem. Soc.*, 80, 5814 (1958).

[9] T. Sato, T. Otsu. *Macromol. Chem.*, 176, 561 (1975).

[10] W.A.Pryor, W.H.Jr.Hendricson. *J. Amer. Chem. Soc.*, 97, 1580 (1975).

In: Synthesis and Properties of Low- and High-Molecular Compounds ISBN 1-59454-716-5
Editor: Gennady E. Zaikov et al., pp. 221-232

Chapter 14

APPLICATION OF LFE EQUATIONS TO ABSORPTION AND CHROMATOGRAPHY, SWELLING OF POLYMERS AND DIFFUSION

R. G. Makitra, A. A. Turovsky and G. E. Zaikov*
L.V.Pisarzhevskii Institute of Physical Chemistry, Ukranium National Academy of Sciences, 3A, Naukova st., Lviv – 79053, Ukraine
*N.M.Emanuel Institute of Biochemical Physics Russian Academy of Sciences, 4, Kosygin st., Moscow 119991, Russia

1. APPLICATION OF LFE EQUATIONS TO ABSORPTION AND CHROMATOGRAPHY

Recently, the attempts to set correlation between absorbability of organic substances α, i.e. the amount of substance absorbed from solution or the gas phase by 1 g of absorbent and their physicochemical properties, were only qualitative. It is found that absorption and molecular weight of absorbed substances are symbate, but only for aliphatic compounds with one functional group. Analogous regularities were observed for other characteristics, such as molar volume, solubility in water, Hensch coefficient π (distribution in octanol-water system), molar refraction, parachor, etc.

In 1985, Kamlet, Abraham *et al.* [2] tried to generalize data [1] on absorption of 38 aliphatic compounds, including alcohols, from aqueous solution by activated coal. The following equation was deduced:

$$y = a_0 + s\pi^* + a\alpha + b\beta + mV, \qquad (1)$$

where V is the molar volume of absorbed substances.

An adequate correlation with $R = 0.974$ was obtained for 37 compounds. In this correlation, the determining factors were molar volume increasing absorbability and basicity reducing it, apparently, due to hydrophilicity, as a result of hydrogen bond formation with water.

In this connection, a modernized equation was suggested for generalizing data on absorption by coals [3] and quantitative regularities for vapor and gas absorption on fullerene C-60 were considered [4].

Progress in quantitative generalization of data on substance adsorption from solutions on adsorbents, as well as gas and vapor adsorption induced application of the same approach in chromatography. In recent 15 years, tens of works by Kamlet, Taft, Abraham *et al.* were published, devoted to application of LFE equations of (1) type for setting a correlation between physicochemical characteristics of substances and the index of their retention on various phases by liquid-liquid chromatography and with respect to the type and composition of the liquid phase. The detailed rendering of the results of these studies would require a separate review. In this Section we mention only the most important among them.

In 1984, it was noted [5] that time of aromatic hydrocarbons retention may not be unambiguously characterized by any factor, though the main effect is caused by molar volume of the substrates. It increases the retention time, whereas H-bond formation effects reduce it. However, a linear correlation ($R = 0.991$) [6] between the known index of Snyder's "chromatographic force" of solvents P [7], developed from data by Rorsnyder, and "bipolarity" index π^x was determined. Unfortunately, it was only made for the so-called "selected" solvents e.g. aliphatic, aprotic and containing no chlorine atoms. As a consequence, in 1985 these authors studied the use of LFE equation for generalization of chromatographic data by Haki and Young [8], who investigated the retention time for aromatic and aliphatic substances on a column with octadecylsilane filler, using methanol-water liquid phase [9]. After elimination of data for so-called silanophilic solvents (amines) the absorption generalizing equation becomes similar to that in [2] and shows that retention time increases with the molar volume. The opposite effect is ability of solutes to nonspecific (π^x) and specific (β) interactions, because they promote interaction of substances with polar, mobile phase capable of forming hydrogen bonds. High efficiency of equations type (1) was also shown for generalization of data by index of retention in columns with different stationary and mobile phases.

The influence of the mobile acetonitrile-water phase composition and temperature of the experiment on retention time for aromatic compounds was also studied [10]. It is found that acetonitrile concentration increase in the mobile phase reduces main coefficients in the LFE equation. Temperature increase causes the same effect. Retention factor logarithm linearly depends on acetonitrile concentration in the mobile phase.

The authors [11, 12] suggested replacing MacHoven molar volume, presented as a ratio of molecular mass division by the substrate density, by Van-der-Waals molecular volume, V_1, computed from molecular models. Such replacement improves the quality of calculations. In particular, joint generalization of data for aliphatic and aromatic compounds became possible, including solids.

As a example, Table 1 shows data on chromatographic capacity factors by Hafkensheid and Tomlison [69], who studied the reverse-phase chromatography of substances in columns with hypersyle ODS and 75 and 50% methanol as eluent. The following highly adequate equation were deduced [11]:

Table 1. Column capacity factors [69] at cleansing by 75 and 50% methanol: compared experiment and calculations by equations (2) and (3) [11]

No.	Solvents	lg exp(k_{75})	Calculation eq. (2)	lg exp(k_{50})	Calculation eq (3)
1.	Methylene chloride	-0.420	-0.506	0.129	0.06
2.	Chloroform	-0.235	-0.203	0.480	0.4780
3.	Carbon tetrachloride	0.145	0.150	0.926	0.926
4.	*n*-Butanol	-0.600	-0.548	-0.054	-0.033
5.	*n*-Pentanol	-0.380	-0.369	0.316	0.261
6.	*n*-Hexanol	-0.163	-0.187	0.550	0.585
7.	Cyclohexane	0.602	0.596	1.507	1.583
8.	Cyclohexanol	-0.390	-0.382	0.244	0.255
9.	Cyclohexanone	-0.530	-0.635	-0.037	-0.140
10.	2-Methylpropanoic acid	-0.680	-0.614	-0.120	-0.054
11	Hexanoic acid	-0.240	-0.240	0.588	0.560
12	Octanoic acid	0.177	0.128	1.288	1.168
13	Diethyl ether	-0.410	0.440	0.056	0.034
14	Ethyl acetale	-0.500	-0.510	-0.075	-0.009
15	Benzene	-0.062	-0.039	0.083	0.098
16	Toluene	0.154	0.159	1.001	1.016
17	Ethylbenzene	0.330	0.350	1.302	1.320
18	Isopropylbenzene	0.476	0.506	1.506	1.578
19	*n*-Propylbenzene	0.530	0.508	1.648	1.581
20	*sec*-Butylbenzene	0.662	0.704	1.803	1.896
21	*p*-Xylene	0.375	0.343	1.3401	1.295
22	Mesitylene	0.593	0.521	1.689	1.588
23	Chlorobenzene	0.114	0.121	1.011	0.990
24	*p*-Chlorotoluene	0.329	0.314	1.350	1.303
25	Nitrobenzene	-0.259	-0.295	0.471	0.457
26	Methyl benzoate	-0.158	-0.116	0.663	0.695
27	Ethyl benzoate	0.025	0.054	0.973	0.976
28	*n*-Propyl benzoate	0.221	0.251	1.300	1.299
29	Benzyl alcohol	-0.610	-0.631	0.025	-0.036

$$\lg k_{75} = (-0.52 \pm 0.04) + (1.84 \pm 0.06)V_1/100 - (0.44 \pm 0.04)\pi^* - (1.55 \pm 0.05)\beta - (0.21 \pm 0.05)\alpha_M; \quad (2)$$
$$n = 29;\ R = 0.995;\ S = 0.044;$$

$$\lg k_{50} = (-0.38 \pm 0.05) + (3.22 \pm 0.06)V_1/100 - (0.44 \pm 0.05)\pi^* - (2.38 \pm 0.06)\beta - (0.04 \pm 0.05)\alpha_M; \quad (3)$$
$$n = 29;\ R = 0.997;\ S = 0.042.$$

In these equations, the common donor factor of hydrogen bond α is replaced by α_M – the difference between α of studied substances and *n*-octanol.

Further development of this approach for various chromatographic columns and a broad selection of aromatic, including polychlorinated substances, was performed in [13, 14], where the effect of mobile phases of different composition were studied. Moreover, a correlation with substrate distribution coefficients in octanol-water system [16] and aqueous solubility was determined. Meanwhile, the limitedness of one-parameter correlations between the retention factor and solvent "polarity" factors as π or E_T, because energy consumption for formation of a cavity was not taken into account in them, was confirmed on the example of series of alkylbenzenes [15]. For binary solvents the retention factor dependence on the mobile phase composition is described by one-parameter equations of E_T [17].

Further on, a detailed investigation of various aspects of multiparameter LFE equation usage in liquid chromatography was performed [18 – 25]. In particular, dependencies on the phase composition were studied, comparisons with distribution coefficients were performed and so on. This approach was also found effective for generalizing data on gas-liquid chromatography [26 – 29]. Recently, the comparison of applicability of type (1) equations was performed [19].

2. Application of LFE Equations to Swelling of Polymers and Diffusion

Despite the existence of numerous experimental data on swelling of synthetic and natural polymers, including coals, and their theoretical generalization, till recent times there was no reliable model of the process, which would allow a correlation of the polymer swelling degree in solvents with physicochemical properties with an adequate accuracy. The known achievements are of either semi-quantitative type or are suitable for separate groups of solvents only, mostly within their homological sequences.

In 1942, the first work with quantitatively studied swelling of raw and vulcanized rubbers in quite many solvents (over 140) was published [30]. The authors made the important conclusion about analogy of polymer swelling and crystalline substance dissolution. However, they failed to obtain quantitative generalization of the data. They only observed that correlation of the swelling degree with dielectric constant of solvents, suggested in 1921 by Ostwald, is of qualitative type only.

Works by Flory [31] on thermodynamics of diluted polymer solutions and Hildebrand theory of irregular solutions [32] are of the fundamental importance for studying swelling of polymers. According to the above-mentioned, the factor defining the polymer swelling degree S (the amount of absorbed solvent in grams, milliliters or moles per 1g of polymer) is enthalpy of polymer mixing with liquids, proportional to cohesive energy density of the polymers. This approach was used by Richards in consideration of data on polyethylene swelling in 52 solvents [36]. It is found that there is no unified dependence of S on δ; for every group of solvents separate parabolic, "bell-shaped" curve was obtained, and data on some solvents do not fit the obtained dependencies at all. The attempts to associate the swelling degree of natural and butadiene-styrene rubbers with the solvent structure or refraction gave just a qualitative interpretation – reduction of solvability of solvents at polar group (OH, NH_2, etc.) injection in the structure was detected [34, 35].

According to the Flory theory, the maximum of polymer swelling should be observed in solvents with the solubility parameter equal or close to that of the polymer. However, molecular masses of polymers, calculated with respect to these suggestions, usually do not correlate with the values, obtained by different methods. Swelling of 12 rubbers in a series of organic solvents was studied in detail [39]. The results were generalized on the basis of the Flory-Rener theory; however, the reliable correlation between S values and physicochemical parameters of solvents was not obtained yet, and calculated solubility parameters of polymers δ and molar volume of the areas between chain crosslinks are 2 – 3 times different from one another with respect to the solvent used. This indicates the limitedness of current theoretical prerequisites. Introduction of some empirical correction coefficients does not eliminate these disadvantages, so the authors recognize [37] the theory of cohesive energy density to be of the qualitative type only. The same conclusion is made in the work [38]: it is emphasized that the primary version of Flory-Huggins calculations is suitable only within homological sequences of solvents. It is also outlined that besides cohesive energy, swelling is affected by other factors. For example, the same results were obtained for swelling of styrene copolymer with divinylbenzene [39], which was explained by different types of interaction between separate functional groups of solvents with the polymer.

These nonconformities induced several attempts to determine effects of other factors on swelling: solvent polarity, viscosity, Reichardt's electrophilicity E_T [40], etc. However, obtained dependencies are also valid within homological sequences of solvents. In 1990's, a series of works by Aminabhavi *et al.* [41] was published, where the absorption degree pf liquids by six polymers were studied, as well as coefficients of their diffusion through corresponded polymeric membranes as a function of the molar volume of solvents. Though such approach is quite logical (the larger molecule is, the more difficult is penetration into the polymer structure), the obtained results may not be considered satisfactory, because linear correlations with numerous deviations were obtained only for separate consideration of groups of solvents – alkanes, esters, cyclic compounds.

Therefore, it may be expected that joint consideration of various types of interactions via LFE equations will be desirable in this case. Actually, for swelling of butadiene-styrene, acrylonitrile and other synthetic rubbers in some solvents, the extended Koppel-Palm equation:

$$\lg S = a_0 + a_1 \frac{n^2 - 1}{n^2 + 2} + a_2 \frac{\varepsilon - 1}{2\varepsilon + 1} + a_3 B + a_4 E_T + a_5 \delta^2, \qquad (4)$$

gave correlation with R = 0.95 – 0.97. However, this happens only after elimination of data on 2 – 4 solvents. For correlation parameter a conditional equilibrium constant of swelling was taken:

$$K = \frac{W}{1 - W},$$

where W is the volumetric part of the solvent in the swollen sample. Table 2 shows W values and experimental and calculated lg$K$ values for butadiene-styrene rubber with 12.5% styrene, and deviations Δlg$K$.

Table 2. Butadiene-styrene rubber swelling in solvents [38]

No.	Solvent	W	$\lg K_{exp}$	$\lg K_{calc}$	$\Delta \lg K$
1	Isooctane	0.5225	-0.0391	-0.5411	-0.5802
2	*n*-Pentane	0.4797	-0.0353	-0.277	-0.1724
3	*n*-Hexane	0.3989	-0.1790	-0.2474	-0.0685
4	*n*-Heptane	0.3491	-0.2706	-0.3158	-0.0452
5	*n*-Decane	0.2167	-0.1461	-0.3943	-0.248
6	*c*-Hexane	0.2448	-0.4893	-0.3039	0.1854
7	CCl_4	0.1768	-0.6680	-0.4710	0.1970
8	Ethyl bromide	0.2132	-0.5661	-0.4239	0.1432
9	Benzene	0.1957	-0.6138	-0.4668	0.1470
10	Chloroform	0.1678	-0.6954	-0.5225	0.1729
11	Dioxane	0.3257	-0.3160	0.4359	0.7519
12	CH_2Cl_2	0.2151	-0.5622	-0.2676	0.2946
13	$CHBr_2$	0.1786	-0.6627	-0.7702	-0.1075
14	Pyridine	0.2833	-0.4031	-0.8019	-0.3988
15	Acetonitrile	0.9524	1.3012	1.2015	-0.0997

After elimination of the most deviating data for swelling in dioxane, 13 solvents were generalized by the following equation:

$$\lg K = 2.443 - (14.04 \pm 1.56)f(n^2) - (4.79 \pm 1.08)f(\varepsilon) +$$
$$+ (1.45 \pm 0.50)10^{-3}B + (6.51 \pm 1.03)10^{-3}\delta^2; \ (5)$$
$$R = 0.762; S = 0.172.$$

(electrophilicity parameter is insignificant).

Of interest is that for butadiene-styrene rubbers, the maximum effect on swelling is caused by chargeability of solvents, which correlates with the presence of benzene rings in the polymer structure. Meanwhile, for acrylonitrile rubbers the determining parameter is the solvent ability to electrophilic solvation [42].

Table 3 shows data on butadiene-acrylonitrile swelling, which are adequately generalized by equation (6). After elimination of data for ethyl bromide and taking into account insignificance of basicity, the following equation is accepted adequate:

$$\lg K = 22.52 - (22.30 \pm 4.52)f(n^2) + (16.02 \pm 5.58)f(\varepsilon) -$$
$$- (0.64 \pm 0.18)E_T + (6.19 \pm 0.61)10^{-3}\delta^2; \ (6)$$
$$n = 14; R = 0.955; S = 0.429.$$

Equations of this type are useful for generalizing data on swelling of acrylonitrile rubbers of different structure and butyl rubber.

Table 3. Butadiene-acrylonitrile rubber (61:39) swelling in solvents – comparison experimental [38] and calculate (eq. (5)) data

No.	Solvent	W	$\lg K_{exp}$	$\lg K_{calc}$	$\Delta \lg K$
1	Isooctane	0.9925	2.1217	1.8818	-0.2400
2	*n*-Pentane	0.9760	1.6092	1.6894	0.0802
3	*n*-Hexane	0.9737	1.5685	1.6838	0.1154
4	*n*-Heptane	0.9805	1.9742	1.5670	-0.4073
5	*n*-Octane	-	-	-	-
6	*n*-Decane	0.9926	2.1275	1.6088	-0.5187
7	*n*-Dodecane	-	-	-	-
8	Hexadecane	-	-	-	-
9	Cyclohexane	0.9672	1.4696	1.7684	0.2987
10	CCl_4	0.5862	0.1513	0.8809	0.7297
11	Ethyl bromide	0.2522	-0.4720	1.6336	2.1056
12	Benzene	0.3311	-0.3054	-0.3860	-0.0806
13	$CHCl_3$	0.1510	-0.7499	-0.8087	-0.0588
14	Dioxane	0.2710	-0.4298	-0.1973	0.2324
15	CH_2Cl_2	0.1563	-0.7322	-0.2497	0.4825
16	Nitrobenzene	-	-	-	-
17	CH_2Cl_2	0.1781	-0.6642	-1.0647	-0.4005
18	Pyridine	0.1637	-0.7083	-0.6822	0.0261
19	Acetonitrile	0.4219	-0.1368	-0.3960	-0.2591

Also, satisfactory results were obtained for data generalization [36] on natural vulcanized rubber swelling in 23 solvents - after elimination of one solvent only. The rest values of S are correlated by the three-parameter equation with $R = 0.962$. Therefore, chargeability and basicity of the solvents promote their penetration into the polymer structure, whereas increasing electrophilicity makes ability to swell worse. Here, polarity and cohesive energy density factors are insignificant [43]. Satisfactory results of generalization were also obtained [44] for polyethylene swelling [33] in several solvents.

Table 4 shows corresponding data on swelling values Q (solvent volume adsorbed per 1g of polymer) for polyethylene with $MM = 9{,}400$ in 26 solvents [33]. They are correlated by equation (4) with $R = 0.940$. After elimination of the most deviating data for chloroform, R increased to 0.955. In this equation chargeability and basicity factors are insignificant. Finally, the correlation of polymer swelling with the solvent properties is adequately described by the following three-parameter equation:

$$\lg Q = 3.153 + (2.12 \pm 1.75)f(n^2) - (0.148 \pm 0.019)E_T +$$
$$+ (1.93 \pm 1.17)10^{-3}\delta^2; (7)$$
$$n = 25;\ R = 0.951;\ S = 0.309.$$

Table 4. Comparison experimental [33] and calculated (eq. (7)) values of polyethylene (MM = 9,400) swelling Q, ml/g

No.	Solvent	Q	$\lg Q_{exp}$	$\lg Q_{calc}$	$\Delta \lg Q$	Q_{calc}
1	Pentane	0.21	-0.6778	-.05862	0.09162	0.26
2	Hexane	0.28	-0.5528	-0.5322	0.0206	0.29
3	Heptane	0.31	-0.5086	-0.5207	-0.0121	0.30
4	Benzene	0.22	-0.6576	-0.6394	0.0182	0.23
5	Toluene	0.25	-0.6021	-0.6171	-0.0150	0.24
6	*m*-Xylene	0.29	-0.5376	-0.5483	-0.0196	0.28
7	*c*-Hexane	0.40	-0.3979	-0.3443	0.0536	0.45
8	Tetralin	0.29	-0.5376	-0.4439	0.0939	0.36
9	Decalin	0.39	-0.4089	-0.3499	0.0590	0.45
10	$CHCl_3$	0.28	-0.5528	-1.4040	-0.8515	0.039
11	CCl_4	0.40	-0.3979	-0.4658	-0.679	0.34
12	Trichloroethylene	0.43	-0.3665	-0.8899	-0.5734	0.13
13	Chlorobenzene	0.25	-0.6021	-1.9258	0.4238	0.094
14	Ethanol	0.002	-2.6990	-2.7242	-0.0252	0.002
15	Propanol	0.024	-2.3979	-2.7938	-0.3958	0.002
16	Pentanol	0.005	-2.3010	-2.6383	-0.3872	0.002
17	*n*-Octanol	0.0009	-3.0458	-2.6091	0.4366	0.002
18	Diethyl ether	0.14	-0.8539	-1.0358	-0.1819	0.09
19	Acetic acid	0.001	-3.0000	-3.2119	-0.2119	0.0006
20	Acetone	0.002	-2.6990	-1.8749	0.824	0.013
21	Ethyl acetate	0.025	-1.6021	-1.3570	0.245	0.044
22	Butyl acetate	0.080	-1.1549	-1.4681	-0.3132	0.034
23	Aniline	0.008	-2.0969	-1.8310	0.2659	0.015
24	Ethylaniline	0.046	-1.6021	1.6647	-0.626	0.022
25	Dimethylaniline	0.110	-0.9586	-0.9411	0.0175	0.11
26	Nitrobenzene	0.019	-1.7213	-1.3564	0.3648	0.044

Aminabhavi [41] indicates the correlation between the swelling degree and molar volume (size) of the solvent molecule, V_m. Actually, taking into account these parameters significantly improves quantitative generalization results on swelling. Application of a six-parameter equation:

$$\lg S = a_0 + a_1\frac{n^2-1}{n^2+2} + a_2\frac{\varepsilon-1}{2\varepsilon+1} + a_3B + a_4E_T + a_5\delta^2 + a_6V_m \quad (8)$$

allowed generalization of data [33] on polyethylene swelling. In this case, it seems that $\lg S$ depends on two parameters only – the molar volume and electrophilicity E_T, which both reduce it, because they are symbate with hydrophilicity parameter of the solvents [45, 46]:

$$\lg S = 2.71 - (0.15 \pm 0.01)E_T + (1.48 \pm 0.85)10^{-3}\delta^2 - (7.95 \pm 1.27)10^{-3}V_m; \quad (9)$$
$R = 0.955$; $s = 0.248$.

Adequate results were also obtained for poly(*cis*-isoprene) swelling generalization by equation (8) [41], but it required addition of nonspecific solvation parameter – the solvent chargeability, which increases lg*S* [47]. The same concerns generalization [36] of crosslinked polybutadiene swelling in 13 solvents, and data on butyl rubber swelling [38].

Equations of type (1) were also used to generalize data on swelling of polymers [54, 55].

Table 5. Comparison experimental [54] and calculated by three-parameter equation (R = 0.991; s = 0.023) values of Illinois No. 6 coal swelling

No.	Solvent	Experimental			Calculated		
		W	S_m 10^3	lgS_m	lgS_m	ΔlgSm	Δ, %
1	Pyridine	1.87	11.00	-1.959	-1.958	-0.001	0.1
2	Dioxane	1.64	7.264	-2.139	-2.143	0.005	0.2
3	Dichloromethane	1.60	7.064	-2.151	-2.179	0.028	1.3
4	Chlorobenzene	1.48	4.264	-2.370	-2.364	-0.006	0.3
5	Isopropanol	1.45	7.489	-2.126	-2.136	0.011	0.5
6	Toluene	1.41	4.450	-2.352	-2.364	0.013	0.5
7	Ethanol	1.40	8.682	-2.061	-2.069	0.008	0.4
8	Benzene	1.38	4.864	-2.313	-2.283	-0.030	1.3
9	Acetonitrile	1.34	8.283	-2.082	-2.056	-0.026	1.2
10	Cyclohexane	1.11	1.307	-2.884	-	-	-

LFE equations adequately correlate both swelling degree, i.e. solvent absorption, and the rate of solvent penetration into the polymer structure.

This approach is also suitable for generalizing data on swelling of natural polymers – coals and lignites – in organic solvents. If correlation of their swelling with solubility [49] or donor and acceptor numbers of the solvents [50] gives an approximate, semi-empirical picture, then generalization of the same data by a five-parameter equation (4) allows obtaining linear dependencies, which correlate well experimental results and swelling features with the substrate types [51 – 53] (all this after elimination of 2 – 3 most deviating solvents). In particular, the lower metamorphized coals are e.g. the higher concentration of acid groups in coals, the more significant basicity of the solvents is. The use of the six-parameter equation (8) allows much better generalization and interpretation of the process features. For example, such generalization of data on coal Illinois No. 6 swelling [54] showed that lg*S* reduces symbate with increase of V_m and increases with basicity *B* of the solvents. Summing up of these two factors gives an adequate linear correlation [55].

Table 7.5 shows data on solvent vapor adsorption by coal *W* [54] (or *S* in moles). There is no clear dependence between *W* and δ^2 and parabolic correlation suggested [54] is just approximate. Therefore, generalization of data on *S* (Table 5) by the six-parameter equation 8) gives the expression with $R = 0.940$; after elimination of deviating data for cyclohexane *R* increases to 0.996. Elimination of insignificant parameters reduces to the following adequate equation:

$$\lg S = -1.96 + (0.655 \pm 0.074)10^{-3}B - (4.12 \pm 0.58)10^{-3}V_m; \quad (10)$$

$R = 0.984$; $s = 0.030$.

The larger solvent molecule size is, i.e. V_m, the more difficult becomes their penetration into the coal structure, whereas interaction of solvent acid groups (-OH, -COOH) promotes such penetration.

LFE equations [55] generalize also well the rate constants of coals swelling (i.e. solvent absorption rates [58]). It is also shown [59] that copper ion diffusion rates through a liquid membrane containing 5-nonylsalicylaldoxime as a complex forming agent similarly correlate with the properties of organic solvents, which form the membrane.

Finally, application of LFE equations for generalization of some biochemical and biological processes should be noted. Taking an organism cell for a protoplasm isolated by a semipermeable membrane, these equations give an opportunity to set a quantitative correlation between properties of organics dissolved in water and their effect on living organism, for example, bacteria phosphorescence decrease [60], goldfish mortality percentage [56], enzyme activity reduction, etc. This specific problem is already discussed in the literature [62, 63], and new works were recently published on this point: distribution of organics in blood and brain [64], necrosis affecting factors [65], solvation effect on medical preparation uptake [66], etc. [67, 68].

Thus the LFE principle, primarily suggested for generalizing data on the effect of solvent properties on the rate of reactions in solutions or spectral characteristics of solutes, became universal, and linear, multiparameter LFE equations makes possible quantitative consideration of solvent or solute property effect on their behavior in all processes proceeding with (or in) the liquid phase.

REFERENCES

[1] Abe I., Hayashi K., and Kitagava M., *Bull. Chem. Soc. Japan*, 1980, vol. 53, p. 1199.

[2] Kamlet M.J., Doherty R.M., Abraham M.H., and Taft R.W., *Carbon*, 1985, vol. 23, p. 549.

[3] Abraham M.H. and Walsh D.P., *J. Chromatogr*, 1992, vol. 627, p. 294.

[4] Abraham M.H., Du C.M., Gate J.W., McGill R.A., and Shuely W.J., *J. Chem. Soc., Chem. Commun.*, p. 1863.

[5] Hanai P. and Hubert J., *J. Chromatogr*, 1984, vol. 302, p. 95.

[6] Abboud J.L.M., Taft R.W., and Kamlet M.J., *J. Chem. Soc., Res. Synop.*, 1984, p. 98.

[7] Snyder L.R., *J. Chromatogr. Sci*, 1978, vol. 16, p. 223.

[8] Haki J.E. and Young A.M., *J. Liq. Chromatogr.*, 1984, vol. 7, p. 675.

[9] Sadek P.C., Carr P.W., and Doherty R.M., *Anal. Chem.*, 1985, vol. 57, p. 2971.

[10] Carr P.W., Doherty R.M., and Kamlet M.J., *Anal. Chem.*, 1986, vol. 58, p. 2674.

[11] Leahy D.E., Carr P.W., Pearlman R.S., Taft F.W., and Kamlet M.J., *Chromatographia*, 1986, vol. 21, p. 473.

[12] Abraham M.H. and McGowan J.C., *Chromatographia,* 1987, vol. 23, p. 243.

[13] Park J.H., Carr P.W., Abraham M.H., Taft R.W., Doherty R.M., and Kamlet M.J., *Chromatographia*, 1988, vol. 25, p. 373.

[14] Kamlet M.J., Abraham M.H., Carr P.W., Doherty R.M., and Taft R.W., *J. Chem. Soc., Perkin Trans. 2*, 1988, p. 2087.

[15] Won Yo Chong and Carr P.W., *Anal. Chem.*,1989, vol. 61, p. 1524.

[16] Jones J.J. and Rutan S.C., *Anal. Chem.*,1991, vol. 63, p. 1318.
[17] Roses M. and Bosch E., *Analyt. Chim. Acta*, 1993, vol. 274, p. 147.
[18] Abraham M.H., J.Andonian-Haftvan J., Whiting G.S., Leo A., and Taft R.W., *J. Chromatogr. A*, 1994, vol. 688, p. 125.
[19] Abraham M.H., Chadha H.S., and Leo A.J., *J. Chromatogr. A*, 1994, vol. 685, p. 203.
[20] Abraham M.H. and Roses V., *J. Phys. Org. Chem.*, 1994, vol. 7, p. 712.
[21] Siebert D.S., Poole C.F., and Abraham M.H., *Analyst*, 1996, vol. 121, p. 511.
[22] Tan L.C., Carr P.W., and Abraham M.H., *J. Chromatogr. A*, 1996, vol. 752, p. 1.
[23] Abraham M.H., Roses V., Pool C.F., and PoolS.K., *J. Phys. Org. Chem.*, 1997, vol. 10, p. 358.
[24] Buszewski B., Gadzala-Kopciuch R.M., and Markuszewski M., *Anal. Chem.*, 1997, vol. 69, p. 3277.
[25] Valko K., Plass M., and Bevan C., *J. Chromatogr. A*, 1998, vol. 797, p. 41.
[26] Abraham M.H., Whiting G.S., and Doherty R.M., *J. Chromatogr.*, 1991, vol. 587, p. 213.
[27] Abraham M.H., Whiting G.S., and Doherty R.M., *J. Chromatogr.*, 1991, vol. 587, p. 229.
[28] Abraham M.H., Hamerton I., and Rose J.B., *J. Chem. Soc., Perkin Trans. 2*, 1991, 1417.
[29] Polyuzhin I.P., Goncharova L.M., and Makitra R.G., *Dopov. NAN Ukraini*, vip. 5, p. 155.
[30] Whitby G.S., Evans A.B., and Pasternack D.S., *Trans. Faraday Soc.*, 1942, vol. 38, p. 269.
[31] Flory P.J., *J. Chem. Phys.*, 1945, vol. 13, p. 453.
[32] Hildebrand J.H., *Solutability of Non-Electrolytes.* Reinhold Publ., New York, 1936.
[33] Richards R.B., *Trans. Faraday Soc.*, 1946, vol. 42, p. 20.
[34] Rostler F.S., Rostler K.S., Morrison R.E., and White R.M., *Rubber Age*, 1946, vol. 59, p. 291.
[35] Rostler F.S. and White R.M., *Rubber Age*, 1947, vol. 61, p. 315.
[36] Scott R.L. and Magat M., *J. Polym. Sci.*, 1949, vol. 4, p. 555.
[37] Munster A., *Koll. Z.*, 1951, vol. 120, p. 141.
[38] Bristow G.M. and Watson W.F., *Trans. Faraday Soc.*, 1958, vol. 54, p.1731.
[39] Erredo L., *Macromolecules*, 1986, vol. 10, p. 1522.
[40] Jonquieres A., Roitand D., and Lochon P., *J. Appl. Polymer Sci.*, 1994, vol. 54, p. 1673.
[41] Aminabhavi T.M., Harogoppad S.B., Khinnavar R.S., and Balangi R.U., *JMS-Rev. Macromol. Phys.*, 1991, vol. 4, p. 433.
[42] Pirih Ya.N. and Makitra R.G., *Ukr. Khim. Zh.*, 1993, vol. 10, p. 1111.
[43] Makitra R.G., Pirih Ya.N., Vasyutin Ya.M., and Midyana G.G., *Ukr. Khim. Zh.*, 1999, vol. 65, p. 64.
[44] Makitra R.G., Pirih Ya.N., and Vasyutin Ya.M., *Ukr. Khim. Zh.*, 1995, vol. 61, p.64.
[45] Makitra R.G., Pirih Ya.N., Zaglad'ko E.A., Turovsky A.A., and Zaikov G.E., *Plastmassy*, 2001, iss. 3, p. 23. (Rus)
[46] Makitra R., Pyrih Ya., Sagladko E., Turovskiy A., and Zaikov G., *J. Appl. Polymer Sci.*, 2001, vol. 81, p. 3133.
[47] Makitra R.G. and Zaglad'ko E.A., *ZhFKh*, 2002, vol. 76, p. 1797. (Rus)

[48] Makitra R.G., Zaglad'ko E.A., Midyana G.G., and Protsailo L.V., *ZhFKh*, 2001, vol. 75, p. 2283. (Rus)

[49] Sanada Y. and HondaH., *Fuel*, 1966, vol. 45, p. 451.

[50] Szeliga J. and Marzek A., *Fuel*, 1983, vol. 63, p. 1229.

[51] Makitra R.G. and Pirih Ya.N., *Khimia Tverdogo Tela*, 1988, iss. 6, p. 41. (Rus)

[52] Makitra R.G. and Pirih Ya.N., *Khimia Tverdogo Tela*, 1992, iss. 6, p. 11. (Rus)

[53] Makitra R.G., Pirih Ya.N., and Vasyutin Ya.M., *Khimia Tverdogo Tela*, 1995, iss. 3, p. 3. (Rus)

[54] Green T.K., Kovac J., and Larsen I.W., *Fuel*, 1984, vol. 62, p. 935.

[55] Makitra R.G. and Pristanskaya R.E., *Khimia Tverdogo Tela*, 2001, iss. 5, p. 3. (Rus)

[56] Abraham M.H., Whiting G.S., and Doherty R.M., *Polymer*, 1992, vol. 33, p. 2162 (1992).

[57] Grate J.M., Klusty M., and McGill R.A., *Analyt. Chem.*, 1992, vol. 64, p. 610.

[58] Aida T., Fuku K., and Fuiji M., *Energy and Fuels*, 1991, vol. 5, p. 79.

[59] Makitra R.G., Yatchishin I.I., and Pyrih Ya.N., *Khim. Tekhnol. Vody*, 2001, vol. 23(2), p. 128. (Rus)

[60] Kamlet M.J., Doherty R.M., and Veish G.D., *Environ. Sci. Technol.*, 1986, vol. 20, p. 696.

[61] Kamlet M.J., Doherty R.M., and Taft R.W., *Environ. Sci. Technol.*, 1987, vol. 21, p. 149.

[62] Abraham M.H., *Pure Appl. Chem.*, 1993, vol. 65, p. 2503.

[63] Cramer C.J., Famini G.R., and Lowren A.H., *Ass. Chem. Res.*, 1993, vol. 26, p. 599.

[64] Chanda H.S., Abraham M.H., and Mitchell R.C., *Bioorg. Med. Chem. Letters*, 1994, vol. 4, p. 2511.

[65] Abraham M.H. and Rafols C., *J. Chem. Soc., Perkin Trans. 2*, 1995, p. 1843.

[66] Gatton J.F., Abraham M.H., and Bradlury M.W., *J. Pharm. Pharmacol.*, 1997, vol. 49, p. 1211.

[67] Alane G., Shaher M., and Nielsen G.D., *Archives Toxicol*, 1998, vol. 72, p. 125.

[68] Abraham M.H., Gola J.M.L., and Kumarsingh R., *J. Chromatogr.*, 2002, vol. 745, p. 1103.

[69] Hafkensheid T.L. and Tomlison E., *Int. J. Pharmaceut.*, 1983, vol. 17(1), p. 1.

In: Synthesis and Properties of Low- and High-Molecular Compounds ISBN 1-59454-716-5
Editor: Gennady E. Zaikov et al., pp. 233-275

Chapter 15

THE EXAMPLES OF HETERO-NANOPHASE KINETIC DESCRIPTION OF PHOTOCHEMICAL REACTIONS

Yu. A. Mikheev and V. G. Zaikov
N.M.Emanuel Institute of Biochemical Physics Russian Academy of Sciences,
4, Kosygin st., Moscow 119991, Russia

The results of kinetic regularity analysis of the model chain reaction of polymers with dibenzoyl peroxide testify about the possibility of considering the heteronanophase kinetic model to be the universal tool for description of chemical transformations, proceeding in NCPM inhomogeneous structural zones in the form of conjugated reaction chains.

Recently, high scientific potential of the heteronanophase model was also demonstrated on the examples of chain oxidative reactions of a series of polymers [1, 2]. It should be noted that the works [1, 2] characterize the beginning of qualitatively new stage in theoretical studies of the polymer oxidation chemical quality. At the present time, many groups of investigators actively work in the branch of polymer oxidation aimed at both solution of applied problems, associated with the control of properties and operation time of polymers, and development of the theory of appropriate chemical reactions. Publications in the literature on these directions are mainly based on kinetic models of liquid-phase homogeneous chain reactions, though works appear in increasing frequency, which indicate the growing dissatisfaction of traditional theoretical description of polymer oxidation processes.

The authors of the present paper understand that introduction of supramolecular heterophase models into the assembly of acknowledged scientific tools, designed for theoretical constructions, requires quite heavy work. However, they believe that this will happen sooner or later and that necessary books, devoted to development of new ideas, will be written in future. In this paper, we will not discuss the polymer oxidation. It should be noted only that presently the associated literature is intensively enriched with publications, containing results of new experimental studies, however, frequently explained on the basis of mutually exclusive postulates.

The paper is devoted to the photochemical heterophase model. The fruitfulness of this model has been already shown in the description of photochemically initiated chain reaction of dibenzoyl peroxide with CTA, PC, PS, and PA-548. Here, its action will be demonstrated on the examples of naphthalene sensitized transformations in glassy-like cellulose triacetate films and poly(methyl methacrylate) chain reaction, proceeding in glassy-like films with participation of photolyzing free macroradicals.

1. A Heterophase Supramolecular Model of the Photochemical Transformation of Naphthalene in Cellulose Triacetate

Regularities of naphthalene (N) photochemical transformation in glassy-like CTA films were studied [3 – 5] simultaneously with the regularities of sensitized polymeric chains. Hence, kinetic features were found which cannot be explained, basing on homogeneous reaction models. In fact, for the first time, the idea of necessary accounting for the heterophase distribution of reaction acts in the matrix of non-crystalline polymer appeared in these works [3 – 5].

It was found that this process was initiated by excited triplet molecules (N^T) and the process of this type was decelerated as the naphthalene concentration increased. The concentration effect revealed was explained with the use of a simplified scheme which suggested that chemical transformations occur with the participation of N^T molecules in structurally isolated zones of the matrix favorable for effecting sensitization events. The same chemically active N^T molecules act as energy donors for unexcited naphthalene molecules occurring in matrix zones unsuitable for sensitization.

The realization of radiation-free *T-T* transition of excitation energy between naphthalene molecules occurring in inhomogeneous nanoscale zones leads to the fact that this aromatic compound acts not only as a sensitizer of the process but also as a quencher of reactive N^T molecules.

Recently, more full kinetic description of naphthalene sensitized transformations was made [6] owing to the accumulated experience on heterophase simulation of complex chemical processes.

1.1. Experimental

The polymer (CTA, $M = 3.3\times10^5$, acetate number 62.5) films 6 - 20 μm in thickness were prepared from a polymer and naphthalene solution in methylene chloride by casting the solution onto the surface of silicate glass and evaporating the solvent. After removal of the solvent, the films were dewetted with water to detach from the glass, and dried in a vacuum for 24 h.

Film samples were placed in a quartz cell, which allowed experiments to be run in vacuum (≈ 0.1 Pa), air, or argon under temperature-controlled conditions. A DRSh-500 high-pressure mercury lamp was used as a light source.

Naphthalene dissolved in CTA films was excited with filtered light that was not absorbable by the polymer ($\nu < 33{,}000$ cm^{-1}, $\lambda > 300$ nm). The spectral characteristics of the light filters used are given in Figure 1b. In this spectral range, the optical density (D) of naphthalene in the films did not exceed 0.1, thus providing uniform absorption of light along the path length. Phototransformation was monitored by following changes in the UV absorption spectra (Figures 1 and 2). (The spectra were recorded with a Specord UV-VIS instrument).

The intensity of UV radiation was determined with the ferrioxalate technique. The relative quantum yields of naphthalene conversion $\gamma_{N,0}$ were calculated from the initial portions of the rate curves. Naphthalene luminescence spectra in CTA films were recorded with a Jobin and Ivon (France) spectro-fluorimeter. The fluorescence decay kinetics was measured on a pulse fluorometer at flash lamp pulse duration of 3 ns. The phosphorescence decay kinetics was measured in the single-photon counting mode using a Nokia (model LP-4050) multichannel pulse analyzer.

The number of scissions of macromolecules n was determined viscometrically in a methylene chloride: methanol solvent mixture (94:6). Calculations were performed according to the equations $[\eta] = 0.016M^{0.76}$ and $n = \dfrac{M_0 - M_t}{M_t}$. Preliminarily, it was found that the polydispersity index of macromolecules ($\dfrac{M_w}{M_n} \approx 1.2$) remained almost unchanged in the course of photosensitized CTA degradation. The value of n was determined by dissolving several samples irradiated for the same period of time. The relative quantum yield of polymer chain scission $\gamma_{n.0}$ was calculated as the ratio of the number of scissions at the beginning of the reaction to the initial concentration of N ($[N]_0$).

The procedure of determining the rate of mechanical damage of the films under the photosensitization of polymer chain scission was also used. The rate of this damage was found from durability isotherms characterizing polymer films in a certain interval of mechanical stress σ (kg/mm^2). Film samples (width of 5 mm and length between the clamps of 22 mm) were loaded in a device with a figure lever, which maintained a constant throughout a run, while measuring the time τ(s) passed before breaking [7]. The loaded samples were irradiated with UV-radiation in a flow-through, fused-silica Dewar vessel in temperature-controlled streams of dry air or oxygen-free nitrogen.

1.2. Phenomenology of the Process

Figures 1 and 2 show changes in the UV absorption spectra of CTA films containing naphthalene at a concentration of 1.4 (Figure 1), 0.1, and 2.9% (Figure 2) under UV radiation with $\lambda > 300$ nm ($\nu < 33{,}000$ cm^{-1}) at room temperature (Figure 1a, Figure 2) and at 91 °C (Figure 1b). The formation of products absorbing the light in the UV spectral region up to $\lambda \sim 380$ nm is observed in all cases. Isosbestic points (crossing points of spectral lines) characteristic of this process are retained up to deep conversion steps. This indicates that the products accumulated do not vary in composition in the course of the reaction.

Taking into account the specific features of variation in absorption spectra in Figures 1 and 2, it may be concluded that two types of products are formed in the reaction. One (A) absorbs light relatively intensely in the region of $\nu = 40{,}000 - 27{,}000$ cm^{-1}. Another (B) shows insignificant absorption in this region. The mixture of compounds A and B is thermally stable, as the heating of CTA films with the products within 3 h at 90°C does not alter their

UV absorption spectra. However, product A is photolyzed by light at $\lambda > 320$ nm ($\nu < 31{,}300$ cm^{-1}), the photodegradation in the presence of air occurring more rapidly than in a vacuum; compounds with insignificant light absorption at $\lambda > 260$ nm ($\nu < 38{,}000$ cm^{-1}) are produced in both cases.

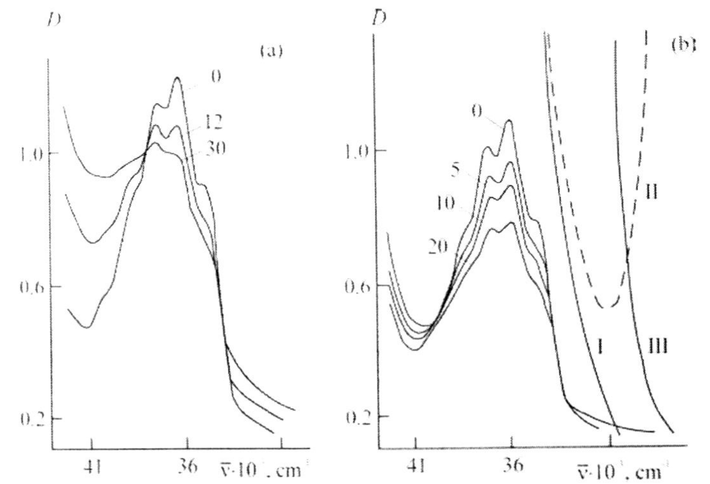

Figure 1. Effect of temperature in transformation of naphthalene UV absorption ($[N]_0 = 1.4\%$) upon photolysis of naphthalene in evacuated films with UV-radiation of $\lambda > 300$ nm (radiation intensity at 313 nm is 1.5×10^{17} cm^{-2}s^{-1}): a – 19°C (film thickness of 15 μm); b – 91°C (film thickness of 13.5 μm). I, II, III – absorption spectra of the light filters used. The Arabic numerals on the curves indicate radiation time in minutes

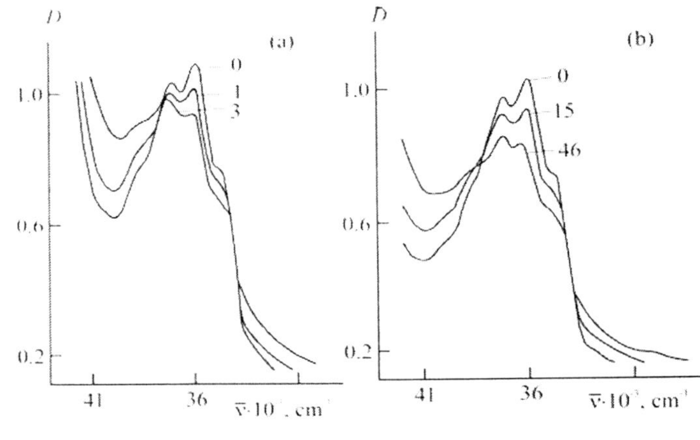

Figure 2. Transformation of naphthalene UV absorption upon its photolysis in evacuated CTA films at different concentrations (T = 17°C, light of $\lambda > 300$ nm, radiation intensity at 313 nm is 1.5×10^{17} cm^{-2}s^{-1}): *a* – $[N]_0 = 0.1\%$ (film thickness of 165 μ); *b* – $[N]_0 = 2.9\%$ (film thickness of 6.5 μm). The Arabic numerals on the curves indicate irradiation time in minutes

It was found [1] that naphthalene phototransformation products were not extractable from the films with methanol, whereas original naphthalene is readily washed out even from 200-μm thick films. The reprecipitation of the polymer with the photolysis products after removal of residual naphthalene with methanol (solvent CH_2Cl_2, and 2 : 1 methanol : water mixture as a precipitating agent) showed that the phototransformation products are attached to macromolecules.

The shape of the absorption spectrum for the products accumulated at different temperatures and different initial naphthalene concentrations remains almost the same in the region of $\lambda > 260$ nm. The absorbance ratio found from this spectrum was taken as a conversion factor for constructing naphthalene consumption rate curves. Typical rate curves for the consumption of N and the buildup of UV-radiation-absorbing products (A) obtained upon radiation of samples in a vacuum ($\lambda > 300$ nm) at different initial concentrations of N are shown in Figure 3.

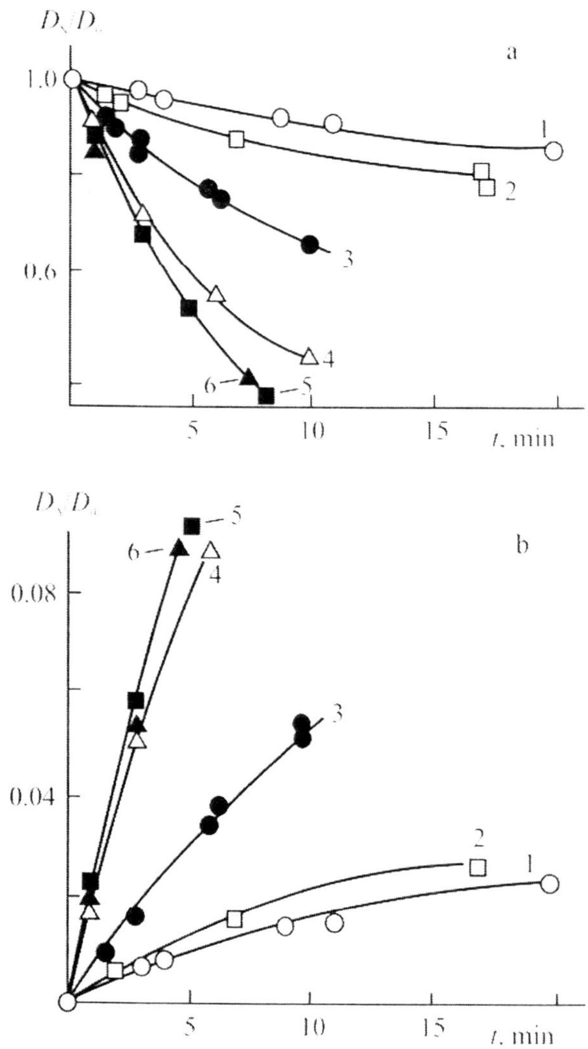

Figure 3. Rate curves for (a) the consumption of naphthalene and (b) formation of product A during the photochemical process in evacuated CTA films at 20°C. D_0 and D_N are the initial and current optical density of naphthalene, respectively, and D_A is that of the product. Naphthalene concentration: (*1*) 1.9, (*2*) 1.0, (*3*) 0.5, (*4*) 0.2, (*5*) 0.1, and (*6*) 0.05% [3]

$$\frac{D(36{,}100\ \mathrm{cm}^{-1})}{D(31{,}250\ \mathrm{cm}^{-1})} = 3.5$$

It turned out that temperature almost does not affect the naphthalene consumption rate but decreases the buildup rate of product A. The apparent activation energy for the formation of A calculated from the initial portions of the rate curves has a negative value (–21 kJ/mol).

In addition, for evacuated samples, it was found that the initial rate of phototransformation of N and the buildup rate of product A depend on the spectral composition of light incident on a sample. For example, in the case of irradiation of a CTA film containing 0.5% naphthalene through interference light filter II (Figure 1b, light at $\lambda >$ 340 nm does not fall on the sample), the quantum yield of naphthalene conversion is 0.3×10^{-2}. At the same time, when filter I (Figure 1b) was used, the quantum yield of naphthalene conversion was 1.2×10^{-2} (the quantum yield was calculated as the ratio of the number of molecules of N reacted to the number of light quanta absorbed by naphthalene in the spectral region limited by filters I and III, Figure 1b). It should be pointed out that filter I transmits light not only in the region of naphthalene absorption but also ten times more intense long-wavelength light with $\lambda >$ 340 nm that is not absorbed by naphthalene and cut by filter III.

The presence of the long-wavelength UV radiation also results in the enhancement of the initial rate of product A formation (by a factor ~2). The influence of long-wavelength UV-radiation was confirmed with the samples containing 0.5% N using two light sources (DRSh-500 mercury lamps with light filters), of which one produced light at $\lambda >$ 290 nm and the other at $\lambda >$ 340 nm. The rate of consumption of N upon simultaneous radiation of samples in vacuum was ~1.5 times as high as that in the case of the single light source with $\lambda >$ 290 nm. Under the same conditions, the formation rate of product A was noticeably higher.

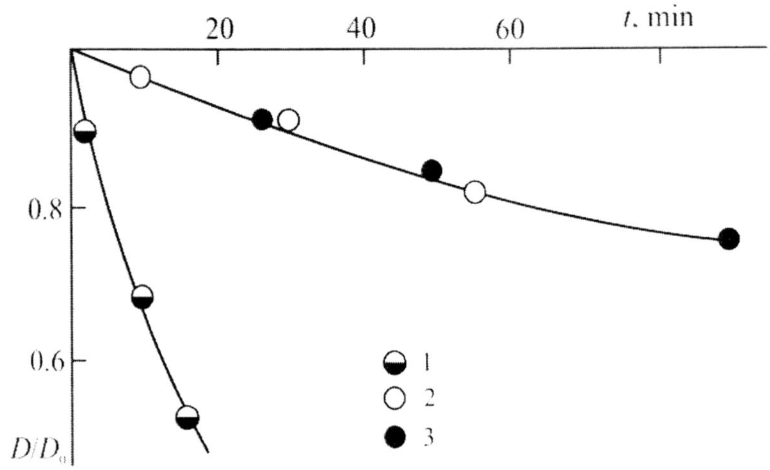

Figure 4. Rate curves for naphthalene consumption in CTA films in (1) a vacuum, (2) air, and (3) xenon at an identical radiation intensity. The initial naphthalene concentration was 0.5% [3]

In the presence of ambient oxygen, the rates of photochemical conversion of N (Figure 4) and the formation of product A, as well as the accumulation of polymer chain scissions [3, 4], considerably (approximately by a factor 10) decrease. The effect of long-wavelength light at λ

> 340 nm is completely eliminated in this case. The inert gas xenon acts in a manner similar to oxygen (an ampoule with the film was filled with xenon up to a pressure of 1 atm after preliminary evacuation) (Figure 4).

Figure 2 depicts isotherms of the mechanical breaking of films (plotted in the $\lg\tau - \sigma$ coordinates) under the conditions of photosensitization (λ > 300 nm, radiation intensity is 5×10^{17} quantum/cm^{2}s) being in air (isotherm *1*) and in a nitrogen atmosphere (isotherm *2*). Both isotherms have rectilinear portions described by the equation

$$\lg\tau = \lg A - \alpha\sigma.$$

Both straight lines have identical coefficients α but differ in coefficients A. The latter corresponds to durability obtained by extrapolation of the linear parts of the isotherms to the axis of ordinates (in these experiments, the $1/A$ value was taken as the rate of structural-mechanical damage of the samples and the relative quantum yield of damage γ_d was determined as the ratio $1/A[N]_0$). Figure 2 shows that the process of structural-mechanical damage is strongly retarded in the presence of air.

It is known that air oxygen effectively quenches the phosphorescence of triplet naphthalene N^T in solid polymers and does not quench the fluorescence of naphthalene molecules [8]. Xenon also deactivates N^T in solid solutions [9]. Hence, it follows that the primary active species in CTA films is excited triplet N^T. This conclusion was confirmed in studying the luminescence of N in CTA films [3]. It turned out that oxygen did not affect the fluorescence of naphthalene molecules. The characteristic fluorescence decay time in the film was invariably 95 ± 5 ns in air or in vacuum over the naphthalene concentration range of 0.025 - 6.7%.

The same films exhibited intense phosphorescence in vacuum; however, the phosphorescence is absent in air because of the high rate of deactivation of N^T. Thus it may be concluded that the photoexcited state of naphthalene reacting with the polymer is a triplet state.

For this photochemical reaction, the presence of a quite characteristic feature should be noted in this case. In fact, an increase in concentration of N in evacuated films from 0.2 to 2% leads to an equal six-fold decrease in the initial relative quantum yields of naphthalene conversion $\gamma_{N,0}$, polymer chain scission γ_n, and structural-mechanical damage γ_d of films under mechanical stress (Figure 5, curves *1* - *3*). The concentration quenching of these processes is described by the empirical equation

$$\gamma_i = \frac{const_{i1}}{(const_{i2} + \mathrm{const}_{i3}[N]_0)}.$$

A similar phenomenon is observed in air-aerated films in which the photochemical process occurs at a much slower rate than in a vacuum (Figure 5, curve 4, 5).

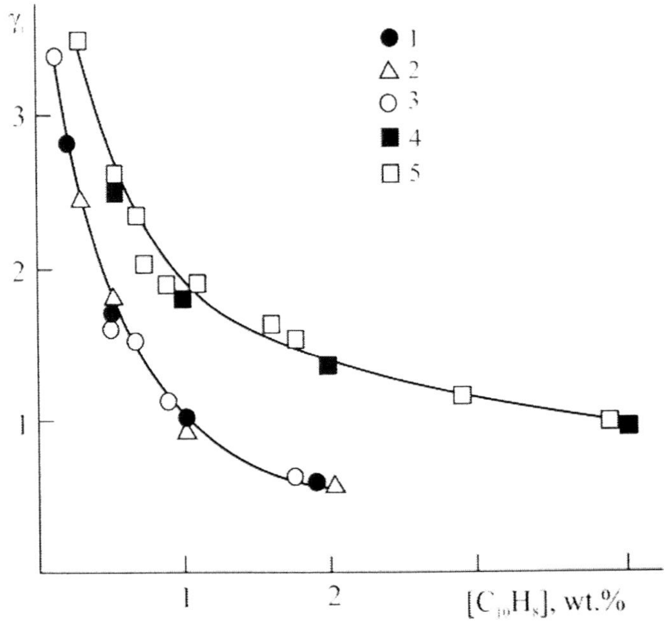

Figure 5. Effect of naphthalene concentration on the relative quantum yields (1 - 3) $\gamma_{N,0}$, $\gamma_{n,0}$, and γ_d in deaerated films and (4, 5) $\gamma_{n.0}$ and γ_d in air-aerated CTA films. Curves 1 - 3 are normalized to the values of $[N]_0 = 1\%$; curves 4 and 5 are displaced to coincide with one another but are not normalized to curves 1 - 3 [5]

At the same time, despite the retardation of the reaction with increasing $[N]_0$, the characteristic phosphorescence decay time varies insignificantly: it remains constant at the level of 1.8 s in the naphthalene concentration range 0.025 - 0.5% or 1.6 and 1.3 s at concentrations of 1 and 2%, respectively.

The experimental results discussed above indicate the dual role of excited triplet N^T. Triplet naphthalene molecules responsible for phosphorescence completely undergo quenching by the action of oxygen, whereas N^T molecules responsible for the sensitization of chemical events are only partly deactivated by oxygen and xenon (although considerably retarded, phototransformation still occurs at a significantly high rate). In addition, the concentration inhibition of the photochemical process has no relation to the characteristic time and naphthalene phosphorescence intensity.

A change in the durability of CTA films containing naphthalene at different UV radiation intensities showed that the rate of structural-mechanical damage in air is directly proportional to the radiation intensity. At the same time, in a nitrogen atmosphere (at an invariable value of α), a quadratic-law dependence of structural-mechanical damage on the UV radiation intensity is observed. A quadratic-law dependence on the UV radiation intensity was also established for the rate of the sensitized scission of macromolecules in evacuated unloaded films [5].

1.3. Kinetic Scheme of Phototransformation

Such features as the quadratic-law dependence of the scission rate of macromolecules on the UV radiation intensity, the effect of additional long-wavelength light on the rate of naphthalene conversion and buildup of product A in evacuated CTA films, and the disappearance of these specific features in the presence of oxygen, at first glance, may be associated with the fact that the active photoexcited state of naphthalene results from the absorption of the second light quantum by the triplet species N^T. It is this assumption that was advanced by Batekha *et al.* [10], who observed an increase in the rate of scission of PMMA macromolecules effected by long wavelength light nonabsorbable by naphthalene.

However, these features of the reaction in evacuated CTA films are displayed simultaneously with the directly proportional dependence of the naphthalene conversion rate and the formation of UV-absorbing product A. This fact makes it possible to rule out the involvement of the doubly excited triplet state of N. To the authors' point of view, it is necessary to take into account, in this case, the secondary photochemical reactions of free radicals produced in the reaction of N^T with CTA macromolecules.

All these relationships can be explained using the heterophase kinetic scheme of the reaction. According to this scheme, the concentration retardation of the photoprocess is due to the quenching of active species N^T by unexcited naphthalene molecules. This is possible in the only case, if sensitization acts proceed in the *s*-zones suitable for this purpose (supernanopore zones, the part of which in the polymer is low), i.e. with participation of N_s^T molecules. At the same time, the acts of phosphorescence and its extinguishing by oxygen proceed in *v*-zones unsuitable for sensitization (incapacious nanopore zones), i.e. with participation of N_v^T molecules. The part of *v*-nanopores in the polymer is high; they accumulate the main amount of additive molecules.

The photo-induced process has the maximum initial rate and occurs at room temperature up to a high conversion degree. This suggests a significantly high rate of exchange with naphthalene molecules between the zones. A simplified supramolecular scheme of an anaerobic photoreaction includes the following steps.

Exchange with naphthalene molecules between *v*- and *s*-zones

$$N_v \leftrightarrow N_s.$$

It is assumed that corresponded equilibrium is not disturbed by the reaction, and thus the following relations are applicable:

$$[N_s] = \alpha[N_v] = \frac{\alpha N}{1+\alpha} \approx \alpha N,$$

$$[N_v] = \frac{[N]}{1+\alpha} \approx N,$$

where parameter α characterizes the low part of molecules N_s: $\alpha << 1$.

Naphthalene molecule excitation to T_v state and further irradiative and radiationless deactivation of excited molecules:

$\mathbf{N_v + h\nu \rightarrow N_v^S;}$

$\mathbf{N_v^S \rightarrow N_v + h\nu_{fluoresc.};}$

$\mathbf{N_v^S \rightsquigarrow N_v^T;}$

$N_v^T \rightarrow N_v + h\nu_{fluoresc.};$

$N_v^T \rightsquigarrow N_v$ (conversion to heat).

Naphthalene excitation to chemically active T_s state (in *s*-zones):

$$N_s + h\nu \rightsquigarrow \xrightarrow{k_{0,h\nu}} N_s^T,$$

where $k_{0,h\nu}$ (s^{-1}) = $2.3\gamma_T I_0 \varepsilon_N$ is the rate constant under the assumption of monochromatic light effect; γ_T is the quantum efficiency of T-states (mol/einstein); I_0 is the intensity of exciting monochromatic UV radiation sized (einstein/cm^{2}s); ε_N is the light absorption coefficient of naphthalene (l/mol·cm).

Active state deactivation by radiationless energy transfer:

$$N_s^T + N_v \xrightarrow{k_1} N_s + N_v^T.$$

Abstraction of an H atom from macromolecules and the formation of the pair hydronaphthyl radical – backbone macroradical:

$$N_s^T \xrightarrow{k_2'(PH_s)=k_2} \{^\bullet NH + P^\bullet\}_s.$$

where

$^\bullet NH \equiv$ 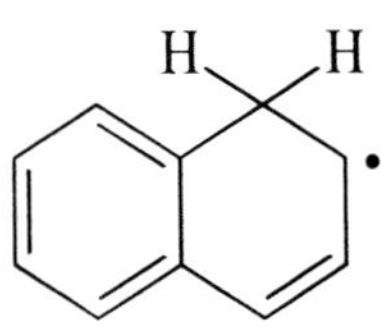

Primary radical pair transformations:

$$\{^\bullet NH + P^\bullet\}_s \xrightarrow{k_3} PNH$$

(recombination with product B_1 formation);

$$\{^\bullet NH + P^\bullet\}_s \xrightarrow{k_{4,h\nu}} \{^\bullet NH + P^{\bullet *}\}_s \rightarrow$$

$\rightarrow \{{}^{\bullet}NH + R^{\bullet}\}_s + n +$ products $\rightarrow$ RNH (B_2)

(photoexcitation of the middle radical $P_s^{\bullet}$ and further occurrence of macromolecule scission (n), end radical $R_s^{\bullet}$, and recombination product B_2. Here the constant $k_{4,hv} = 2.3\gamma_4 I_0 \varepsilon_4$; γ_4 and ε_4 are quantum efficiency of scissions and light absorption coefficient of macroradical, respectively); (absorption of long wavelength UV-radiation (ν_1, intensity I_1) by the hydronaphthyl radical [11] followed by opening of one of the rings in the hydronaphthyl radical yielding the radical pair $\{{}^{=}NH^{\bullet} + P^{\bullet}\}$ and recombinative conversion of this pair into unsaturated compound A_1; $k_{5,hv,1} = 2.3\gamma_A I_1 \varepsilon_{NH^{\bullet}}$ is the rate constant, assuming that the incident light is monochromatic).

$$\{{}^{\bullet}NH + P^{\bullet}\}_S \xrightarrow{k_{5,h\nu,1}} \{{}^{\bullet}NH^{*} + P^{\bullet}\}_S \longrightarrow$$

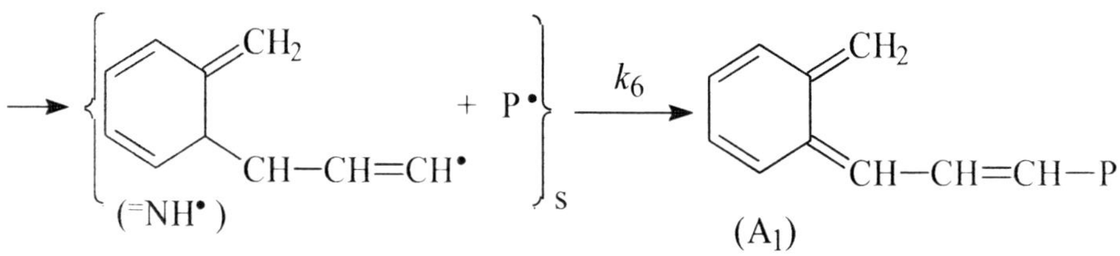

The enhancement of naphthalene conversion by the action of long wavelength UV-radiation (I_1) can be associated with the scavenging of N molecules by radical pairs:

$$\{{}^{=}NH^{\bullet} + P^{\bullet}\}_S + N_s \xrightarrow{k_7} \{{}^{\bullet}NNH + P^{\bullet}\}_S \rightarrow \text{HNNP } (A_2).$$

Applying the steady concentration condition to active particles in the current scheme and accounting for the inequality

$$k_3 > (k_{4,hv} + k_{5,hv,1}),$$

one can simply obtain expressions for initial rates of:

naphthalene consumption

$$w_{N,0} = \frac{d[N]}{dt} = \frac{k_2 k_{0,hv}[N]_0}{k_2 + k_1[N]_0}\left\{1 + \frac{k_7 k_{5,hv,1}}{k_3(k_6 + k_7 \alpha [N]_0)}\right\},$$

$$(\gamma_N \sim \frac{w_{N,0}}{[N]_0});$$

macromolecule scission:

$$w_{n,0} = \frac{ak_2 k_{4,h\nu} k_{0,h\nu} [N]_0}{(k_2 + k_1 [N]_0) k_3} \sim I_0^2,$$

$$(\gamma_n \sim \frac{w_{n,0}}{[N]_0});$$

accumulation of unsaturated products A_1, A_2:

$$w_{A,0} = \frac{ak_2 k_{5,h\nu,1} k_{0,h\nu} [N]_0}{(k_2 + k_1 [N]_0) k_3}.$$

These expressions explain the influence of the additional source of long wavelength UV-radiation on the naphthalene consumption rate and the rate of formation of products A (comprising A_1 and A_2), as well as the presence of the quadratic-law dependence of the macromolecule scission rate on UV radiation intensity in the spectral region of naphthalene absorption. The directly proportional relation of the initial rate $w_{N,0}$ and $w_{A,0}$ to I_0 must hold because of a rather large spectral gap between the long wavelength absorption bands of naphthalene and hydronaphthyl radicals $h\nu_1 < h\nu$.

This reduced scheme is consistent with the kinetic features of anaerobic phototransformation of naphthalene (a detailed scheme must cope with the fact that macromolecule scission events involve backbone radicals with free valence in the C_1 and C_4 positions of glucopyranose rings). In addition, it takes into account the sufficiently fast migration of initiator molecules in the glassy CTA matrix. The migration of naphthalene replenishes sensitizing molecules N_s and provides bimolecular deactivation of triplets N_s^T and grafting of naphthalene moieties to macromolecules.

When oxygen is present in the films, it oxidizes the radicals $^{\bullet}$NH and $^{=}$NH$^{\bullet}$, inhibiting the formation of products A and B. Oxygen also quenches the N_v^T states completely and the N_s^T states incompletely, probably because of the nonequivalence of the physical properties of these species occurring in different structural zones of the matrix.

1.4. Nonequivalent Properties of Dopant Molecules in Unequal Nanophases

According to the supramolecular scheme of the photoprocess considered above, dopant compounds occurring in unequal structural zones of a glassy polymer matrix acquire nonequivalent physical properties. This fact is clearly displayed by the different abilities of aromatic compounds to phosphoresce when they are introduced into glassy films in different manners, namely, from a common solution by evaporation of the volatile solvent (films 2) and by absorption of a dopant from the vapor phase (films 1). In this respect, experiments on photoexcitation of naphthalene, α-naphthol, and biphenyl phosphorescence in CTA and PMMA films placed in the inert gas CO_2 are very illustrative.

For example, when UV-radiation exciting aromatic molecules ($300 < \lambda < 385$ nm) is removed, films 2 prepared from a common polymer and dopant solution in methylene chloride exhibit visually detectable bright phosphorescence decaying within ~2 s. In contrast, absorption-doped glassy films 1 do not phosphoresce under identical conditions 2.

In addition, both types of the films also differ in the rate of photochemical conversion of naphthalene in air (λ > 300 nm, 22°C, naphthalene desorption during the photochemical reaction is negligible): the photoreaction rate in films 2 is much lower rather than in films 1.

The results discussed agree with the heterophase kinetic model of the processes proposed above. For example, phosphorescing triplets N^T are detected only in films 2 (the authors believe that they occur in tight nanopores and do not take part in sensitization of the photoprocess). In such airaerated films, the phototransformation rate is relatively low, but the process develops owing to exchange by naphthalene molecules between zones.

In films 1, as already noted, phosphorescence is not observed in the absence of oxygen; however, the rate of the photoprocess in air is high. It may be assumed that N molecules absorbed in these films are almost completely localized in zones with supernanopores (this assumption is supported by the fact that the rate of naphthalene desorption from films 1 is much higher rather than from films 2). The absence of phosphorescence indicates the existence of considerable structural hindrances in films 1 to naphthalene migration from *s*-zones to *v*-zones with tight nanopores. Meanwhile, films 2 are characterized by rather rapid naphthalene exchange between zones that provides for the occurrence of the photoprocess (but naphthalene desorption from these films has an extremely low rate).

The combination of these findings indicates that, when films are formed by the evaporation of a volatile solvent, the dissolved dopant affects the process of self-organization of the polymer chains into a supramolecular heterophase carcass-micelle system. It may be suggested that glassy films 2 differ from films 1 in their having perfect (less permeable) walls of the paracrystalline carcass and, simultaneously, higher dynamics of the units of spongy micelles in the *pc*-carcass cells.

The nonequivalence of the rate of photosensitized reactions in unequal nanophases of glassy polymers is confirmed by the results of naphthalene fluorescence quenching experiments. For example, it was shown in [12] that the fluorescence of excited singlet naphthalene molecules N^S in air-aerated PMMA films could be quenched by Tinuvin P, but this did not affect the naphthalene degradation rate. Naphthalene is consumed in a process whose rate is not determined by the concentration of species responsible for fluorescence. Under such conditions, primary chemical events are defined [12] as inevitable in character. However, in the absence of oxygen, Tinuvin P decelerates the photochemical process in accordance with a decrease in the concentration of N excited singlet molecules.

Based on their results, Kutsenova and Karpukhin [12] assumed that the inevitable reaction occurs in matrix cells with a specific structure. By varying oxygen concentration in the films, they found that oxygen did not take part immediately in the inevitable reaction event. However, the inevitable reaction was not detected in the absence of oxygen.

Turning to a consideration in terms of the hetero-nanophase model discussed above, the observed facts can be qualitatively rationalized as follows.

As in the case of CTA, the primary chemical events in PMMA films occur in supernanopores in which dopant molecules rest mostly on the walls in an adsorbed state. The adsorbed N_s^T molecules also sensitize chemical events in the presence of oxygen since they are deactivated by oxygen less effectively as compared to the N_v^T molecules (these occur in oxygen-saturated incapacious nanopore zones). The zones of tight nanopores accumulate the major amount of dopant compounds, and it is in these zones that the process of quenching of fluorescing naphthalene molecules N_v^S by Tinuvin P is realized.

Phosphorescing molecules N_v^T are produced from molecules N_v^S via the $S \rightarrow T$ conversion of electronic excitation energy and are rapidly deactivated in the presence of oxygen. For this reason, the deactivation of N_v^S molecules by Tinuvin P in air-aerated PMMA films does not affect the reaction sensitization rate. On the other hand, N_v^T molecules produced from N_v^S molecules in the absence of oxygen have a sufficiently long lifetime (1.7 s) and, as follows from the experimental data [12], are capable of transferring triplet excitation energy in the PMMA matrix via a non-radiative *T-T* pathway to naphthalene molecules occurring in supernanopores. For this reason, the quenching of fluorescing molecules N_v^S realized in the absence of oxygen inhibits the N_v^T yield and decelerates naphthalene photodegradation process.

To put it differently, in deaerated PMMA films, along with the excitation of N_s molecules by the absorption of UV-radiation, there is another, fairly effective excitation pathway associated with the nonradiative *T-T* energy transfer from tight nanopores to supernanopores. The reaction model considered for CTA samples does not account for the transfer of energy of electronic excitation in this direction; however, in the general case, based on the results obtained in [12], this possibility cannot be ruled out.

2. Kinetic Model of Poly(Methyl Methacrylate) Photochemical Degradation

2.1. The Modern State of Ideas about the Mechanism of PMMA Photolysis

Poly(methyl methacrylate) is the representative of acrylic polymers, widely applied in various branches of technology, medicine and household activities. Possessing good mechanical and optical properties, it has early become the target for investigations by photochemists. The studies of PMMA photochemical degradation were started 40 years ago and by now relatively sufficient amount of publications on this subject. Meanwhile, it should be ascertained that during last 40 years the total material related to this problem was not sufficiently generalized and was not completed by creation of a model of the basic direction in the photochemical process. It is clear now that the difficulty in constructing an adequate kinetic model of PMMA photolysis is definitely associated the absence of an information in the literature on the existence of supramolecular nanophases in NCPM systems and their role in chemical polymeric transformations.

The primary investigations have already indicated that UV-radiation absorption by PMMA esteric groups (the wavelength of light in the maximum of the absorption band is $\lambda_{max} = 214$ nm, $\varepsilon_{max} = 156$ l/mol·cm [13]) induces the decay of these groups to free radicals and is accompanied by macromolecular backbone breaks. Future transformations of free radicals lead to the formation of volatile products of the reaction: CO, CO_2, formic acid methyl ester ($HCOOCH_3$), methanol (CH_3OH), methane (CH_4), and H_2.

In the literature, much attention is paid to the problem of PMMA molecular mass variation during the photolysis process. It is found that variation of the polymer molecular mass at absorption of rather low doses of UV photons is stipulated by random macromolecular backbone scissions. Hence, at the initial stages of the phototransformation, intermolecular crosslinks are formed neither in the presence, nor in the absence of oxygen in the samples [14 – 19], and the rate of macromolecule break accumulation is constant which linearly depends upon the intensity of UV radiation. Experimental quantum efficiencies of macromolecular scissions, determined by different authors monochromatic light with $\lambda = 254$ nm), are significantly different: $\gamma_{n,air} = 2.3\times10^{-3}$ [14], $\gamma_n = 12\times10^{-3}$ [15], $\gamma_{n,air} = (13 - 18)\times10^{-3}$ and $\gamma_n = (22 - 40)\times10^{-3}$ [16], $\gamma_{n,air} = 3.2\times10^{-2}$ and $\gamma_n = 5\times10^{-2}$ [17, 18], $\gamma_{n,air} = 8.7\times10^{-3}$ and $\gamma_n = 4.8\times10^{-3}$ [19] (here $\gamma_{n,air}$ characterizes the photoprocess proceeding in the films in air, and γ_n in the absence of oxygen).

In later works [20, 21], relatively intense monochromatic UV-radiation at wavelengths $\lambda > 250$ nm in the spectrum region with extremely low PMMA extinction coefficients (below $\varepsilon_{254} = 0.37$ l/mol·cm [22]). The following values were found: $\gamma_{n,air} = 2.1\times10^{-4}$, 2.4×10^{-4}, and 4.1×10^{-4} for $\lambda = 260$, 280, and 300 nm [20], and $\gamma_n = 0.84\times10^{-4}$, 2.06×10^{-4}, 4.21×10^{-4}, 1.23×10^{-4}, 0, and 0 for $\lambda = 260$, 280, 300, 320, 400, and 500 nm [21], respectively. It should be said that PMMA samples [20, 21] were prepared from solution in acetone, which traces might remain in the samples. In conditions of UV-radiation, acetone traces may be a photosensibilizer responsible for the dependencies $\gamma_{n,air}(\lambda)$ and $\gamma_n(\lambda)$ mentioned above. These dependencies fall outside the region of the self UV-radiation absorption by the polymer and are characterized by λ_{max} at 300 nm and are identical in shape to the UV absorption band of acetone [23]. Meanwhile, the acetone-induced contribution of photosensitization into photolysis at the wavelength equal 260 nm must be minimal so that the mentioned quantum efficiencies for $\lambda = 260$ nm prove that that of macromolecule scissions at direct PMMA photolysis is much lower than 1.

Application of the ESR method demonstrated that end macroradicals ($\sim CH_2(CH_3)C^{\bullet}(COOCH_3) \equiv R^{\bullet}_{end}$), simultaneously, with photo-induced macromolecular backbone scissions are formed. The proportions of the backbone scissions and $R^{\bullet}_{end}$ radical formation were qualitatively compared [19]. It was found that in photolyzed polymer films, thoroughly purified from the monomer, the rate of $R^{\bullet}_{end}$ radical formation is, approximately, five times lower than the rate of macromolecule scissions.

It is common knowledge that at enough high temperature $R^{\bullet}_{end}$ radicals formed under photolysis conditions undergo depolymerization with extraction of the monomer molecules (MMA) [13, 24]. However, at room temperature (and in the range $T < 50°C$) MMA extraction process is practically absent under PMMA photolysis conditions [13, 24, 25]. At T_{room}, depolymerization is not also observed under conditions of PMMA macromolecule scission induction by ionizing radiation [26] and active free radicals $Cl^{\bullet}$ [27].

In the work [25], by using thoroughly purified polymer samples which macromolecules were labeled by radioactive carbon isotope C^{14} in four different positions:

$\sim CH_2C(CH_3)(C^{14}OOCCH_3)\sim$ (I),

$\sim CH_2C(CH_3)(COOCC^{14}H_3)\sim$ (II),

$\sim CH_2C^{14}(CH_3)(COOCCH_3)\sim$ (III),

$\sim CH_2C(C^{14}H_3)(COOCCH_3)\sim$ (IV),

the yields of photolysis (λ = 254 nm) gas products were studied. Hence, radioactivity of volatile reaction products was deteremined, accumulated during 50-hour radiation exposure of samples in quarts ampoules, evacuated to 10^{-4} mmHg (during that time the pressure in the ampoules increase to 6 - 7 mmHg), and in ampoules with nitric oxide at 10 mmHg pressure. Radioactivity of the initial PMMA and volatile products of photolysis was measured after their combustion to water and CO_2. The experimental results [25], for the sake of demonstrativeness converted per the primary radioactivity of the polymer, are shown in the Table below.

Relative radioactivity I/I_0 of gas products of PMMA photolysis by light with λ = 254 nm

Polymer	Polymer I_0, pulse/s·mmol CO_2	I/I_0 of gas reaction products	
		In vacuum	In NO, P = 40 mmHg
I	300	2.77	1.00
II	238	1.97	0.54
III	195	0.06	0.16
IV	312	0.05	0.11

As follows from the Table, PMMA photolysis in vacuum leads to concentrating of radioactive carbon in the volatile fraction in the cases, if C^{14} atoms participate in side esteric $COOCH_3$ groups. Vice versa, if C^{14} atoms are located in the macromolecular backbone or α-CH_3 groups (samples III and IV), the volatile products of photolysis are not practically radioactive compared with the combustion products of the initial labeled PMMA. This proves the utmost absence of depolymerization process and, simultaneously, indicates the main direction of photolysis which is $COOCH_3$ group decay.

The experimental results [25] allow, simultaneously, a conclusion about a clear slowing down of the process of PMMA esteric group degradation in the presence of nitric oxide. It is common knowledge that NO molecules possess unpaired electrons and, being the simplest stable radicals, are capable of accepting free radicals formed in photolysis. For this reason, in due course, nitric oxide was used for separation of the chain mechanism of photochemical reactions [23]. The Table clearly shows that in the experiments with nitric oxide the rate of $COOCH_3$ group decay is slowed down by 2.77 - 3.6 times versus the tests in vacuum. This fact proves the presence of the chain mechanism of photolysis of ester groups which degrade with participation of free radicals.

Data in the literature on the quantitative composition of volatile products of PMMA photolysis are ambiguous. For example, by the gas chromatography method [16], it was found that among volatile compounds methanol (γ(MeOH) = 0.48) and methyl formate ($\gamma(HCOOCH_3)$ = 0.14) dominated. Moreover, CO, CO_2, CH_4 and H_2 were also detected; their quantum yields were not measured. Note that in the work [16] a significant quantity of MMA was detected. Meanwhile, in view of the above-said, this fact could not be associated with the photolysis process. It shall be explained by the fact that for the purpose of releasing volatile reaction products, the authors heated photolyzed samples to 110°C. In the current case, depolymerization resulted from thermal impact on photolyzed PMMA.

In the work [24], by the mass-spectrometry method, volatile products of photolysis were studied. It was found that the effect of non-filtered light from a mercury lamp of middle pressure (DRSh-1000) induced a release of sufficient quantities of CO_2 and methyl formate. The formation of methyl formate as a main reaction product was also observed in [28].

To the authors' point of view, the observed noncompliance in the quantitative gas products of PMMA photolysis may reflect a structural-physical difference of the tested samples induced by particular methods of their preparation. For example, in the work [29], samples were prepared by the freeze-drying technique. For this purpose, a polymer solution in benzene was frozen first and then sublimated in vacuum from the frost state. The structure of dilatant samples obtained in this manner corresponds to microporous adsorbents and possesses well-developed system of supernanopores.

The gas chromatographic analysis of volatile products of photolysis of such samples [29] indicated the presence of CO, methyl formate and methanol in them in the 1 : 2 : 4 amount ratio, i.e. methanol represented the main product of $COOCH_3$ group decay. It is not improbable that unequal composition of the volatile products of photolysis is caused by a difference in the rates of competing secondary reactions of free methoxycarbonyl radicals, proceeding in nanopores which different in dynamics of the volume pulsations. For instance, as mentioned above, the dilatant samples prepared by the technique described [29] possess a large quantity of supernanopores (the supernanopore content may also be relatively high in the samples prepared from thermodynamically poor solvents). Photo-induced macromolecule scissions proceeding in supernanopores are capable of increasing the rate of internal stress relaxation and, by increasing frequencies and amplitudes of the volume pulsations of nanopores, may change the rate of chemical acts.

In accordance with the heteronanophase process model, the acts of photochemical breaks of macromolecular backbones must proceed directly in supernanopores (Section 1). This is proved by a result in [29] which indicates a relatively high yield of macromolecule breaks compared to results by other authors, namely, one break per 19 molecules of volatile compounds. Meanwhile, in the photolysis of film samples, the yield of macromolecule breaks is much lower than that of the volatile products [19, 30], giving the ratio 1 : 75 [19].

It should be said that the process of functional group degradation in PMMA was also studied [19] by IR-spectroscopy method; it was found that the quantum yield of $COOCH_3$ group decay approached 1 (which is close to the efficiency of CH_2 group consumption, whereas optical density of IR absorption bands of α-methyl groups is decreased very slowly). Hence, since the films used were relatively thick (10 - 15 μm), the change of optical density of the IR bands in the frequency range of 1,100 – 1,300 cm^{-1} was analyzed. These bands possess decreased intensity compared to the band at 1,730 cm^{-1} of ester C=O-groups. However, a kinetics recorded by these IR bands is somewhat distorted due to spectral agitations stipulated by the intermolecular interaction of neighbor ester groups.

Later on, the IR-spectroscopy method has been used in the study of photolysis of thin PMMA films (0.5 – 1.5 μm) [13] applied on NaCl plates. In these tests, ester group consumption kinetics was recorded by a band of C=O bond valence oscillations (1,730 cm^{-1}) up to high transformation degrees. The results in [13] allowed obtaining more precise value of the initial quantum yield of ester group degradation, found equal 0.5 for UV-radiation with λ =254 nm. Preliminarily, it was found that the half-width of the band 1,730 cm^{-1} ($\Delta\nu = 27 \pm 1$

cm^{-1}) was invariable during the photolysis; that is why the following formula may be used in calculations:

$$C = C_0 \frac{D_{1730}}{D_{0,1730}},$$

where C and C_0 are the concentrations of ester groups, current and initial, respectively; D and D_0 are corresponded optical densities.

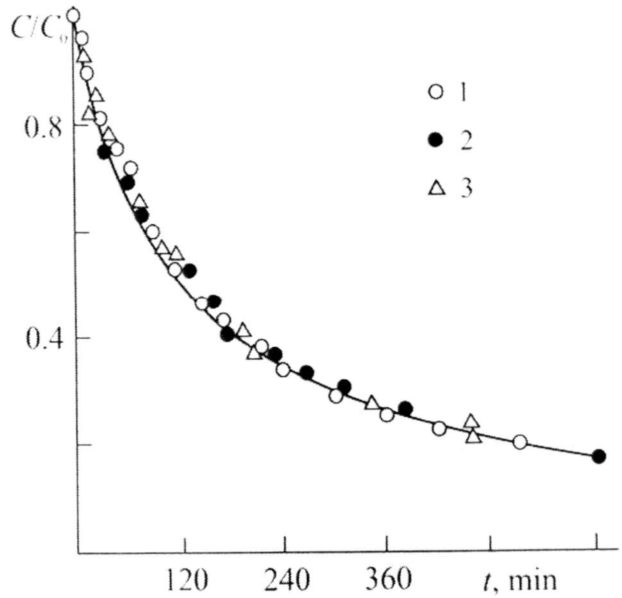

Figure 6. Kinetic curves of ester group photodecomposition for evacuated PMMA films absorbing non-filtered UV-radiation of intensity (*1*) $I_0 = 2.1\times10^{16}$ photon/cm^2·s, (*2*) $1.28\times10\ I_0$, (*3*) $3.7\ I_0$. (Source of light is middle-pressure Hg-lamp, DRSh-500, data of work [5])

The kinetic curves of ester group consumption, obtained [13] at three different UV radiation intensities of a high-pressure mercury lamp, are shown in Figure 6. These curves completely transform onto one another with respect to linear dependence of the reaction rate on UV-radiation intensity. The generalized curve in Figure 6 is calculated by the equation:

$$\frac{C}{C_0} = (1 + KC_0 t)^{-1}, \qquad (2.1)$$

typical of the second kinetic order reaction (here $KC_0 = 0.0083\ min^{-1}$). Clearly the curve complies well with the experimental points up to 80% transformation.

As mentioned above, the authors [19] have found approximately equal, high decay rate of side $COOCH_3$ and CH_2 groups, located in the backbones of PMMA macromolecules. This fact groups with extremely low rate of macromolecule breaks, thus it may be suggested that unsaturated C=C bonds ($P^=$ groups) located in middle parts of macromolecules will be the main polymeric product of the reaction. Actually, $P^{=}$ group formation was detected in [31]. They display an absorption band in the UV region with a maximum at λ_{max} = 195 – 200 nm (Figure 7) and high extinction parameter ε_{max} = 11,500 l/mol·cm. (A concentration of accumulated $P^{=}$ groups required for calculation of the extinction parameter was determined by the ozone treatment method. Ozone rapidly oxidizes unsaturated bonds that allows their quantitative analysis.)

The kinetics of $P^{=}$ group accumulation during photolysis of PMMA films was recorded [32] and then improved [13]. The experiments indicated that the initial rate of this process was directly proportional to UV radiation intensity, and the initial quantum yield of $P^{=}$ groups under radiation by a monochromatic light with the wavelength 254 nm equaled 0.5, i.e. the same as for $COOCH_3$ group decay. (Under radiation by filtered UV-radiation with λ > 280 nm, no absorption band of $P^{=}$ groups is observed.)

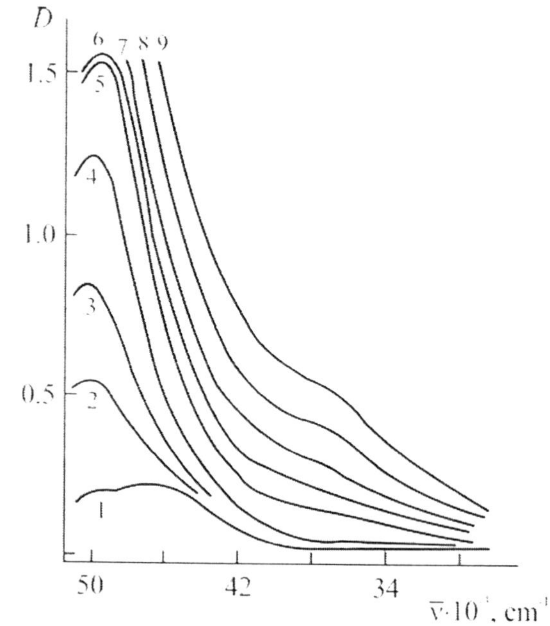

Figure 7. Evolution of UV absorption spectrum for evacuated PMMA films (1 μm thickness) absorbing non-filtered radiation of DRSh-500 lamp (intensity $I_0 = 2\times10^{16}$ photon/cm^2·s); irradiation time is (1) 0, (2) 12, (3) 25, (4) 60, (5) 300, (6) 510, (7) 920, (8) 1,060, (9) 1,560 s (data of work [22, 31])

Resorting to the spectra in Figure 7, one may observe that during an increase of $P^{=}$ group absorption band the maximum is gradually shifted towards the long wavelength region of the spectrum. This is caused by an instrumental artifact that is scattering of the short-wave UV component of a deuterium lamp on optical parts (prisms and mirrors) inside the spectrophotometer. The short-wave radiation scattered inside the device distorts a signal formed on a detector of monochromatic light flux, passed through the film under analysis. Taking this distortion into account with the help of a known technique, the author [13] gives specified values of λ_{max} = 196 nm and ε_{max} = 11,500 l/mol·cm. Later on, on a modernized instrument, it was found [33] that the absorption band maximum of $P^{=}$ groups accumulated at PMMA film photolysis was steadily located at λ_{max} = 195 nm.

Figure 7 also shows that PMMA photolysis is accompanied by an increase of optical density in the form of a structureless background in the frequency range of 50,000 – 30,000 cm^{-1} (200 - 330 nm). This effect is induced by a decrease of film transparency as a result of light scattering on voids formed in the films due to $COOCH_3$ group decaying and desorption of its volatile products from the films. A broad structureless band of $D(\lambda)$ dependence, induced by light scattering and called the 'turbidity spectrum' in the literature, usually corresponds to the following dependence:

$$D = const\,\lambda^{-n}$$

Or

$$\lg D = \lg const - n\lg\lambda.$$

Based on the value found (n = 3.7) and using the approach from [34], the author [13] estimates a diameter of voids formed as ≈ 80 nm. This result indicates that elementary voids generated during the photolysis ('holes' the volume of which equals volume of ester groups) are not homogeneously distributed in the matrix, but coalesce with one another. To put it differently, a 'free volume' injected photochemically is, in fact, incompatible with the polymer.

UV-radiation losses for scattering on the voids are summed up with those for absorption by accumulated photolysis products. Besides $P^{=}$ groups, macromolecular products of PMMA photolysis contain compounds with chromophoric groups located at the ends of macromolecules and consisting of conjugated C=C and C=O bonds: $\sim CH{=}C(CH_3)C({=}O)OCH_3$ (their absorption band possesses a maximum at λ = 214 - 217 nm), formed in much less amounts. Moreover, these products contain compounds with $\lambda_{max} \approx 280$ nm (which are probably macromolecular aldehydes). However, the rates of these products formation and the rate of turbidity spectrum intensification are much lower than that of $P^{=}$ group accumulation.

With respect to the above-said, the authors [13, 32] give a kinetic equation, describing $P^{=}$ group accumulation process with an approach of the limiting concentration:

$$[P^{=}] = [P^{=}]_{\infty}[1 - \exp(-kt)], \quad (2.2)$$

($[P^{=}]_{\infty}$ value improved in [13] equals 1.4 mol/l).

Figure 8 shows kinetic curves in semi-logarithmic coordinates, corresponded to linear anamorphoses of the equation (2.2):

$$\lg\frac{[P^{=}]_{\infty}}{[P^{=}]_{\infty} - [P^{=}]} = 0.434kt.$$

Clearly these plots represent straight lines, proving that the phenomenological equation (2.2) comply with the experimental points.

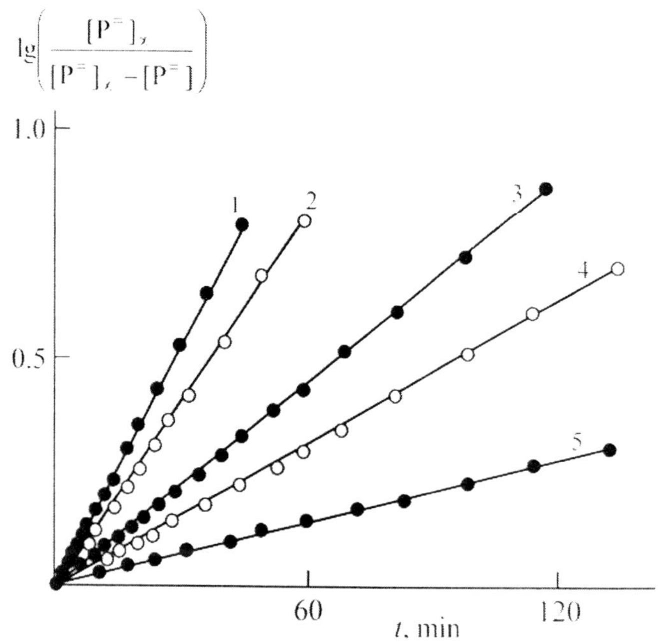

Figure 8. Kinetic curves of macromolecular C=C group accumulation plotted in semi-logarithmic coordinates for evacuated PMMA films (0.5 μm thick), absorbing non-filtered radiation of DRSh-500 lamp; radiation intensities are (*1*) $I_0 = 4.74\times10^{16}$ photon/cm^2·s, (*2*) 0.75 I_0, (*3*) 0.44 I_0, (*4*) 0.27 I_0, (*5*) 0.13 I_0

2.2. The Features of 'Free Volume' in the PMMA Matrix

During PMMA pyrolysis, $P^=$ groups are accumulated with simultaneous, continuous initiation of free radicals and with participation of these radicals in $COOCH_3$ group decay, which is testified by inhibition of this process in the presence of nitric oxide. Meanwhile, it is common knowledge that in reactions with free radicals compounds with unsaturated C=C bonds usually possess a high chemical activity. For example, the activation energy of alkyl radical reaction with liquid olefin molecules is, as a rule, below 5 kcal/mol, whereas that of hydrogen atom detachment from liquid hydrocarbons by alkyl radicals equals 8 - 10 kcal/mol [35]. Owing to the ability of accepting free radicals, compounds with C=C bonds are used as indicators of the chain mechanism of photolysis [23]. However, taking into account high limiting concentration $[P^=]_\infty = 1.4$ mol/kg, one may conclude that unsaturated macromolecular groups formed in photolysis of glassy PMMA films display rather low reactivity with free radicals.

The situation observed is of the more interest, because the 'free volume' shaped as elementary voids, cleared as a result of $COOCH_3$ group removal, is continuously generated during PMMA photolysis.

Remind that the molar volumes of PMMA monomeric units and $COOCH_3$ groups equal 85.6 and 42 cm^3/mol [36], respectively. This means that in the initial polymer ester groups occupy almost a half of the total volume. For this reason, ester group detachment and desorption of their degradation products into the gas phase in glassy films is accompanied by generation of a sufficient 'free volume'. The fact of void accumulation during PMMA photolysis, clearly detected by turbidity spectra observed, allows an assessment of the scientific consistency of the models widely used in the literature, based on the free volume idea.

If one bases on the idea that mechanical properties of non-crystalline polymers are defined by a part of free volume and, correspondingly, by the intensity of chain units' combinatorial exchange of positions, an increase of the part of the free volume in the polymer must be expressed in intensification of molecular-segmental mobility and pliability of the polymer to mechanical impacts. To put it differently, filling a highly-viscous system with void at preservation of combinatorial properties of the system must be expressed in viscosity decrease and plastic deformation rate increase.

According to positron annihilation measurements results, in initial glassy PMMA samples the free volume equals V_0 = 34.7 cm^3/kg [37], and the average radius of subnanopores (called holes in the literature) equals 0.27 nm [38]. $COOCH_3$ group has a similar average radius (0.255 nm), therefore, in the case of decaying of 1 mol/kg of $COOCH_3$ groups in PMMA sample, ≈ 1 mol/kg holes must occur in it. At uniform (combinatorial) distribution of these holes in the sample, total free volume would equal $V = V_0 + V_{h\nu} = 76.7$ cm^3/kg. If 80% of ester groups decay (that corresponds to the maximum degree of PMMA film photolysis in Figure 6), the free volume equal $V_{h\nu}$ = 8 mol/kg × 42 cm^3/mol = 256 cm^3/kg would be injected to the sample.

Thus if the material of non-crystalline polymer represented a highly-viscous liquid, a significant increase of plasticization effect, intensification of molecular-segmental mobility and, as a consequence, an increase of unsaturated $P^=$ group activity in relation to free radicals in the course of photolysis should be expected. Meanwhile, the variation in mechanical properties of PMMA films during photolysis indicates an increase of their friability. Simultaneously, kinetic curves shown in Figure 8 are described by the mono-exponential law (equation (2.2)) independently of the amount of $COOCH_3$ groups decayed; moreover, the limiting value $[P^=]_\infty$ = 1.4 mol/l approached in the reaction is preserved for a long time, despite the continuing degradation of ester groups and the void generation in the glassy film matrix.

The attention should also be paid to the fact that according to turbidity spectra, mean radii and volumes of voids stabilized in the polymer are much higher than those of elementary 'holes', remaining after ester group degradation. As mentioned above, the assessment of the void size [13] gave ≈ 80 nm (which gives the radius ≈ 40 nm). Using the calculation technique, specially developed for determination of void radii in PMMA [39, 40], for the turbidity spectrum index $n = 3.7$ an average radius of stabilized void inhomogeneity will give 14 nm. Thus the nanopore volume (11,500 nm^3) significantly exceeds the volume of the 'hole', formed after removal of one $COOCH_3$ group (0.07 nm^3). This fact unambiguously indicates that a void injected to PMMA is distributed inside the matrix non-uniformly. Clearly separate subnanopores, occurred at ester group decay, coalesce with one another, forming large pores. To put it differently, the 'free volume' generated in glassy PMMA is incompatible with the polymer and does not plasticize the inside material of *gs*-micelles. Apparently, the void coalescence in the system characterized by the supramolecular spongy organization of polymeric chains proceeds in the course of void extraction to the space between *gs*-micelles. Coalescence of nanovoids to larger voids also contributes into damaging of the carcass-micellar structure of glassy polymer, which is displayed by an increase of friability of photolyzed films.

The fact of free volume incompatibility with the polymer may be displayed visually, not using turbidity spectrum analysis. For this purpose, a PMMA film radiated by a sufficiently high UV dose, but preserved high optical transparency in the visible region of the spectrum, must be placed to an alcohol or heated in water up to ≈ 90°C, or heated dry up to 90 - 100°C. As treated so, the photolyzed film rapidly becomes white and nontransparent due to formation of rather large voids sized up to 1 μm in it (which is comparable to the wavelength of the visible light). Thus one can make a conclusion that special increase of molecular-segmental mobility by plasticization or heating of the films does not transform a system of stabilized voids to a system of homogeneously distributed free volume holes. Conversely, further coalescence of the void and increase of the pores happens in this case.

The described situation is not the unique one, typical of PMMA only. For example, a long exposure of transparent films from polyacrylic acid, as well as from copolymer of allylbarbituric acid and acrylic acid, in a solar radiation chamber at 70°C makes them nontransparent, eggshell [41]. In these cases, light scattering is increased due to quite high molecular-segmental mobility directly under photolysis conditions.

One should note that presently wide-spread models that use the idea of a free volume in polymers are, in fact, formulated not in the classical manner of the liquid-phase combinatorial (homogeneous) systems. The 'free volume' term often represents just a traditional vestige in explanations of results of the experiments, where really functioning voids are considered as the structured system property. For this reason, a special term of 'frozen in' free volume has been introduced (refer, for example, to [37]). As follows from the current book, this 'frozen in' free volume is physically corresponded to nanopores or supernanopores in the state of more or less active fluctuational pulsations.

2.3. Structure and Properties of Free Macroradicals Formed in PMMA Photolysis

Turning to the problem of PMMA photolysis mechanism, it should be said that by now the investigators of this process limit themselves with formal indications on monomolecular reactions of chemical bond photodissociation, proceeding in side $COOCH_3$ groups. Meanwhile, the fact of slowing down of ester group photo-degradation by nitric oxide, as well as a combination of kinetic monoexponential law of unsaturated $P^{=}$ groups' accumulation with the kinetic second order of consumption of ester groups testify about more complex mechanism of the process, in which an important role is played by light radical reactions with macromolecules and secondary photochemical reactions of free macroradicals.

The structure and properties of macroradicals formed in PMMA macromolecule reactions with active light radicals were studied well by the ESR method in [11, 42 – 46]; in this case, in [42 – 46] the radicals were generated with the help of photolyzing iron salts – chlorides and complex Fe(III) compounds. It was found that at 77 K three types of primary macroradicals were stabilized:

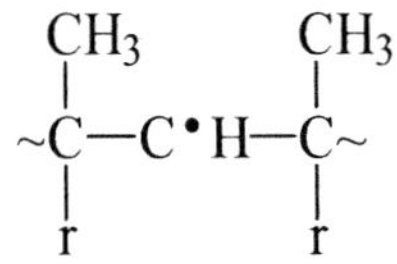 ($P_1^{\bullet}$) (here r≡COOCH$_3$); 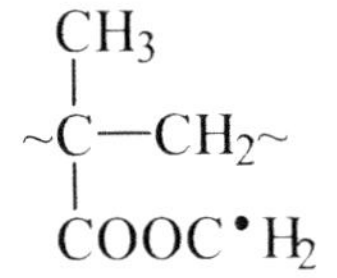 ($R_1^{\bullet}$);

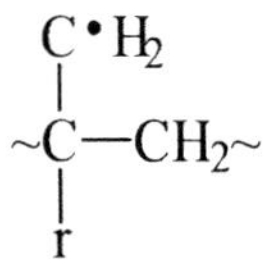 ($R_2^{\bullet}$).

These radicals differ in their photochemical properties and thermal stability. For example, radicals $R_2^{\bullet}$ are not highly sensitive to the impact of near UV and visible light regions of the wavelengths. Radicals $P_1^{\bullet}$ decay under the impact of UV-radiation in the range $\lambda < 300$ nm (the extinction parameter of $P_1^{\bullet}$ radicals at the wavelength $\lambda = 254$ nm equals 1,200 ± 300 l/mol·cm [11]):

$$P_1^{\bullet} + h\nu \rightarrow \sim CH{=}C(CH_3)\sim (P^{=}) + r^{\bullet}. \qquad (2.I)$$

Radicals $R_1^{\bullet}$ are photolyzed (at 77 K) by UV-radiation in the wavelength range of 340 – 390 nm (with the extinction parameter at $\lambda_{max} = 370$ nm equal $\varepsilon_{max} = 600$ l/mol·cm [11]):

$R_1^{\bullet} + h\nu \rightarrow \sim C(CH_3)(C^{\bullet}{=}O)\sim (P_2C^{\bullet}O) + H_2CO$ (the main reaction),

$R_1^{\bullet} + h\nu \rightarrow \sim C(CH_3)(CHO)\sim + HC^{\bullet}O$ (secondary reaction with low yield).

In their turn, $P_2C^{\bullet}O$ radicals are capable of decaying in the effect of light in a wide range of wavelengths ($\lambda < 650$ nm, $\varepsilon_{254} = 1{,}000$ l/mol·cm [11]), forming $P_2^{\bullet}$ macroradicals:

$$P_2C^{\bullet}O + h\nu \rightarrow P_2^{\bullet} (\sim CH_2C^{\bullet}(CH_3)CH_2\sim) + CO.$$

Note that the sequence of photochemical reactions

$$P_1^{\bullet} \rightarrow P_2C^{\bullet}O \rightarrow P_2^{\bullet}$$

was also demonstrated on PMMA samples, preliminarily treated by γ-radiolysis [47].

In a mixture of macroradicals stabilized in PMMA samples by monochromatic UV-radiation ($\lambda = 254$ nm, 77 K), radicals $P_1^{\bullet}$ are the most inactive in thermal reaction. More active $R_1^{\bullet}$ and $R_2^{\bullet}$ radicals are replaced by $P_1^{\bullet}$ at heating of photolyzed samples from 77 to 170 K; moreover, $P_1^{\bullet}$ radicals are thermally stable up to 240 K [11].

As mentioned above, in glassy PMMA films, the process of photochemical backbone break proceeds at a rate by 1.5 – 2 orders of magnitude lower than that of ester group decaying. It is found that this process may proceed by thermal decay of $P_1^{\bullet}$ and $P_2^{\bullet}$ radicals [11, 48]:

$$P_1^{\bullet} \rightarrow \sim CH{=}C(CH_3)(COOCH_3) + {}^{\bullet}CH_2C(CH_3)(COOCH_3)\sim (R_4^{\bullet}), \qquad (2.II)$$

$P_2^{\bullet} \rightarrow \sim CH_2(CH_3){=}CH_2 + C^{\bullet}(CH_3)(COOCH_3)CH_2\sim (R^{\bullet}_{end})$. (2.III)

The more so, in the matrix of powder-like PMMA samples, $P_1^{\bullet}$ radicals are capable of not only photochemical detachment of $COOCH_3$ groups, but also with some probability by thermal activation (at room temperature) [49].

Photolysis of glassy PMMA films by light with λ = 254 nm at room temperature is accompanied by accumulation of $R^{\bullet}_{end}$ radicals stable in the absence of oxygen. As already mentioned, the rate of their accumulation is, approximately, 5-fold below the total rate of macromolecule breaks [19]. This indicates proceeding of two reactions: (2.II) and (2.III).

The study of PMMA photolysis in liquid solutions using the spin trap method showed that contrary to block polymer, macromolecular backbone breaks mainly proceed by the reaction (2.II), whereas contribution of the reaction (2.III), most likely, is negligibly low [11, 50, 51].

It should be noted that the quantum yield of macromolecule breaks in glassy PMMA films is much lower, than at PMMA photolysis (λ = 254 nm) in liquid solutions. This was found in [52] using optically pure solvents: dioxane and methylene chloride, for which radiation absorption at λ = 254 nm was insignificant (PMMA concentration in solutions equaled 5 g/l). In these cases, quantum yields in the absence of oxygen equal: in dioxane γ_n = 0.145 – 0.188; in methylene chloride γ_n = 0.133 – 0.149.

Another important difference of photochemical reaction of PMMA in liquid solutions is that in this case, just an insignificant change in absorption spectra is observed [52], whereas photolysis of the films leads to growth of intensive absorption band of $P^{=}$ groups at λ_{max} = 195 nm. Since spectrally pure ethers are not self-absorptive in the spectrum region of λ > 200 nm [23], it may be concluded that in liquid solutions the break of macromolecules is the main result of PMMA photolysis, and $P^{=}$ groups are not formed. In this connection, the mechanism of $HCOOCH_3$ molecule detachment in the primary photochemical acts must be excluded from the consideration. This fact indicates that $P^{=}$ groups formed in the glassy films are the products of secondary transformations of macroradicals.

In accordance with the above-said, the mechanism of PMMA photolysis in liquid solutions can be presented by the following scheme:

$PH + h\nu \rightarrow \sim C(CH_3)(OCO^{*}CH_3)CH_2\sim \rightarrow \sim C(CH_3)(C^{\bullet}O)CH_2\sim + CH_3O^{\bullet}$,

$CH_3O^{\bullet}\ (HOCH_2^{\bullet}) + SH \rightarrow CH_3OH + S^{\bullet}$,

$\sim C(CH_3)(C^{\bullet}O)CH_2\sim \rightarrow \sim C(CH_3)(CHO)CH^{\bullet}\sim \rightarrow R_4^{\bullet}$ (polymeric chain break),

$\sim C(CH_3)(C^{\bullet}O)CH_2\sim + SH \rightarrow \sim C(CH_3)(CHO)CH_2\sim + S^{\bullet}$,

$R_4^{\bullet} + SH \rightarrow R_4H + S^{\bullet}$,

$2S^{\bullet} \rightarrow$ products.

2.4. Structure of Unsaturated Groups in Photolyzed PMMA Macromolecules

As follows from the material discussed above, the formation of unsaturated groups during photolysis of block PMMA samples (at room temperature) is induced by reactions of macromolecules with free radicals of decayed ester groups. Since methylene groups possess higher reactivity to free radicals than methyl ones, one may expect the dominance of $P_1^{\bullet}$ radical formation, and then $P^{=}$ group formation by the reaction (2.I).

The occurrence of unsaturated groups with different structure, namely:

$$\sim\underset{\underset{\displaystyle CH_2}{\|}}{C}CH_2\sim \quad (P_1^{=})$$

seems low-probable.

The corresponded process requires formation of a side $R_2^{\bullet}$ radical which then must undergo thermal or photochemical act with radical $r^{\bullet}$ detachment. However, it was mentioned above that $R_2^{\bullet}$ radicals did not practically absorb UV-radiation in this spectrum region and are intensively replaced by $P_1^{\bullet}$ radicals which decreases the probability of their photolysis with elimination of $r^{\bullet}$ radicals.

Formation of $P_1^{=}$ structures was suggested [13], for the benefit of which the occurrence of low-intensive IR-absorption band at 1,640 cm^{-1} during PMMA film photolysis was considered. This assumption was based on the fact that IR-bands of C=C bond valence oscillations in ethers displayed a remarkable property associated with the effect of alkyl substituting agents. In particular, in liquid olefins, possessing $P^{=}$ type groups, the absorption bands of C=C bonds usually possess a maximum at 1,670 cm^{-1}, whereas the bands of $P_1^{=}$ type structures are located at 1,640 cm^{-1}. Meanwhile, in the book [53] it is emphasized that such subdivision of frequencies is unacceptable for olefin compounds containing conjugated C=C and C=O bonds. Conjugation induces some agitation of C=C bond oscillation and their IR-band shift to 1,647 – 1,621 cm^{-1} frequencies, combined with a significant increase of IR-light absorption intensity. Similar shift of C=C bond IR-bands happens as a result of insignificant mechanical stresses in the atomic skeleton of the molecules [53].

Note that similar mechanical stresses are quite natural for polymeric chains participating in the *gs*-micelle structure. Moreover, at PMMA photolysis end C=C-C=O groups conjugated double bonds are formed.

Thus occurrence of a weak band in the range of 1,640 – 1,645 cm^{-1} in IR spectrum of photolyzed PMMA films may not be the basis for proving the $P_1^{=}$ structure.

At the same time, the $P^{=}$ structure is proved, for example, by the data [19] which show that optical density of the IR band, devoted to α-methyl groups (1,388 cm^{-1}), is decreased very slowly during photolysis, contrary to high rate of optical density decrease for CH_2 groups (1,465 and 2,948 cm^{-1}).

The direct proof of the structure of $P^{=}$ groups formed by the equation (2.I) was obtained with the help of ESR method [49] in the study of photogenerated C=C bond reaction with nitric dioxide. In this work, C=C bonds were accumulated up to maximal concentration 0.3 - 0.4 mol/kg, radiating a thin layer of thoroughly purified PMMA powder in a quartz ampoule with monochromatic UV-radiation (λ = 254 nm, T =293 K, photolysis duration 16 h) at continuous mixing. Powder-like samples were prepared by polymer precipitation by ethanol from solution in methylene chloride.

It has been found that C=C bond reaction with nitric dioxide results in formation of two kinds of nitroxyl radicals: dialkyl nitroxyls

$$R'–N(O^{\bullet})–R'',$$

where R' and R'' are alkyl groups with tertiary C atoms, and acylalkyl nitroxyls

$$R'–N(O^{\bullet})C(=O)–R''.$$

The studied kinetics of nytroxyls' accumulation testifies about the absence of the induction period and the presence of direct proportion between the initial rate of nitroxyl accumulation and NO_2 concentration in the polymer. Based on kinetic regularities of formation and structure of nitroxyls, the authors have made a conclusion that stable R'–N(O$^{\bullet}$)–R'' radicals are synthesized in 'cells', not requiring diffusion of macroradicals and intermediate macromolecular nitro-compounds. To put it differently, the appropriate reagents do not leave the nanopores.

The sequence of transformations proceeding is described by the following scheme:

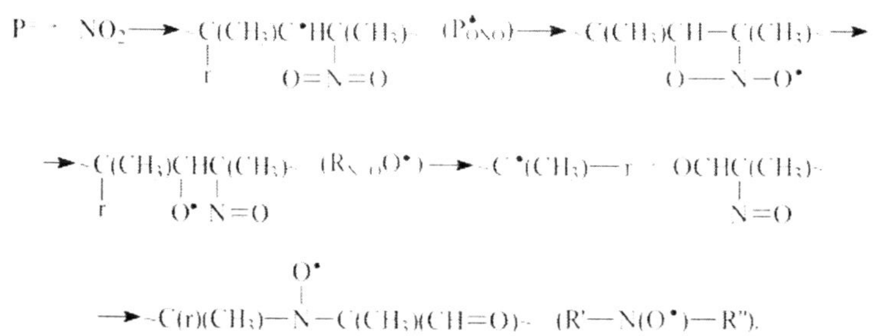

In [49], the authors suggest that for proceeding of such 'intracellular' reaction, the small-scale vibrational-rotational motions of reacting units of macromolecules (or to put it differently, motions of the units inside the fluctuationally pulsating nanopores) are sufficient.

The formation of acylalkyl nitroxyl radicals testifies about proceeding of thermal acts of $COOCH_3$ (r$^{\bullet}$) radical detachment in powder-like samples. The appropriate reactions are shown by the following scheme [49]:

$$P^{\bullet}_{ONO} + PH \rightarrow PH_{ONO} + P_1^{\bullet},$$
$$P_1^{\bullet}\ (P^{\bullet}_{ONO}) \rightarrow P^{=} + r^{\bullet},$$
$$r^{\bullet} + R_{N=O}OH \rightarrow \sim CH(OH)–C(CH_3)\sim\ (R'–N(O^{\bullet})C(=O)–R'').$$
$$|$$
$$O^{\bullet}–NCOOCH_3$$

As follows from the results obtained [49], if $P_1^{=}$ structures are present in the samples, their amounts are extremely low. Actually, $P_1^{=}$ groups must react with NO_2, forming iminoxyls >C=N–O$^{\bullet}$:

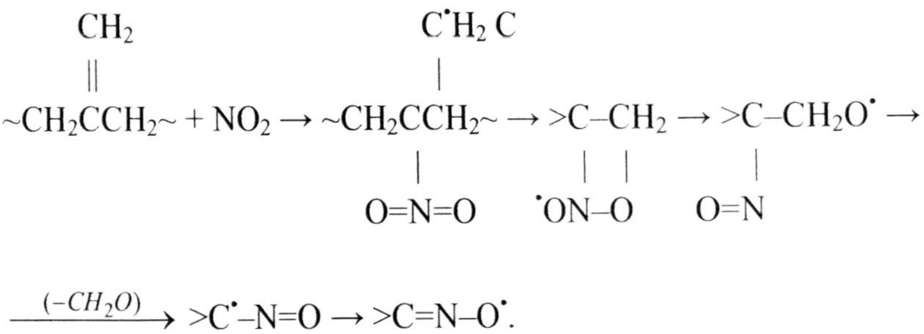

Iminoxyls differ from nitroxyls by typical ESR spectrum; however, they were not observed [49].

2.5. Structure of Free Radicals Stabilized at PMMA Photolysis in Nitric Oxide

Nitric oxide (NO) is the effective acceptor of free radicals [23] and decreases the rate of PMMA photolysis [25]. Having unpaired electrons, NO molecules add free radicals and, simultaneously, form nitroso-compounds, which also are traps for free radicals. This property was used [54] in the study of PMMA photolysis features by the ESR method. The study was performed with powder-like samples, prepared by polymer precipitation from solution in methylene chloride by ethanol.

It was found [54] that photolysis of such samples at 25°C by unfiltered UV-radiation from middle pressure mercury lamp (DRSh-1000) in the absence of O_2 and NO leads to the formation of $R^{\bullet}_{end}$ end radicals, possessing a typical nine-line ESR spectrum. Under the effect of gaseous nitric oxide (NO) on the samples with accumulated $R^{\bullet}_{end}$ radicals, the latter are terminated at a high rate. If the same samples are radiated by unfiltered light in NO atmosphere, ESR spectra display a signal belonged to acylalkyl nitroxyl radicals, whereas signals of other radicals are absent. However, if the samples are radiated through a light filter cutting off a part of short-wave radiation and transmitting UV-radiation with $\lambda > 260$ nm, then the ESR spectrum displays an additional signal belonged to iminoxyl radicals. As compared with acylalkyl nitroxyls, it is low intensive and is the most clearly detected by ESR method for the samples, dissolved in benzene.

ESR signal from acylalkyl nitroxyl radicals testifies about generation of free methoxy carbonyl radicals under PMMA photolysis conditions, which interact with nitric oxide dissolved in the polymer, having no time to decay and forming nitroso-compounds:

$$COOCH_3 + NO \rightarrow O{=}NCOOCH_3.$$

A low-molecular nitroso-compound migrates in a powder-like sample by the system of nanopores and interacts with macroradicals formed during photolysis. These radicals are $P_{2,1}^{\bullet}$

ones ($P_2^{\bullet}$ type), formed as a result of $P^{=}$ groups' interaction with migrating $^{\bullet}COOCH_3$ ($r^{\bullet}$) radicals:

$$P^{=} + r^{\bullet} \rightarrow \sim CHC^{\bullet}(CH_3)CH_2\sim \ (P_{2,1}^{\bullet}),$$

$$\qquad | \qquad COOCH_3$$

$$P_{2,1}^{\bullet} + O{=}NCOOCH_3 \rightarrow {>}CHC(CH_3)CH_2\sim \equiv R'{-}N(O^{\bullet})C({=}O){-}R''.$$

$$\qquad | \qquad O^{\bullet}{-}NCOOCH_3$$

Synthesis of iminoxyl radicals is explained as follows. As noted before, the maximum of UV-radiation absorption band of radicals $P_1^{\bullet}$ falls on $\lambda_{max} = 254$ nm [11]. That is why the use of a light filter cutting off the light with $\lambda < 260$ nm slows down the rate of radical $P_1^{\bullet}$ photo-decay, increasing their lifetime and the probability of interaction with nitric oxide:

$$P_1^{\bullet} + NO \rightarrow \sim CH(N{=}O)\sim \rightarrow {>}C{=}NOH.$$

Hence, an oxym formed reacts with light radicals then, transforming into an iminoxyl radical:

$$>C{=}NOH + r^{\bullet} \rightarrow {>}C{=}NO^{\bullet} + HCOOCH_3.$$

Thus the effect of UV-radiation spectral composition on radical stabilization in the presence of NO, detected before [54], proves the presence of intermediate photochemical reactions of $P_1^{\bullet}$ macroradicals (equation (2.I)).

Note also the results of recently published work, in which photochemical reactions with participation of free radicals are studied on PMMA samples, doped by a complex salt $(NH_4)_2Ce(NO_3)_6$ (cerium ammonium nitrate, CAN) [55]. This salt is demonstrative, because it combines the property of photoinitiator and the source of nitric oxides in itself. Samples containing CAN were prepared using aerosil with the specific surface of 300 m^2/g. First, CAN was applied from aqueous solution on the aerosil surface. Then modified aerosil was injected to PMMA (50 wt.%), mixing with 5% polymer solution in chloroform and evaporating the solvent. Weights (50 mg) of powder samples were placed to ampoules, designed for ESR spectra measurements, and radiated by filtered light ($\lambda > 280$ nm) of mercury lamp DRSh-500.

CAN salt displays an intense UV-radiation absorption band at $\lambda_{max} = 305$ nm and under conditions of the experiment decays giving free NO_3 radicals:

$$Ce^{4+}NO_3^{-} + h\nu \rightarrow Ce^{3+} + NO_3.$$

NO_3 radicals possess three light absorption bands in the range of 500 – 700 nm with high extinction coefficients and are able to dissociate by two pathways:

$$NO_3 + h\nu_1\ (\lambda < 570\ \text{nm}) \rightarrow NO_2 + O,$$

$NO_3 + h\nu_2$ (λ < 620 nm) → NO + O_2.

Thus CAN salt is the source of NO, NO_2 and O. Atomic oxygen is rather active in hydrogen detachment reactions, and thus formed $HO^{\bullet}$ radical is also capable of detaching hydrogen atoms from surrounding macromolecules.

Implementation of the above-enumerated photochemical acts in poly(methyl methacrylate) (T_{room}, vacuum ~ 10^{-3} mmHg) is combined with formation of dialkyl nitroxyl and acylalkyl nitroxyl macroradicals, clearly detected by the ESR method. In these tests, the mechanism of stable radical synthesis includes intermediate stages of $P_1^{\bullet}$ radical formation by hydrogen atom detachment from the most unstable C-H bonds in methylene groups of macromolecules by oxygen atoms and hydroxyl radicals and the stages of $P_1^{\bullet}$ radical photolysis with methoxy carbonyl radicals' detachment (equation (2.I)). Groups $P^{=}$ formed by the reaction (2.I) then react with NO_2, producing dialkyl nitroxyls R'–N(O$^{\bullet}$)–R" by the above-shown scheme or add $^{\bullet}COOCH_3$ radicals, producing alkyl macroradicals $P_{2,1}^{\bullet}$. Further on, either the above-discussed reaction:

$P_{2,1}^{\bullet}$ + O=NCOOCH$_3$,

or acts:

$P_{2,1}^{\bullet}$ + NO → $P_{2,1}$–N=O,

$P_{2,1}$–N=O + $^{\bullet}COOCH_3$ → $P_{2,1}$–N(O$^{\bullet}$)COOCH$_3$,

providing formation of acylalkyl nitroxyl radicals, are performed.

2.6. The Effect of Internal Physical Structure of PMMA Samples on the Transformation Rate of Unsaturated and Ester Groups

In accordance with the previous results, $P^{=}$ groups accumulated (maximal concentration 0.4 mol/kg) during powder PMMA sample photolysis possess relatively high activity in reactions with free radicals $^{\bullet}COOCH_3$ and even with low-active radicals NO_2. Vice versa, $P^{=}$ groups formed during photolysis of optically transparent films differs by relatively low activity in reactions with free radicals and, as mentioned above, reach high stationary concentration $[P^{=}]_{\infty}$ = 1.4 mol/l. This can be explained by structural-mechanical differences of powder samples from transparent films.

Actually, the powder-like samples are dilatants, i.e. *gs*-micelles composing them are bulky stretched and fixed by a rigid *pc*-carcass. Groups $P^{=}$ stabilized in such *gs*-micelles under photolysis conditions obtain relatively high steric accessibility to free radicals and are capable of easy change of a conformation of their atomic skeleton in a reaction act. Vice versa, in optically transparent films $P^{=}$ groups are formed on the surface of incapacious nanopores, which sizes (and fluctuation dynamics) are strictly regulated by close packing of chains inside *gs*-micelles. In this case, relatively high density of the material in *gs*-micelles is fixed by a firm supramolecular *pc*-carcass of a glassy polymer. As mentioned above, the 'holes' injected during photochemical degradation of $COOCH_3$ groups are not superposed with the dense molecular-chain sponge, but are released from *gs*-micelles and form inter-micellar large voids. Hence, the average size of nanopores in *gs*-micelle nanophases does not change and unfavorable steric conditions for $P^{=}$ groups' reaction with free radicals are preserved, at least, till 80% transformation.

Remind that overcoming of steric barriers existing in incapacious nanopores and proceeding of $P^{=}$ groups' reaction with free radicals require highly intense volume pulsations of the nanopores. Such pulsations are infrequent events in *gs*-micelles of glassy films. This fact must be taken into account during development of the reaction scheme related to the main direction of photolysis of glassy PMMA films.

A photochemical degradation of the side ester groups (with simultaneous formation of C=C bonds on macromolecules) and kinetic sensitivity of the photoprocess to physical structure of the initial samples are typical not only of PMMA. Qualitatively similar pathways of changes in UV- and IR-spectra are also detected for films from poly(*n*-butyl methacrylate), poly(*tert*-butyl methacrylate) poly(*iso*-propyl methacrylate) and butyl methacrylate copolymer with methacrylic acid (5% COOH groups) [56]. It was found [56] that films of the mentioned copolymer prepared from solutions in thermodynamically good and poor solvents were significantly different in globule sizes, observed on electron micrographs. Such structural-physical difference leads to both unequal physicomechanical properties and unequal rates of photochemical degradation of ester groups. As a consequence, the films with small dense globules display lower rate of the photochemical reaction. This fact may be explained by the fact that denser samples with small globules-microreactors display reduced amounts of supernanopores and reduced probability of implementation of primary photodissociation acts of ester groups.

2.7. The Mechanism of Glassy Film Photolysis

As mentioned above, the ideas about the presence of only dissociation of photo-excited ester groups still dominate in the works, devoted to direct photolysis of PMMA, and secondary photochemical reactions of macroradicals are not taken into account. One more reason, why this is so, is that the effective quantum yield of $COOCH_3$ group dissociation does not exceed 1. However, this cannot be the proof of the non-chain mechanism of photochemical reaction. Actually, in the process of photolysis proceeds by a heterophase mechanism, i.e. in structurally inhomogeneous nanophases, primary photochemical acts of dissociation with free radical formation proceed most actively in supernanopore zones. The frequency of chemical bond dissociation acts with formation of free radicals in incapacious nanopores of *v*-zones must be extremely low; thus the rate of free valences termination will be equivalently low, too. In such a case, long kinetic chains may be realized in *v*-zones even if the effective quantum yield of the chain reaction products does not approach 1.

The heterophase kinetic scheme of PMMA photolysis, including transformations in *s*- and *v*-zones, is discussed in [57]. It neglects translation of free radicals from *s*- to *v*-zones suggesting the presence of practically invincible structural obstacles for light radical migration in this direction. Such situation is typical, for example, of glassy CTA films with absorbed naphthalene (refer to 1.4). At the same time, it is suggested that reverse migration of light radicals (from *v*- to *s*-zones) proceeds at a definite, though rather low rate and that such migration provides for linear termination of kinetic *v*-chains.

The Scheme of Reaction Chains in V-Zones

Firstly, the transformations proceeding in supernanopore zones shall be considered. In this connection, note that the average thickness of these zones in PMMA films is suggested to be ≈ 10 times lower than that of the films. Taking into account the local type of the process development in s-zones of *gs*-micelles, it is believed that the experimental quantum yields of macromolecular backbone breaks obtained (for example, $\gamma_n = 4.8\times10^{-3}$ [19]) are underestimated, because UV-radiation, really providing the breaks, is not absorbed by the whole thickness of the film, but in s-zones only. The same relates to quantum yields of end macroradicals ($R_{end}^{\bullet}$) accumulation.

Taking into account kinetic regularities of macromolecule breaks and accumulation of stabilized $R_{end}^{\bullet}$ radicals at a rate 5-fold slower than the total rates of macromolecule breaks [19], the following conclusions can be made:

1. Total photochemical process of macromolecule breaks includes two parallel pathways, one of which leads to formation of $R_{end}^{\bullet}$ radicals.
2. $R_{end}^{\bullet}$ radicals are accumulated at a constant rate during a long time since the very beginning of photolysis that testifies about a rapid approaching of a stationary concentration of all radicals, which are $R_{end}^{\bullet}$ predecessors.
3. Radical $R_{end}^{\bullet}$ formation acts indicate the facts of kinetic chains' termination and, simultaneously, the facts of macromolecule breaks with participation of intermediate $P_2^{\bullet}$ macroradicals (equation (2.III)). The latter only provide for some part in the total process of macromolecule breaks.
4. Parallel acts of macromolecule chain breaks, independent of $P_2^{\bullet}$ radicals (and not giving $R_{end}^{\bullet}$ radicals), must proceed by $P_1^{\bullet}$ macroradical dissociation (equation (2.II)).

The above-said can be adequately presented by the s-reaction scheme, shown below, in accordance with which primary acts of photodissociation of ester groups, proceeding in s-zones:

$$\text{i) } PH_s + h\nu \rightarrow \underset{\displaystyle {}^{*}O{=}COCH_3}{\underset{|}{\sim CH_2C(CH_3)_s\sim}}\ (PH_s^{*}) \xrightarrow{k'_{i,s}} \underset{\displaystyle O{=}C^{\bullet}}{\underset{|}{\sim CH_2C(CH_3)_s\sim}}\ (P_2C^{\bullet}O_s) +$$

$$+ CH_3O_s^{\bullet},$$

$$P_2C^{\bullet}O_s + PH_s \rightarrow P_2CH{=}O + P_{1,s}^{\bullet},$$
$$CH_3O_s^{\bullet} + PH_s \rightarrow CH_3OH + P_{1,s}^{\bullet},$$

$$\text{ii) } PH_s^{*} \xrightarrow{k''_{i,s}} \underset{\displaystyle HOC^{\bullet}OCH_3}{\underset{|}{\sim CH^{\bullet}C(CH_3)_s\sim}} \xrightarrow{(h\nu)} \underset{\displaystyle O{=}COCH_3}{\underset{|}{\sim CH^{\bullet}C(CH_3)\sim_s}}\ (P_{1,s}^{\bullet}) + H_s^{\bullet},$$

$$H_s^{\bullet} + PH_s \rightarrow H_2 + P_{1,s}^{\bullet},$$

$$\text{iii) } PH_s^* \xrightarrow{k'''_{i,3}} \sim CH^{\bullet}C(CH_3)_s\sim \rightarrow \sim CH^{\bullet}C(CH_3)_s\sim \;(P_{1,s}^{\bullet}) + CH_{3,s}^{\bullet},$$

$$\qquad\qquad | \qquad\qquad\qquad\qquad |$$

$$\qquad HOC^{\bullet}OCH_3 \qquad\qquad HOC{=}O$$

$$CH_{3,s}^{\bullet} + PH_s \rightarrow CH_4 + P_{1,s}^{\bullet},$$

lead to formation of middle radicals. Schematically, these acts can be presented as follows:

$$PH_s + h\nu \xrightarrow{k_{i,s}} 2P_{1,s}^{\bullet}.$$

Further transformations cause breaks of macromolecules:

$$P_{1,s}^{\bullet} \xrightarrow{k_{1,s}} \sim CH{=}C(CH_3)(COOCH_3) + {}^{\bullet}CH_2C(CH_3)(COOCH_3)\sim_s (R_{4,s}^{\bullet}),$$

kinetic chain propagation:

$$R_{4,s}^{\bullet} + PH_s \xrightarrow{k_{2,s}} R_4H + P_{1,s}^{\bullet},$$

and kinetic chain termination that proceeds by formation of $R_{1,s}^{\bullet}$ macroradicals and further transformations:

$$R_{4,s}^{\bullet} + PH_s \xrightarrow{k_{t,s}} R_4H + \sim C(CH_3)(COOCH_2^{\bullet})\sim_s (R_{1,s}^{\bullet}),$$

$$R_{1,s}^{\bullet}\ (+\ h\nu) \rightarrow P_2C^{\bullet}O + CH_2O,$$

$$P_2C^{\bullet}O \rightarrow P_2^{\bullet} + CO,$$

$$P_2^{\bullet} \rightarrow R_{end}^{\bullet} + \sim CH(CH_3){=}CH_2.$$

The current s-scheme supports an assumption that in *s*-zones $P_{1,s}^{\bullet}$ radicals mostly enter the thermal acts of polymeric chain break and allows composing a system of algebraic equations, using the steady state condition for free radicals:

$$\frac{d[P_{1,s}^{\bullet}]}{dt} = 2k_{i,s}C - k_{1,s}[P_{1,s}^{\bullet}] + k_{2,s}[R_{4,s}^{\bullet}]C = 0,$$

$$\frac{d[R_{4,s}^{\bullet}]}{dt} = k_{1,s}[P_{1,s}^{\bullet}] - k_{2,s}[R_{4,s}^{\bullet}] - k_{t,s}[R_{4,s}^{\bullet}]C = 0,$$

where C is the concentration of polymer monomeric units, equivalent to $COOCH_3$ group concentration. Solving these simultaneous equations, one can deduce the reaction rate balance equation for free radical initiation and termination:

$$2k_{i,s}C = k_{t,s}[R_{4,s}^{\bullet}]C;$$

quasi-stationary concentration:

$$[R_{4,s}^{\bullet}] = \frac{2k_{i,s}}{k_{t,s}};$$

and then express the rates for macromolecule breaks and end radical ($R_{end}^{\bullet}$) accumulation:

$$\frac{dn_s}{dt} = k_{1,s}[P_{1,s}^{\bullet}] + k_{t,s}[R_{4,s}^{\bullet}]C = \left(\frac{k_{1,s}(k_{2,s} + k_{t,s})}{k_{t,s}} + 1\right) \cdot 2k_{i,s}C, \tag{2.3}$$

$$\frac{d[R_{end}^{\bullet}]}{dt} = k_{t,s}[R_{4,s}^{\bullet}]C = 2k_{i,s}C.$$

Here, in accordance with the experiment, one can get

$$\frac{dn}{dt} > \frac{d[R_{end}^{\bullet}]}{dt}.$$

For rather thin films, the rate constant of $COOCH_3$ group photochemical dissociation, participating in these equations, equals

$$k_{i,s} = 2.3\, I_0 \gamma_{i,s} \varepsilon_{COOCH3}.$$

The equation (2.3) characterizes the local process of macromolecule breaks in s-zones, the material part of which in the samples equals α_s. The experimentally determined break rate, calculated per sample, equals

$$\frac{dn}{dt} = \alpha_s \frac{dn_s}{dt}.$$

The Scheme of Reaction Chains in V-Zones

Reactions in v-zones must begin with the primary acts of photochemical dissociation of $COOCH_3$ groups directly inside the v-zones, nanopores in which are highly incapacious and, consequently, the quantum yield is extremely low ($\gamma_{i,v} << \gamma_{i,s}$):

$$PH_v + h\nu \xrightarrow{k_{i,v}} 2P_1^{\bullet};$$

$$P_1^{\bullet} + h\nu_1 \xrightarrow{k_1} P^{=} + r^{\bullet};$$

$$r^{\bullet} + PH_v \xrightarrow{k_2} rH + P_1^{\bullet}$$

(H atom detachment from methyl group of a macromolecule);

$$r^{\bullet} + PH \xrightarrow{k_2'} r_1^{\bullet} + CO, CO_2$$

(free methoxy carbonyl dissociation inside a nanopore, for example, happening at its collision with an ester group of leading to formation of $^{\bullet}OCH_3$ or $^{\bullet}CH_3$ radicals, denoted by $r_1^{\bullet}$ in this scheme);

$$r_1^{\bullet} + PH \rightarrow r_1H + P_1^{\bullet};$$

$$P_1^{\bullet} + CO \rightarrow P_1C^{\bullet}O;$$

$$P_1C^{\bullet}O + PH \rightarrow P_1CH{=}O + P_1^{\bullet}$$

(these reactions explain low CO output compared with CH_3OH and formation of aldehyde groups, possessing a weak UV-radiation absorption band at 280 nm),

$$r^{\bullet} \xrightarrow{k_t} r_s^{\bullet}$$

(kinetic chain termination).

It is suggested that kinetic v-chains are terminated by $^{\bullet}COOCH_3$ radicals transition from *v*- to *s*-zones of *gs*-micelles. It is also assumed that small-size aggressive $^{\bullet}OCH_3$ and $^{\bullet}CH_3$ radicals interact with CH_2 groups of macromolecules so rapidly that their loss due to migration from *v*- to *s*-zones may be neglected.

Groups $P^{=}$ formed in kinetic *v*-chain propagation acts are completely inactive in reactions with free radicals, if they are located in incapacious nanopores. Proceeding of this reaction requires receiving of a high-power thermofluctuational pulse by a nanopore or $P^{=}$ group which will provide a series of pulsations in the increased volume. Corresponded structural-mechanical acts of reactivity modulation can be written down in the form of a reversible reaction scheme:

$$P^{=} \xrightarrow{k_f} P_f^{=},$$

$$P_f^{=} \xrightarrow{k_{-f}} P^{=},$$

believing that at the exchange of structural-mechanical states the equilibrium is not disturbed by a chemical reaction and the expression:

$$K_{e,f} = \frac{[P_f^{=}]}{[P^{=}]} = \frac{k_f}{k_{-f}}$$

determines the equilibrium constant between fluctuation-excited and unexcited states of $P^{=}$ groups (e.g. $[P_f^{=}] = K_{e,f}[P^{=}]$).

The fluctuation-excited $P_f^{=}$ groups differ from unexcited $P^{=}$ groups in the ability to add free radicals. Since light radicals are fast consumed in competing reactions with methylene groups of macromolecules, one may suggest that $P_f^{=}$ groups preferably react with macroradicals which have a free valence on side methylene groups ($R_2^{\bullet}$). Hence, reproduction of $R_2^{\bullet}$ radicals as a result of photochemical acts provides for proceeding of a chain reaction consuming $P_f^{=}$ groups. The appropriate transformations can be presented by the following scheme:

$$P_1^{\bullet} + h\nu \xrightarrow{k_3} \sim CH_2C(COOCH_3)(C^{\bullet}H_2)CH_2\sim \ (R_2^{\bullet}) \text{ (photoisomerization);}$$

$$R_2^{\bullet} + PH \xrightarrow{k_4} R_2H + P_1^{\bullet};$$

$$R_2^{\bullet} + P_f^{=} \xrightarrow{k_5} \sim CH(R_2)C^{\bullet}(CH_3)CH_2\sim \ (P_{2,1}^{\bullet});$$

$$P_{2,1}^{\bullet} + h\nu \xrightarrow{k_6} \sim C(COOCH_3)(C^{\bullet}H_2)CH_2\sim \ (R_2^{\bullet}) \text{ (photoisomerization [11]).}$$

The presented scheme of v-reactions enables to express the system of simultaneous algebraic equations with respect to the steady state of free radical concentration:

$$\frac{d[P_1^{\bullet}]}{dt} = 2k_{i,v}C - k_1[P_1^{\bullet}] + k_2[r^{\bullet}]C + k_2'[r^{\bullet}]C - k_3[P_1^{\bullet}] + k_4[R_2^{\bullet}]C = 0, \quad (2.4)$$

$$\frac{d[r^{\bullet}]}{dt} = k_1[P_1^{\bullet}] - k_2[r^{\bullet}]C - k_2'[r^{\bullet}]C - k_t[r^{\bullet}] = 0, \quad (2.5)$$

$$\frac{d[R_2^{\bullet}]}{dt} = k_3[P_1^{\bullet}] - k_4[R_2^{\bullet}]C - k_5[R_2^{\bullet}][P_f^{=}] + k_6[P_{2,1}^{\bullet}] = 0, \quad (2.6)$$

$$\frac{d[P_{2,1}^{\bullet}]}{dt} = k_5[R_2^{\bullet}][P_f^{=}] - k_6[P_{2,1}^{\bullet}] = 0. \quad (2.7)$$

Summing up these equations, the rate balance condition for reaction v-chain initiation and termination:

$$2k_{i,v}C = k_t[r^\bullet]$$

and concentration of free methoxy carbonyl radicals:

$$[r^\bullet] = \frac{2k_{i,v}C}{k_t}$$

are obtained. According to the present v-scheme, the rate of ester groups' consumption equals:

$$-\frac{dC}{dt} = 2k_{i,v}C + k_1[P_1^\bullet].$$

Neglecting the first summand in this expression by the condition of long reaction chains and accounting for the equation (2.5), the differential second order kinetic equation by ester groups is obtained:

$$-\frac{dC}{dt} = k_1[P_1^\bullet] = (k_2 + k'_2)[r^\bullet]C = \frac{(k_2 + k'_2)\cdot 2k_{i,v}C^2}{k_t} = ak_{i,v}C^2, \tag{2.8}$$

where $a = \dfrac{2(k_2 + k'_2)k_{i,v}}{k_t}$; $k_{i,v} = 2.3I_0\gamma_{i,v}\varepsilon_{COOCH3}$; $\gamma_{i,v} << \gamma_{i,s}$.

The $P^=$ group accumulation rate represents the difference between rates of their formation and consumption:

$$\frac{d[P^=]}{dt} = k_1[P_1^\bullet] - k_5[R_2^\bullet][P_f^=] = k_1[P_1^\bullet] - k_5[R_2^\bullet]K_{e,f}[P^=].$$

The value $[R_2^\bullet]$ present in this expression is determined from equations (2.6) and (2.7):

$$[R_2^\bullet] = \frac{k_3[P_1^\bullet]}{k_4C},$$

wherefrom it is obtained:

$$\frac{d[P^=]}{dt} = ak_{i,v}C^2 - \frac{k_5k_3[P_1^\bullet]K_{e,f}[P^=]}{k_4C} = ak_{i,v}C^2 - abk_{i,v}C[P^=], \tag{2.9.}$$

where $b = \dfrac{k_5 k_3 K_{e,f}}{k_4}$.

Equations (2.8) and (2.9) characterize the main direction of photochemical transformations, proceeding in *v*-zones of *gs*-micelles of glassy PMMA films. They correlate well with experimental kinetic laws of $COOCH_3$ group consumption and $P^=$ group accumulation. (Note that the accumulation rate of unsaturated C=C bonds in *s*-zones is by one and half or two orders of magnitude lower than in *v*-zones.) For example, in accordance with the theoretical presentations, initial rates of both macroscopic processes must be equal at the same direct proportionality with UV-radiation intensity:

$$-\left(\frac{dC}{dt}\right)_0 = \left(\frac{d[P^=]}{dt}\right)_0 = ak_{i,v}C^2.$$

This complies with the fact determined in [13]:

$$\gamma_{COOCH3} = \gamma_{C=C} = 0.5.$$

Moreover, as predicted in the theory, kinetic laws of both processes must be fundamentally different. If ester groups are consumed in accordance with the second order equation (equation (2.1) represents an integral form of equation (2.8)), then accumulation of $P^=$ groups in *v*-zones must be stopped, when the limiting concentration is reached long before complete consumption of the ester groups. If at a low dose of dissociated ester groups (i.e. when the consumption of ester groups can be neglected and their concentration is accepted constant) the limiting concentration of $P^=$ groups is obtained, the equation (2.9) is reduced to the following:

$$\frac{d[P^=]}{dt} = m(p - [P^=]),$$

where $m = abk_{i,v}C$ and $p = \dfrac{C}{b}$ are accepted to be constants.

By integrating the above expression the following exponential equation is obtained:

$$[P^=] = [P^=]_\infty[1 - \exp(-mt)], \quad (2.10)$$

where $[P^=]_\infty = p$.

The equation (2.10) completely reproduces the experimentally determined equation (2.2). Meanwhile, due to its approximation type, the latter may not describe the change of $P^=$ group concentration at high transformation levels. If description of the process at high doses of dissociated ester groups is required, two equations (2.8) and (2.9) must be solved simultaneously, for example, by one numerical procedure or another.

In liquid solutions, chemically active free radicals participate in the self-diffusion process, continuously and rapidly exchanging positions with the liquid molecules. As a result of such exchange, they interact more or less rapidly with the medium molecules and with one another, terminating in recombination or disproportionation. Under these conditions, the lifetime of free radicals can be basically determined by thermal reactions, which may significantly decrease the probability of radical reactions, induced by absorption of photons.

In contrast with the liquids, macromolecule units in the *gs*-micelle sponge do not participate in the combinatorial exchange of positions. For this reason, macroradicals located in nanopores of glassy polymers lose a significant part of their activity in thermal reactions. Before terminating in recombination or disproportionation acts, free valences must undergo more or less long-term migration in the sponge during numerous pulsations of nanopores. Two free valences recombine only when occur inside the same pulsating nanopore that requires specifically active pulsations and the sponge restructuring in the meeting zone of free valences. A low frequency of such structural-mechanical acts may significantly increase the probability of photochemical reactions of macroradicals even at their rather low concentrations [11, 58, 59].

The above considered hetero-nanophase model of PMMA photolysis enables to explain the reason for a noticeable inconsistency in quantum yields of macromolecular backbone breaks, cited in different publications. This may be a consequence of unequal conditions for forming the carcass-micellar structure, providing unequal material parts of the *s*-zones (α_s, equation (2.3)) in the tested samples. To put it differently, the mentioned feature may be associated with impossibility to reproduce the internal structure of the samples.

Non-reproducibility of the internal structure can be considered as a natural event in the world of polymers which accompanies the application of solvents with unequal thermodynamic quality and associates with unequal rates of solvent evaporation, unequal temperature and jelly formation (glass transition) rate of the samples. (In this connection, remind that the photolysis rate of butyl methacrylate copolymer with methacrylic acid is highly dependent on the solvent used for film preparation [56]). Meanwhile, the common methods of quantum yield determination in photochemical reactions are based upon the idea of the homogeneity of non-crystalline films and they do not take into account specific heterogeneity of the nanostructural scale and its sensitivity to the sample formation conditions.

Unequal conditions of PMMA sample formation are also sufficient for the value of residual internal stresses in *gs*-micelles, on which the size and frequencies of nanopore pulsations in *v*-zones of micelles depend. In their turn, unequal sizes and fluctuation dynamics of *v*-nanopores in different PMMA samples may change the ratio of rate constants k_2 and k_2' and, as a consequence, the yields of methyl formate in relation to methanol, methane, CO and CO_2, as it has been observed in works by different authors.

According to [13], the initial rate of photochemical accumulation of $P^=$ groups in PMMA films is independent of the presence of air and additives of sterically hindered phenols (4-methyl-2,6-di-*tert*-butylphenol and methylene-2,2'-bis-(4-methyl-6-*tert*-butylphenol)) in them, injected in 0.5% concentrations. These facts are inconsistent with slowing down of the process in the presence of nitric oxide; however, they display a simple explanation. The fact is that light radicals formed in PMMA photolysis in the presence of air in the films are oxidized giving free peroxyl radicals. The latter participate in the kinetic chain propagation, reacting with macromolecules:

$$r^{\bullet} + O_2 \rightarrow rOO^{\bullet},$$

$$rOO^{\bullet} + PH \rightarrow CH_3OC(O)OOH\ (rOOH) + P_1^{\bullet},$$

$$(CH_3O^{\bullet} \leftrightarrow HOC^{\bullet}H_2) + O_2 \rightarrow HOCH_2OO^{\bullet} \rightarrow HOC^{\bullet}HOOH \rightarrow HOCH{=}O + {}^{\bullet}OH,$$

$$CH_3 + O_2 \rightarrow CH_3OO^{\bullet} \rightarrow {}^{\bullet}CH_2OOH \rightarrow CH_2{=}O + {}^{\bullet}OH,$$

$$PH + {}^{\bullet}OH \rightarrow H_2O + P_1^{\bullet}.$$

Hence, kinetic chains are terminated by migration of the largest $rOO^{\bullet}$ radicals among mobile ones and highly reactive hydroxyls react with macromolecules. Thus at the initial stage of PMMA photooxidation, the mechanism of light radical participation in kinetic chain propagation is invariable, and the presence of oxygen in the films does not affect the initial rate of photo-induced dissociation of ester groups. At the highest stages of photolysis in the presence of air, concentration of $P^{=}$ groups does not yet equal to the limiting value 1.4 mol/l and decreases, passing through the lower maximum point [5]. The extreme character of $P^{=}$ group accumulation curves in the presence of air testifies about the oxidation rate increase for unsaturated C=C bonds during the process. This fact may be explained by occurrence of an additional source of free radicals which may be, for example, accumulated $CH_3OC(O)OOH$ hydroperoxide.

So far as concerns photolysis of the films with additives of sterically hindered phenols, it is common knowledge that phenols are capable of reacting with light radicals that leads to formation of free phenoxyls and σ-complexes. Both phenoxyls and σ-complexes possess high extinction parameters in the spectrum region at $\lambda < 400$ nm. As the UV photons are absorbed, these radicals transit to the electron-induced state and obtain a possibility to detach H atoms from macromolecules [11], forming $P_1^{\bullet}$ radicals.

Stable aromatic compounds are practically unable to initiate free radicals in v-zones (refer to Section 1), therefore, the formation rate of phenoxyls and radical σ-complexes in the experimental conditions [13] was only determined by the extremely low rate of primary photodissociation acts of ester groups. Not participating in initiation and termination acts, phenols transformed to transmitters of photodissociation kinetic chains of the ester groups.

In recently published review [60] devoted to photolysis of polyacrylates, traditional, developed long ago ideas on the mechanism of PMMA degradation in the full absence of any information about kinetic features of the main direction of PMMA photolysis are discussed. Meanwhile, currently described specific kinetic laws of conjugated processes of ester group consumption and $P^{=}$ group accumulation are of the fundamental importance for both practical application of PMMA and evaluation of a new kinetic model of the chain reactions. Clearly the new hetero-nanophase) model has displayed high scientific efficiency for the description of both thermal chain reactions and complex photochemical processes, thus giving an additional proof of the true value of the supramolecular carcass-micellar model of the non-crystalline phase of polymer, presented in this book.

REFERENCES

[1] Mikheev Yu.A., Guseva L.N., and Zaikov G.E., *Uspekhi Khimii*, 1997, vol. 66(1), 1 - 30. (Rus)

[2] Mikheev Yu.A. and Zaikov G.E., *Uspekhi Khimii*, 2000, vol. 69(3), pp. 249 - 282. (Rus); *Russian Chemical Reviews*, 2000, vol. 69(3), pp. 2312 - 260 (Engl. transl.)

[3] Guseva L.N., Mikheev Yu.A., and Toptygin D.Ya., *Izv. AN SSSR, Ser. Khim.*, 1974, No. 9, pp. 1988 - 1993. (Rus)

[4] Guseva L.N., Mikheev Yu.A., and Toptygin D.Ya., *Dokl. AN SSSR*, 1975, vol. 220(6), pp. 1356 - 1359. (Rus)

[5] Guseva L.N., Yu.A. Mikheev, Rogova L.S., and Toptygin D.Ya., *Dokl. AN SSSR*, 1975, vol. 224(5), pp. 1077 - 1080. (Rus)

[6] Mikheev Yu.A., Guseva L.N., and Zaikov G.E., *Vysokomol. Soed.*, 2002, vol. A44(5), pp. 758 - 767. (Rus); *Polymer Science, Ser.* A, 2002, vol. 44(5), pp. 454 - 462, (Engl. transl.)

[7] Mikheev Yu.A., Guseva L.N., Rogova L.S., and Toptygin D.Ya., *Polym. Photochem.*, 1982, vol. 2(6), pp. 457 - 474.

[8] Czarnecki St. and Kryszewski M., *J. Polym. Sci., Part A: Polym. Chem Ed.*, 1963, vol. 1(10), pp. 3067 - 3077.

[9] Siegel S. and Judeikis H.S., *J. Chem. Phys.*, 1968, vol. 48(4), pp. 1613 - 1619.

[10] Batekha I.G., Shekk Yu.B., Krysanov S.A., and Alfimov M.V., *Dokl. AN SSSR*, 1971, vol. 197(3), pp. 614 - 617. (Rus)

[11] M. Ya. Melnikov, and V. A. Smirnov, *Photochemistry of Organic Radicals*, Moscow, Izd. Moskovskogo Universiteta, 1994. (Rus)

[12] Kutsenova A.V. and Karpukhin O.N., *Izv. AN SSSR, Ser. Khim.*, 1976, No. 6, pp. 1301 - 1306. (Rus)

[13] Popravko T.S., *PhD Thesis on Chemistry*, Moscow, IKhF AN SSSR, 1985. (Rus)

[14] Shultz A.R., *J. Phys. Chem.*, 1961, vol. 65(6), pp. 967 - 974.

[15] Charlsby A. and Thomas D.K., *Proc. Roy. Soc.*, 1962, vol. A269(1336), pp. 104 - 123.

[16] Fox R.B., Isaaks L.A., and Stokes S., *J. Polym. Sci.*, 1963, vol. A1(3), pp. 1079 - 1086.

[17] Gardner D.G. and Henry G.A., *J. Polym. Sci, Part B*, 1967, vol. 5(1), pp. 101 - 104.

[18] Gardner D.G. and Epstein L.M., *J.Chem. Phys.*, 1961, vol. 34(5), pp. 1653 - 1660.

[19] Shlyapintokh V.Ya. and Goldenberg V.I., *Eur. Polym J.*, 1974, vol. 10(8), pp. 679 - 684.

[20] Torikai A., Ohno M., and Fueki K., *J. Appl. Polym. Sci.*, 1990, vol. 41(5-6), pp. 1023 - 1032.

[21] Mitsuoka T., Torikai A., and Fueki K., *J. Appl. Polym. Sci.*, 1993, vol. 47(10), pp. 1027 - 1032.

[22] Warnock M. and Gardner D.G., *J. Appl. Polym. Sci.*, 1968, vol. 12(10), pp. 2325 - 2337.

[23] Calvert J. and Pitts J., *Photochemistry*, Moscow, Mir, 1968. (Rus)

[24] Yasina L.L. and Pudov V.S., *Vysokomol. Soed.*, 1973, vol. A15(6), pp. 1291 - 1296. (Rus)

[25] Frolova M.I., Nevskii L.V., and Ryabov A.V., *Vysokomol. Soed.*, 1961, vol. 3(6), pp. 877 - 881. (Rus)

[26] Todd A., *J. Polym. Sci.*, 1960, vol. 42(139), pp. 223 - 241.

[27] Mikheev Yu.A., Popravko T.S., Yasina L.L., and Toptygin D.Ya., *Vysokomol. Soed.*, 1973, vol. A15(11), pp. 2470 - 2476. (Rus)

[28] Gupta A., Liang R., Tsay F.D., and Moacanin J., *Macromolecules*, 1980, vol. 13(6), pp. 1696 - 1703.

[29] Allison J.T., *J. Polym. Sci.*, 1966, A-1, vol. 4(5), pp. 1209 - 1221.

[30] Gunder O.A., Vlasov V.G., Koval' A.I., and Krasovitskii B.M., *Plast. Massy*, 1968, No. 6, pp. 3 - 5. (Rus)

[31] Mikheev Yu.A., Popravko T.S., and Toptygin D.Ya., *Dokl. AN SSSR*, 1973, vol. 210(1), pp. 148 - 150. (Rus)

[32] Popravko T.S., Mikheev Yu.A., and Toptygin D.Ya., *Dokl. AN SSSR*, 1977, vol. 232(4), pp. 856 - 859. (Rus)

[33] Shirai M., Yamamoto T., and Tsunooka M., *Polym. Degrad. Stab.*, 1999, vol. 63(3), pp. 481 - 487.

[34] Heller W., Klevens H.B., and Oppenheimer H., *J. Chem. Phys.*, 1946, vol. 14(9), pp. 566 - 567.

[35] Semenov N.N., *On Some Problems of Chemical Kinetics and Reactivity (Free Radicals and Chain Reactions)*, Moscow, Izdat AN SSSR, 1958. (Rus)

[36] Van Krevelen D.W., *Properties of Polymers. Correlations With Chemical Structure*, Amsterdam, Elsevier, 1972.

[37] Van Krevelen D.W., *Properties and Structure of Polymers,* Moscow, Khimia, 1976. (Russ. transl.)

[38] Boersma A., Cangialosi D., and Ricken S.J., *Polym. Deg. Stab.*, 2003, vol. 79(3), pp. 427 - 438.

[39] Mohamed H.F.M., El-Sayed A.M.A., and Abd-Elsadek G.G., *Polym. Deg. Stab.*, 2001, vol. 71(1), pp. 93 - 97.

[40] Zhurkov S.N., Marikhin V.A., and Slutsker A.I., *Fizika Tverdogo Tela,* 1959, vol. 1(7), pp. 1159 - 1164. (Rus)

[41] Slutsker A.I. and Marikhin V.A., *Optika i Spekroskopia*, 1961, vol. 10(4), pp. 612 - 517. (Rus)

[42] Kargin V.A., Pis'menko I.V., and Cherneva E.P., *Vysokomol. Soed.*, 1968, vol. A10(4), pp. 846 - 858. (Rus)

[43] Pariyskii G.B., Davydov E.Ya., Zaitseva N.I., and Toptygin D.Ya., *Izv. AN SSSR, Ser. Khim.*, 1972, no. 2, pp. 281 - 289. (Rus)

[44] Pariyskii G.B., Davydov E.Ya., and Toptygin D.Ya., *Izv. AN SSSR, Ser. Khim.*, 1972, No. 10, pp. 2207 - 2212. (Rus)

[45] Pariyskii G.B., Davydov E. Ya., and Toptygin D.Ya., *Vysokomol. Soed.,* 1975, vol. A17(7), pp. 1504 - 1509. (Rus)

[46] Zaitseva N.I., Pokholok T.V., Pariyskii G.B., and Toptygin D.Ya., *Dokl. AN SSSR*, 1976, vol. 229(4), pp. 906 - 909. (Rus)

[47] Toptygin D.Ya., *DSc Thesis,* Kazan, Kaz. Gos. Politekh. Inst., 1977. (Rus)

[48] Tanaka M., Ioshida H., and Ichikawa T., *Polym. J.*, 1990, vol. 22(9), pp. 835 - 841.

[49] Zaitseva N.I., Pokholok T.V., Pariyskii G.B., and Toptygin D.Ya., *Kinetika i Kataliz*, 1984, vol. 25(4), pp. 799 - 807. (Rus)

[50] Pokholok T.V., Pariyskii G.B., and Bragina G.O., *Vysokomol. Soed.*, 1989, vol. A31(10), pp. 2049 - 2055. (Rus)

[51] Sohma J. and Tabata M., *Eur. Polym. J.*, 1980, vol. 16(7), pp. 587 - 588.
[52] Tabata M. and Sohma J., *Eur. Polym. J.*, 1980, vol. 16(7), pp. 589 - 595.
[53] Fox R.B. and Price T.R., *J. Appl. Polym. Sci.*, 1967, vol. 11(11), pp. 2373 - 2379.
[54] Bellami L., *Infrared Spectra of Complex Molecules*, Moscow, Inostrannaya Literatura, 1963. (Rus)
[55] Gaponova I.S., Pariyiskii G.B., and Toptygin D.Ya., *Vysokomol. Soed.*, 1988, vol. 30(2), pp. 262 - 268. (Rus)
[56] Davydov E.Ya., Gaponova I.S., and Pariyiskii G.B., *Vysokomol. Soed.*, 2003, vol. 45(4), pp. 585 - 587. (Rus); *Polymer Science*, 2003, vol. A45(4), pp. 346 - 351. (Engl. transl.)
[57] Kanevskaya E.A., Schepilov A.M., and Zubov P.I., *Vysokomol. Soed.*, 1970, vol. 12(9), pp. 1943 - 1948. (Rus)
[58] Mikheev Yu.A. and Ershov Yu.A., *Zhurnal Fizicheskoi Khimii*, 2003 (in press). (Rus)
[59] Shlyapintokh V.Ya., *Photochemical Transformations and Stabilization of Polymers*, Moscow, Khimia, 1979. (Rus)
[60] Milinchuk V.K., Klinshpont E.R., and Pshezhetskii S.Ya., *Macroradicals*, Moscow, Khimia, 1980. (Rus)
[61] Hrdlovič P., *Polymer News*, 2001, vol. 26(3), pp. 86 - 96.

In: Synthesis and Properties of Low- and High-Molecular Compounds ISBN 1-59454-716-5
Editor: Gennady E. Zaikov et al., pp. 277-288

Chapter 16

HETEROPHASE SUPRAMOLECULAR MODEL OF PHOTOCHEMICAL TRANSFORMATION OF NAPHTHALENE IN CELLULOSE TRIACETATE

Yu. A. Mikheev, V. G. Zaikov and I. V. Savenkova*
N.M.Emanuel Institute of Biochemical Physics Russian Academy of Sciences,
4, Kosygin st., Moscow 119991, Russia
*Kursk State Technologycal University, 94, 50 years of October, Kursk, Russia

Naphthalene excitation by UV-light in glassy cellulose triacetate films induces formation of polymeric free radicals, polymer chain break and addition of naphthalene fractures to macromolecules. In the absence of oxygen, the naphthalene consumption rate increases in direct proportion to UV-light intensity, whereas the rate of polymeric chain breaks varies in proportion to quadratic intensity. The process is initiated by singly excited triplet naphthalene molecules localized in the structural matrix zones, where they are incapable of irradiative deactivation. The features of phototransformation are explained in the framework of the hetero-nanophase kinetic model of the process, taking into account the radiationless translation of triplet excitation energy to naphthalene molecules present in the zones, where sensitization is absent and only triplet state deactivation is performed.

Kinetics of the photochemical naphthalene (N) transformation in evacuated glass CTA films does not comply with homogeneous reaction models. In works published over 25 years ago [1 – 3], it has been found that triplet-excited N^T molecules are initiators of this process, which itself is slowed down with N concentration increase.

The observed concentration effect was explained with the help of a simplified scheme, according to which chemical acts proceed with participation of N^T molecules in structurally separate zones of the matrix favorable for implementation of sensitization acts. The same chemically active N^T molecules are also donors of energy for unexcited N molecules, located in the matrix zones unfavorable for sensitization.

Realization of the radiationless $T - T$ translation of excitation energy between naphthalene molecules, present in heterogeneous zones of the nanostructural scale, makes this aromatic compound the process sensitizer, as well as active N^T molecule extinguisher.

The study was aimed at specification and systematizing of kinetic regularities for a photochemical naphthalene transformation in glass CTA combined with the kinetics of induced degradation and modification of macromolecules and, based on this, at development of a kinetic model of the process using the ideas of supramolecular heterogeneous-heterophase reactions, developed in [4, 5].

EXPERIMENTAL

The polymer (CTA, $M = 3.3\times10^5$, acetate number 62.5), prepared as a cotton-wool by re-precipitation, was thoroughly purifies from aromatic additives by extraction by methanol. Analytically pure naphthalene was additionally sublimated. Films 6 – 20 μm thick were prepared from polymer and naphthalene solution in methylene chloride. The solution was distributed by the silicate glass surface and the solvent evaporated. After solvent removal, the films were stratified by water and dried in vacuum during 24 hours.

Film samples were placed to a quartz cuvette which allows test performance in vacuum (10^{-4} – 10^{-6} Pa), in air and xenon under temperature-stabilized conditions. For the light source, high-pressure mercury lamp DRSh-500 was used.

Naphthalene (N) dissolved in CTA films was excited by filtered light not absorbed by the polymer ($v < 33{,}000$ cm^{-1}, $\lambda > 300$ nm). In this spectrum region, optical density of the samples was below 0.1 that provided for uniform light absorption in the sample thickness. The phototransformation was searched for by changes in UV absorption spectra which were measured by a Specord UV-VIS instrument.

UV-radiation intensity was controlled with the help of ferrioxalate technique. Relative quantum yields of naphthalene consumption ($\gamma_{N,0}$) were calculated by the initial parts of kinetic curves.

Luminescence spectra of N in CTA films were recorded on a spectrofluorimeter Jobin and Ivon (France). Fluorescence decay kinetics was recorded on a pulse fluorometer with the pulse lamp flash duration of 3 ns, In the mode of photon counting with the help of a multichannel pulse analyzer Nokia (model LP-4050).

The number of macromolecule breaks n was determined viscosimetrically, using methylene chloride : methanol mixture (94 : 6). The calculations were performed by the equations:

$$[\eta] = 0.016\, M^{0.76}$$

and

$$n = \frac{M_0 - M_t}{M_t}.$$

Preliminarily, it was found that macromolecule polydispersity index $\left(\frac{M_w}{M_n} \approx 1.2\right)$ is practically invariable during photosensitized degradation. The number n was determined by dissolving several samples, obtained during equal times. The relative quantum yield of polymeric chain breaks ($\gamma_{N,0}$) was calculated as the ratio of the number of breaks at the reaction beginning and the initial N concentration.

The technique for determination of the rate of structural-mechanical damage of the films at photosensitization of polymeric chain breaks was also used. The rate of such damage was found from the durability isotherms, characterizing polymeric films in a definite range of mechanical stress (σ, kg/mm^2). The film samples (width 5 mm and length between clips 22 mm) were loaded on a device with a shaped lever which supported constant σ during the experiment, and the time period τ (s) to degradation was determined [6]. Loaded samples were UV-light radiated in a flow quartz Dewar vessel in temperature-stabilized flows of dried air or nitrogen, purified from oxygen additive.

RESULTS

The change of UV absorption of CTA films containing naphthalene in concentrations 1.4, 0.1 and 2.9% by light with λ >300 nm (ν< 33,000 cm^{-1}) at room temperature and 91°C were show. In all cases, formation of the reaction products absorbing light in the UV-region of the spectrum up to λ ~ 380 nm was observed. Isobestic points (the cross-points of spectral lines) typical of this process were preserved to high transformation stages. This indicated invariability of the composition of products accumulated during the reaction.

Taking into account the features of absorption spectra changes, one may conclude about products of two types' formation in the reaction (A and B). One (A) absorbs light relatively intensively in the range of ν = 40,000 – 27,000 cm^{-1}. Another one (B) possesses an insignificant absorption in the range. A mixture of compounds A and B is thermally stable, because heating of CTA films with the products during 3 hours at 90°C does not change their UV absorption spectrum. However, the former product A is photolyzed by light with λ > 320 nm (ν < 31,300 cm^{-1}), moreover, in the presence of air photodegradation proceeds at a higher rate than in vacuum. In both cases, compounds with insufficient light absorption in the range of λ > 260 nm (ν < 38,000 cm^{-1}) are formed.

It was found [1] that phototransformation products of naphthalene were not extracted by methanol from the films, whereas the primary N was easily washed out from the films even 200 μm thick. Polymer re-precipitation with photolysis products, performed after N residues removal by methanol (solvent CH_2Cl_2, precipitator – methanol : water = 2 : 1 mixture), indicated addition of the phototransformation products to macromolecules.

The absorption spectrum shape of reaction products accumulated at various temperatures and different initial N concentrations remain practically the same in the range λ > 260 nm. The ratio of optical densities

$$\frac{D(36{,}100\,\text{cm}^{-1})}{D(31{,}250\,\text{cm}^{-1})} = 3.5,$$

obtained from this spectrum, was taken for a conversion factor in composing kinetic curves of N consumption. Typical kinetic curves of N consumption and accumulation of UV-absorbing reaction products (A), obtained at sample preparation in vacuum (λ > 300 nm) at different initial N concentrations were composed.

It has been found that temperature does not practically affect the rate of N consumption, but it decreases the rate of products A. The effective activation energy of their accumulation, calculated by the initial parts of kinetic curves, is negative ≈-5 kcal/mol (-21 kJ/mol).

Moreover, for evacuated samples a dependence of the initial rate of N phototransformation and product A accumulation on the spectral composition of light was observed. For example, as CTA films with 0.5% naphthalene concentration are radiated through an interference light filter (wavelengths λ > 340 nm are not transmitted), the quantum yield[1] of N consumption equals 0.3×10^{-2}. At the same time, in the case of another filter used, the quantum yield increased to 1.2×10^{-2}. It should be emphasized that the first filter transmits light not only in the region of N absorption, but also 10 times more intense long-wavelength light with λ > 340 nm, not absorbed by naphthalene and cut off by another filter.

The presence of the long-wavelength IV-radiation also leads to an increase of the initial rate of product A accumulation (by 2 times, approximately).

The effect of long-wavelength UV-light was proved on the samples containing 0.5% N, using two light sources (mercury lamps DRSh-500, equipped with light filters), one of which transmitted light with λ > 290 nm, and another with λ > 340 nm. The rate of N consumption at simultaneous radiation of samples in vacuum is 1.5-fold higher than that under the effect of only one light source with λ > 290 nm. Under these conditions, the rate of the product A accumulation is significantly increased.

In the presence of air oxygen, the rates of photochemical N consumption and product A accumulation are noticeably decreased (by 10 times, approximately), as well as the rate of polymeric chain break accumulation [1, 2]. Hence, the effect of the long-wavelength light with λ > 340 nm is almost completely neglected. The inert gas xenon acts similar to oxygen (after preliminary evacuation, an ampoule with the film was filled with xenon to 1 atm pressure).

Isotherms of mechanical degradation of the films (plotted in $\lg\tau$ - σ coordinates) under photosensitization conditions in air and nitrogen were obtained. Both isotherms possess linear intersects described by the equation

$$\lg\tau = \lg A - \alpha\sigma.$$

Both lines possess equal coefficients α, but different coefficients A. The latter correspond to durability obtained by extrapolation of linear parts of the isotherms on the axis of ordinates. In these experiments $1/A$ value was taken for the rate of the structural-mechanical damage of the samples, and the relative quantum yield of the damage γ_d were determined [3, 6] as the

[1] The quantum yield was calculated as a relation of the number of reacted N molecules and the number of light quanta, absorbed by naphthalene in the spectral region under consideration.

ration $1/A$[N]). Clearly the process of structural mechanical damage is significantly slowed down under the effect of air.

It is common knowledge that air oxygen effectively decays fluorescence of triplet naphthalene N^T in solid polymers [7]. Xenon also deactivates N^T in solid solutions [8]. Thus an assumption follows that triplet-excited N^T is the primary active particle in CTA films.

The corresponded fact was proved in the studies of N luminescence in CTA films [2]. Characteristic time of fluorescence decay in the films was constant, equal 95 ± 5 ns in air and in vacuum in the range of naphthalene concentration 0.25 – 6.7%.

The same films possessed an intense fluorescence in vacuum; however, in air it was not detected due to high rate of N^T deactivation. Thus it may be concluded that photoexcited naphthalene state reacting with the polymer is the triplet one.

Hence, for the current photochemical reaction the presence of quite typical feature shall be outlined. The fast is that the concentration increase of N in evacuated films from 0.2 to 2% causes equal, 6-fold decrease of initial quantum yields of N consumption ($\gamma_{N,0}$), polymeric chain breaks (γ_{n0}), and structural-mechanical damage (γ_d) of the films under mechanical stress. The concentration slowing down of the mentioned processes is described by the empirical equation:

$$\gamma_i = \frac{const_{i1}}{const_{i2} + const_{i3}[N]}.$$

Similar event also takes place in aerated films, where photochemical process proceeds much slower that in vacuum.

At the same time, despite slowing down of the reaction with [N] increase, the characteristic time of fluorescence decay varies insignificantly: in the N concentration range of 0.025 – 0.5%, it is constant and equals q.8 s, and at concentrations 1 and 2% it is 1.66 and 1.3 s, respectively.

The experimental results under consideration indicate the dual role of triplet-excited N^T. While N^T molecules responsible for fluorescence are fully decayed under the effect of oxygen, N^T molecules responsible for sensitization of chemical acts are just partly deactivated by oxygen and xenon (the phototransformation, though significantly slowed down, yet proceeds at enough high rate). Moreover, the concentration slowing down of the photochemical process is performed without any connection to the characteristic time and naphthalene fluorescence intensity.

A variation of durability of CTA films with naphthalene at different UV-radiation intensities showed that the rate of the structural-mechanical damage in air is in direct proportion to the radiation intensity. At the same time, in nitrogen (at constant coefficient α) the quadratic dependence of structural-mechanical damage on UV-radiation intensity is observed. The quadratic dependence on UV-radiation intensity was also observed for the rate process of sensitized breaks of macromolecules in evacuated unloaded films [3].

Discussion

Kinetic Scheme of Phototransformation

Such features as the quadratic dependence of the macromolecular break rate on UV-radiation intensity, the effect of addition long-wavelength light on the rates of naphthalene consumption and reaction product A accumulation in evacuated CTA films, as well as oxygen-induced disappearing of these features, for the first glance, might be associated with the fact that active photoexcited state of naphthalene occurs as a result of the second quantum of light absorption by triplet N^T. This very assumption was made in [9], where the rate increase of PMMA macromolecule breaks induced by the long wavelength light, not absorbed by naphthalene.

However, the mentioned reaction features in evacuated CTA films are displayed simultaneously with direct proportion of the naphthalene consumption rate and accumulation of the product A, absorbing UV-light. This fact allows an exclusion of participation of two-fold excited triplet states of N. In this case, according to the authors' point of view, the attention should be paid to secondary photochemical reactions of free radicals formed at N^T interaction with CTA macromolecules.

The totality of the above-enumerated regularities can be explained with the help of the heterophase kinetic scheme of the reaction, in accordance with which the concentration slowing down of the photoprocess is provided by active N^T molecule decaying by unexcited N molecules. This is possible in the only case, if sensitization acts proceed in s-zones suitable for this purpose (these zones are the zones of supernanopores, the concentration of which in the polymer is low [5]), i.e. with participation of N^T molecules. Simultaneously, phosphorescence acts and its decay by oxygen proceed in v-zones (the zones of incapacious nanopores [5]) unsuitable for sensitization, i.e. with participation of N_v^T molecules. (The part of v-nanopores in the polymer is high; they accumulate the main amount of additive molecules.)

The photoprocess possesses the maximal initial rate and proceeds at room temperature to high transformation stages. This indicates quite high exchange rate of N molecules between zones. The reduced supramolecular scheme of anaerobic photoreaction includes the stages present below:

1. Naphthalene molecule exchange between *v*- and *s*-zones:

$$\mathbf{N_v \leftrightarrow N_s}$$

(it is assumed that its equilibrium is not disturbed by the reaction, thus the following relationships are applicable:

$$[N_s] = \alpha[N_v] = \frac{\alpha[N]}{1+\alpha} \approx \alpha N,$$

$$[N_v] = \frac{[N]}{1+\alpha} \approx N,$$

which reflect the small part of N_s molecules: $\alpha << 1$).

2. Excitation of naphthalene molecules to T_v-state and subsequent irradiative and radiationless deactivation of excited molecules:

$$\mathbf{N_v + h\nu \rightarrow N_v^S},$$

$$\mathbf{N_v^S \rightarrow N_v + h\nu_{fluoresc}},$$

$$\mathbf{N_v^S \rightsquigarrow N_v^T},$$

$$N_v^T \rightarrow N_v + h\nu_{fluoresc},$$

$$N_v^T \rightsquigarrow N_v \text{ (conversion to heat)}.$$

3. Naphthalene excitation into chemically active T_s-state:

$$N_s + h\nu \rightsquigarrow \xrightarrow{k_{0,h\nu}} N_s^T,$$

where $k_{0,h\nu} = \gamma_T I_0 \varepsilon_N$ is the rate constant under the assumption of monochromatic light effect; γ_T is the quantum yield of T-states; I_0 is the intensity of exciting monochromatic UV-light; ε_N is the light absorption coefficient of naphthalene.

4. Deactivation of an active state by radiationless energy transfer:

$$N_s^T + N_v \xrightarrow{k_1} N_s + N_v^T.$$

5. H atom detachment from macromolecules and formation of hydronaphthyl radical - middle macroradical couple:

$$N_s^T \xrightarrow{k_2'(PH)=k_2} \{^{\bullet}NH + P^{\bullet}\}_s,$$

where

$^{\bullet}NH \equiv$ 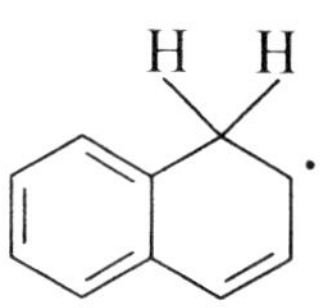

6. Primary radical pair transformations:

$$\{^{\bullet}\mathrm{NH} + \mathrm{P}^{\bullet}\}_s \xrightarrow{k_3} \mathrm{PNH} \text{ (recombination with product } \mathrm{B}_1 \text{ formation)};$$

$$\{^{\bullet}\mathrm{NH} + \mathrm{P}^{\bullet}\}_s \xrightarrow{k_{4,h\nu}} \{^{\bullet}\mathrm{NH} + \mathrm{P}^{\bullet *}\}_s \rightarrow \{^{\bullet}\mathrm{NH} + \mathrm{R}^{\bullet}\}_s + n \rightarrow \mathrm{RNH}$$

(photoexcitation of the middle radical $P_s^{\bullet}$ and further occurrence of a macromolecule break (n), end radical $R_s^{\bullet}$ and the recombination product B_2; here constant $k_{4,h\nu} = \gamma_4 I_0 \varepsilon_4$; γ_4 and ε_4 are the quantum yield of breaks and light absorption coefficient of macroradical, respectively);

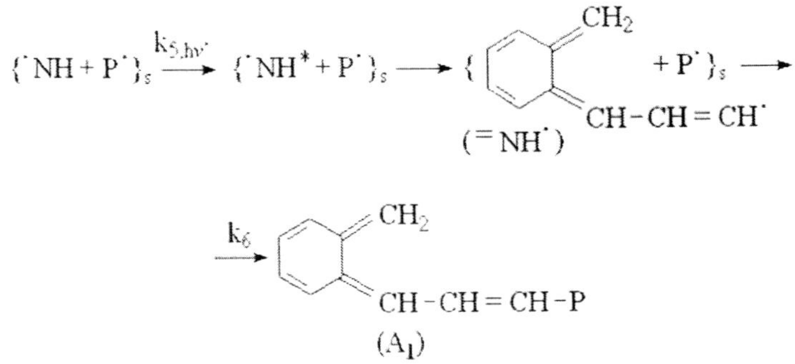

(long-wavelength UV-light absorption (ν', intensity I_1) by hydronaphthyl radical; subsequent disclosure of one ring in hydronaphthyl radical with formation of $\{^{=}\mathrm{NH}^{\bullet} + \mathrm{P}^{\bullet}\}$ radical pair and recombination transformation of this pair to unsaturated compound A_1; $k_{5,h\nu'} = \gamma_A I_1 \varepsilon_{NH}$ is the rate constant, written down in the suggestion of monochromatic light).

7. Speeding up of naphthalene consumption induced by long-wavelength UV-light (I_1) may be associated with accepting of N molecules by radical pairs:

$$\{^{=}\mathrm{NH}^{\bullet} + \mathrm{P}^{\bullet}\}_s + \mathrm{N}_s \xrightarrow{k_7} \{^{\bullet}\mathrm{NNH} + \mathrm{P}^{\bullet}\}_s \rightarrow \mathrm{HNNP}\ (\mathrm{A}_2).$$

Applying the steady state concentration to active particles in the current scheme (and accounting for the inequality $k_3 > (k_{4,h\nu} + k_{5,h\nu'})$, the following expressions can be easily deduced:

naphthalene consumption rate

$$w_N = \frac{d[\mathrm{N}]}{dt} = \frac{k_2 k_{0,h\nu}[\mathrm{N}]}{k_2 + k_1[\mathrm{N}]}\left\{1 + \frac{k_7 k_{5,h\nu'}}{k_3\left(k_6 + k_7\alpha[\mathrm{N}]\right)}\right\},$$

$$\gamma_N \sim \frac{w_N}{[\mathrm{N}]};$$

macromolecule break rate:

$$w_{\mathrm{n}} = \frac{\alpha k_2 k_{4,h\nu} k_{0,h\nu}[\mathrm{N}]}{(k_2 + k_1[\mathrm{N}])k_3} \sim I_0^2,$$

$$\gamma_{\mathrm{n}} \sim \frac{w_{\mathrm{n}}}{[\mathrm{N}]};$$

the accumulation rate of unsaturated A_1 and A_2 products:

$$w_{\mathrm{A}} = \frac{\alpha k_2 k_{5,h\nu'} k_{0,h\nu}[\mathrm{N}]}{(k_2 + k_1[\mathrm{N}])k_3}.$$

The above-shown expressions explain the effect of additional long-wavelength UV-light on N consumption rate and the rate of product A accumulation (including A_1 and A_2 products), as well as the presence of a quadratic dependence of the macromolecule break rate on UV-radiation intensity in the spectral region of naphthalene absorption. Therefore, the direct proportionality of initial rates $w_{\mathrm{N},0}$ and $w_{\mathrm{A},0}$ to I_0 must be fulfilled due to large enough spectral interval between long-wavelength absorption bands of naphthalene and hydronaphthyl radicals: $h\nu' < h\nu$.

The presence of constant k_3 in denominators of expressions for w_{n} and w_{A} may be responsible for low negative activation energies observed: E_{n}, $E_{\mathrm{A}} \approx -21$ kJ/mol.

The reduced scheme under consideration complies with the regularities of anaerobic phototransformation of naphthalene (the detailed scheme must take into account the fact that middle radicals with a free valence in positions C_1 andC_2 on glucopyranose rings participate in macromolecule break acts). It accounts for enough fast migration of initiator molecules in glassy CTA matrix. N migration restores sensitizing N_s molecules, provides for bimolecular deactivation of N_s^T triplets and formation of grafted naphthalene groups on macromolecules.

In the presence of oxygens in the films, the latter oxidizes $^{\bullet}$NH and $^{=}$NH$^{\bullet}$ radicals, inhibiting formation of A and B products. It also completely decays N_v^T states and N_s^T ones incompletely, probably, because of non-equivalence of physical properties of these particles, located in different structural zones of the matrix.

The Display of Non-Equivalence of Additive Molecule Properties in Heterogeneous Nanophases

In accordance with the above-considered supramolecular scheme of the photoprocess, additive compounds, occurring in heterogeneous structural zones of glassy polymer matrix, acquire unequal physical properties. This fact is clearly displayed in unequal ability of aromatic compounds to phosphoresce, if they are injected to glassy films by different methods, namely, from combined solution by volatile solvent evaporation (films 1) and by additive absorption from the vapor phase (films 2). In this connection, tests on photoexcitation of phosphorescence of naphthalene, α-naphthol and diphenyl in CTA and PMMA films, placed to the inert gas CO_2, may be the demonstrative experiment [10].

For example, if UV-light, exciting aromatic compound molecules, is removed ($300 < \lambda < 385$ nm), then films 1 prepared from the combined solution of the polymer and an additive in methylene chloride display bright phosphorescence, decaying during 3 s, approximately. In the case of naphthalene, phosphorescence is green (λ_{max} = 495 nm, $\tau_{phosphoresc.}$ = 1.7 s); α-naphthol gives green phosphorescence, too; diphenyl gives blue light.

On the contrary, the initially pure glassy films are transformed as a result of absorption of the above-mentioned compounds to films 2, which under equal conditions do not phosphoresce.

Moreover, the films of both types also differ by the rates of photochemical transformation of naphthalene in air ($\lambda > 300$ nm, 22°C, N desorption level during photochemical reaction is negligibly small): the photoreaction rate in films 1 is much lower than in films 2.

The mentioned results correlate with the above heterophase-kinetic model of the process. For example, phosphorescing triplets N^T are observed in the films 1 only (it is assumed that they are located in incapacious nanopores and do not participate in sensitization of the photoprocess). In such aerated films, the rate of phototransformation is relatively low, but the process proceeds owing to N molecule exchange between zones.

As mentioned above, in the films 2 in the absence of oxygen phosphorescence is not observed, however, in air the photoprocess rate is high. It may be suggested that absorbed N molecules in them are almost completely localized in zones with supernanopores (this suggestion is testified by the fact that the naphthalene desorption rate from films 2 is much higher than from films 1 [10]). The absence of phosphorescence in them indicates the existence of sufficient structural hindrances for naphthalene displacement to incapacious nanopore zones. At the same time, quite rapid exchange of naphthalene between zones is typical of films 1; it provides for the photoprocess proceeding (but naphthalene desorption from the zones proceeds at extremely low rate [10]).

A combination of the mentioned facts indicates the effect of dissolved additive on the self-organization of polymeric chains to a supramolecular hetero-nanophase carcass-micellar system at formation of the films during volatile solvent evaporation. It may be believed that glassy films 1 differ from films 2 by more perfect (less permeable) walls of the paracrystalline carcass and, simultaneously, by higher dynamics of spongy micelle units in carcass cells [11, 12].

The nonequivalence of the rates of photosensitized reactions in heterogeneous nanophases of glassy polymers is proved in experiments with naphthalene phosphorescence decay. For example, it is shown [13] that in aerated PMMA films fluorescence of singlet-excited naphthalene molecules N^S can be decayed by tinuvin P, but this does not affect the rate of naphthalene dissociation. The latter is consumed in the process, the rate of which is not defined by the concentration of particles responsible for fluorescence. Under such conditions, according to definition by the authors [13], primary chemical acts are inevitable. However, in the absence of oxygen tinuvin P slows the photochemical process down in accordance with a decrease of singlet-excited naphthalene molecule concentration.

Based on their results, the authors [13] have suggested that the inevitable reaction proceeds in matrix cells of a specific structure. Varying oxygen concentration in the films, the authors found that oxygen did not participate directly in the inevitable reaction act. Meanwhile, in the absence of oxygen the inevitable reaction was not observed.

Transferring to terms of the considered hetero-nanophase model, one may give the following qualitative description of the mentioned facts.

Similar to the case of CTA, primary chemical acts in PMMA films proceed in supernanopores, in which additive molecules spend the main time adsorbed to the walls. Adsorbed N_s^T molecules also sensitize chemical acts in the presence of oxygen, because they are deactivated by oxygen less effectively compared with N_v^T molecules (the latter are present in incapacious nanopore zones saturated with oxygen). The zones of incapacious nanopores accumulate the main amount of additive compounds and directly in them fluorescing naphthalene molecules N_v^S are decayed by tinuvin P.

Phosphorescing N_v^T molecules are formed from fluorescing N_v^S molecules, resulting the $S \rightarrow T$ conversion of electron excitation energy, and in the presence of oxygen they are rapidly deactivated. This is the reason why deactivation of N_v^S molecules by tinuvin P in aerated PMMA films does not affect the rate of reaction sensitization. On the other hand, N_v^T molecules formed from N_v^S ones in the absence of oxygen possess quite long lifetime (1.7 s) and, as follows from the experiments [13], in PMMA matrix possess the ability to transmit irradiationlessly the energy of triplet excitation to naphthalene molecules, located in supernanopores. For this reason, the decay of fluorescing N_v^S molecules proceeding in the absence of oxygen slows photodegradation of naphthalene down.

To put it differently, besides activation of N_s molecules by means of light absorption, in deaerated PMMA films an additional quite effective pathway of excitation, associated with radiationless *T-T* transmission of energy from incapacious nanopores to supernanopores, acts. The reaction model discussed for CTA samples does not take into account transmission of electron excitation energy in this direction; however, in general case, based on the results [13], such possibility should be taken into account.

CONCLUSION

Previously, it was shown that supramolecular heterophase models of chemical transformations possess high advantages in the description of kinetic features of chain reactions of autooxidation before the traditional homogeneous model of liquid-phase oxidation of hydrocarbons [4, 5].

In this Section, the method of heterophase-kinetic modeling is used in description of a complex photochemical process of transformations sensitized by naphthalene in glassy cellulose triacetate films. The considered supramolecular model of the mentioned process quite fully reflects the presence of heterogeneous nanophases in non-crystalline polymers, which cause the dominant influence on physical and chemical properties of additive moleculaes.

REFERENCES

[1] Guseva L.N., Mikheev Yu.A., and Toptygin D.Ya., *Izv. AN SSSR, Ser. Khim.*, 1974, No. 9, p. 1988. (Rus)

[2] Guseva L.N., Mikheev Yu.A., and Toptygin D.Ya., *Doklady AN SSSR*, 1975, vol. 220(6), p. 1356. (Rus)

[3] Guseva L.N., Mikheev Yu.A., Rogova L.S., and Toptygin D.Ya., *Doklady AN SSSR*, 1975, vol. 224(5), p. 1077. (Rus)
[4] Mikheev Yu.A., Guseva L.N., and Zaikov G.E., *Uspekhi Khimii*, 1997, vol. 66(1), p. 1. (Rus)
[5] Mikheev Yu.A. and Zaikov G.E., *Uspekhi Khimii*, 2000, vol. 69(3), p. 249. (Rus)
[6] Guseva L.N., Mikheev Yu.A., Rogova L.S., and Toptygin D.Ya., *Polym. Photochem.*, 1982, vol. 2(6), p. 457.
[7] Czarnecki St. and Kryszewski M., *J. Polymer Sci.*, 1963, vol. A1(10), p. 3067.
[8] Siegel S. and Judeikis H.S., *J. Chem. Phys.*, 1968, vol. 48(4), p. 1613.
[9] Batekha I.G., Shekk Yu.B., Kryisanov S.A., and Alfimov M.V., *Doklady AN SSSR*, 1971, vol. 197(3), p. 614. (Rus)
[10] Mikheev Yu.A. and Guseva L.N., *Khim. Fizika*, 1991, vol. 10(5), p. 724. (Rus)
[11] Mikheev Yu.A., Guseva L.N., and Zaikov G.E., *Khim. Fizika*, 1996, vol. 15(1), p. 7. (Rus)
[12] Mikheev Yu.A. and Guseva L.N., *Russ. J. Phys. Chem.*, 2000, vol. 74, Suppl. 3, p. S460.
[13] Kutsenova A.V. and Karpukhin O.N., *Izv. AN SSSR, Ser. Khim.*, 1976, No. 6, p. 1301. (Rus)

In: Synthesis and Properties of Low- and High-Molecular Compounds ISBN 1-59454-716-5
Editor: Gennady E. Zaikov et al., pp. 289-319

Chapter 17

INTENSIFICATION MASS TRANSFER PROCESSES IN FAST LIQUID-PHASE CHEMICAL REACTIONS

***V. P. Zakharov*[1], *A. G. Mukhametzyanova*[2], *G. S. Dyakonov*[2], *Al. Al. Berlin*[3] *and G. E. Zaikov*[4]**

[1]Bashkir State University, ul. Frunze 32, Ufa, 450074 Bashkortostan, Russia
[2]Kazan State Technological University, K. Marks str. 68, 420015, Kazan, Russia
[3]Institute of Chemical Physics, Russian Academy of Sciences, ul. Kosygina 4, Moscow, 119991, Russia
[4]Institute of Biochemical Physics, Russian Academy of Sciences, ul. Kosygina 4, Moscow, 117334, Russia

ABSTRACT

Fundamental regularities of turbulent mixing of one-phase flows worked out in this paper allow significantly deepening and extending of novel part of theoretical technology concerning fast chemical processes proceeding in turbulent regime. The analysis of physical picture of reaction mixture turbulent movement in tubular canals of various construction determines the possibility of quantitative and scientifically-founded approach to the selection of optimal reaction zone geometry under any fast chemical processes proceeding with the aim of reduction of diffusion limitations and creation of uniform conditions under synthetic products production.

Key word/Phrase index. fast chemical reaction, liquid phase, turbulent mixing, mixing time, self-similar regime, tubular apparatus

PROBLEMS OF CARRYING OUT FAST CHEMICAL PROCESSES

In chemistry there are examples of extremely fast processes proceeding in liquid phase, when chemical reactions rates are comparable or higher than rates of reagents' mixing. A lot of processes of ion and free-radical polymerization, chlorination, hydrochlorination and sulfation of olefins, alkylation of alkanes by alkenes, chlorination of aromatic hydrocarbons, etc. relate to such extremely fast processes [1, 2]. Cationic (electrophilic) polymerization of isobutylene that may be considered as a classical model of fast chemical reaction attracts the greatest attention for theoretical investigation among fast polymerization reactions [3, 4]. It is because this process is theoretically clear in general and of high practical importance.

In industry oligo- and polyisobutylenes with molecular mass (MM) 112-50000 and higher are produced by cationic polymerization of isobutylene in the presence of $AlCl_3$ in hydrocarbons (butane and others) or chlorinated hydrocarbons (ethyl or methyl chloride, etc.) medium at 173-353 K in stirred reactors of $1{,}5 \div 30$ m^3 volume and complex construction [3]. Reactors are equipped by advanced inside and outside heat-exchanging surfaces (130 m^2 and higher) with liquid ethylene or ammonia as refrigerants, intensive mixers providing linear rates of reaction mass movement of $1 \div 10$ m/sec order for cooling and necessary productivity control according to thermal and material balance. Medium reagents residence time in reaction zone is about $(1{,}8 \div 3{,}6) \cdot 10^3$ sec [1].

Constants of initiation and chain propagation (**k_i, k_p**) are lower than $10^5 \div 10^6$ l/mole·sec [4, 5], and determine characteristic time of chemical reaction equal to $10^{-1} \div 10^{-3}$ sec at real initial catalyst and monomer concentrations. It means that isobutylene polymerization proceeds by 100% in places where reagents are introduced into the apparatus (within less than $1 \div 10$ cm from catalyst introduction) and process is limited by reagents mixing, i.e. process proceeds in diffusion field. Heat accumulation in the reaction system at high turbulence of reaction mixture movement leads to the oscillation temperature change in reaction zone in time [5]. In topochemical aspect fast polymerization reaction proceeds as "torch" with characteristic gradients of reagents temperature and concentration by coordinates of reaction zone [5, 6].

Shape of forming reaction front is analogous to that under burning reaction [7, 8]. In this case the main reactor volume is not enabled in chemical process and presents ballast in a sense increasing reagents residence time in reaction zone that promotes by-products formation. Furthermore, reaction zone doesn't reach reactor's walls and the use of external heat removal is ineffective [1, 2, 4, 9]. That is why thermostating of fast polymerization processes in industrial and laboratory production is difficult enough. Gradients of polymers MM and MMD are observed in process course in reaction zone volume due to non-isothermality [10].

It is important that dependence of medium MM on reagents concentration, and also significant MMD broadening at initial monomer concentration increase are the macroscopic consequences of local polymerization proceeding. At the same time polymer MM according to kinetic scheme [5] is totally determined by chain transfer to monomer and predicts independence of MM and MMD on catalyst and monomer concentration in isothermal regime [1]. Moreover, catalyst and monomer solutions are introduced into reactor irregularly as a rule and because of high polymerization rates catalyst and monomer don't have enough time to mix well with reaction mass. This particularity causes additional non-stability in reactor operating, MMD broadening and reduction of resulting product MM [5].

It was found that mentioned regularities of fast polymerization were applied to any fast processes including low-molecular synthesis in flow [11].

Thus, using traditional approach for instrumental typography of fast chemical reactions both under polymer synthesis and low-molecular products production in flow leads to the uncontrolled processes and nonoptimal quality of resulted products [1, 2, 3, 12]. That is why it is of great importance to find optimal conditions for fast chemical reactions carrying out.

It is worth saying that fast chemical processes should be studied and carried out in stream conditions in tubular reaction vessel with ideal mixing, i.e. in high-turbulence flows [1, 7]. It is expedient on account of several reasons. First, carrying out of fast reactions in a stream limited by impermeable wall presents the most convenient and natural way of their investigation. Second, under realization of such reactions in classical stirred tank reactors it is in principle impossible to provide effective heat- and mass-transfer for the time commensurable with chemical reaction time. Third, turbulence conditions of moving stream allow carrying out fast chemical processes with maximum intensity for least time and in minimum volume. Forth, investigation of reactions in stationary stream with turbulence mixing is in principle easier and more effective than under single proceeding under closed volume conditions. At last, under fast reactions realization in stream it is possible to vary characteristic mixing time $\tau_{mix} = R^2/D_т$ (**R** – radius of stream (flow) limited by impermeable wall) and, in particular to make it commensurable with chemical reaction characteristic time $\tau_{ch} = 1/k_d$ (k_d – constant of active sites deactivation).

First of all, it was necessary to solve at least three problems [9]:

a. fast mixing of two and more reagents, especially different in density and viscosity (following condition must be fulfilled in ideal – $\tau_{mix} \leq \tau_{ch}$);
b. reagents residence time in reaction zone ($\tau_r = L/V$) shouldn't be significantly higher than time of chemical reaction because of slower secondary reactions following condition must be fulfilled in ideal – $\tau_r \approx \tau_{ch}$);
c. removal of large quantity of heat evolving in substantially small reaction zone volume or realization of conditions when a very fast temperature increase in this zone doesn't influence on chemical reaction course and quality of resulted polymers.

As fast chemical processes proceed in diffusion regime, so for revealing of regularities and specificity of their realization it is necessary to use macro-kinetic approach describing chemical reactions with consideration of mass- and heat-transfer [13]. On the base of this approach to modelling of fast polymerization processes regularities of proceeding of such reactions were revealed by the example of isobutylene cationic polymerization [5, 10]. In particular, it was found that many of problems under fast chemical reactions may be solved by creation of turbulence high enough in reaction zone. The last fact led to the development and wide use of tubular turbulent apparatus in industry [1, 2, 9, 12, 14].

Turbulent Mixing of One-Phase Mediums

Mixing in liquid phases is the most commonly used method for increasing of turbulence level in reaction zone, intensification of heat- and mass-transfer processes in chemical and other branches of industry [15]. With the aim of reception of homogeneous by structure and properties polymer product it is necessary to provide under polymerization the equal conditions in total reaction volume. It is possible to realize by intensive mixing of reaction medium when homogeneous fields of reactants concentrations are formed at $\tau_{mix} < \tau_{ch}$

condition. Traditionally used for this aim apparatus of large volume with mechanical mixers as a rule can not adequately provide the homogeneity of fields of reactants concentrations along reaction volume under fast chemical reactions especially when working with highviscosity mediums [10]. For example, system viscosity under polymerization (from 10^{-3} to 10^2-10^3 Pa·sec), high constants of propagation reaction rate ($k_p > 10^2$·l/mole·sec), a large amount of evolving heat (60-100 kDj/mole) determine sharp rise of temperature in reaction volume at the catalyst and monomer delivery point right up to heat explosion [17].

The interest in compact apparatus allowing along with specific output creating of high turbulence level in mixing zone grew recently [18]. As they showed in [19] intensity of turbulence approaches 50÷70% in cylindrical apparatus with turbulence promoters (for undisturbed flow in plain canals this value was 1÷3%). Apparatus with turbulence promoters [20], including those of divergent-convergent design [21] don't contain internal moving elements and are able to provide homogeneity of conditions for both chemical and mass-transfer physical processes. Application of tubular turbulent apparatus for processes limited by mass-transfer stage is determined by possibility of their control by increasing of turbulence level under reagents mixing. The last fact required the development of theoretical methods for studying of characteristics of liquid flows turbulence mixing in tubular canals as a base of fast chemical processes carrying out in optimal conditions and intensification of heat- and mass-transfer.

It is well known that radial introduction of reagents into apparatus in comparison with coaxial method provides better mixing in reaction zone. In particular, in [1] on the base of Navie-Stocks equations in combination with K-ε turbulence model it was shown that significant improvement of flows mixing under other equal conditions can be reached only by change of way of reagents introduction. Change of initial turbulence level influences on mixing characteristics as at coaxial, so at radial introduction. Experimental and calculation data [8] indicate on essential improvement of mixing and increase of effective mass and heat diffusion if there are circulating zones. Formation of the last ones is reached by application of various mechanisms [22] in combination with the rise of flows speeds [23]. In particular central one-shot catalyst introduction into reaction zone under fast polymerization processes is less effective than catalyst introduction by outside ring. The best results are observed not for coaxial, but for radial introduction of one of the components if there is conical extension in the initial part of reaction zone [24].

Nevertheless, it was shown in [16] that mixing of liquid flows differing in density and especially in viscosity is a very complex problem. Suffice it to say that in spite of unlimited solubility of concentrated sulfuric acid ($\rho = 1{,}8$ g/cm^3, $\mu = 27{,}8$ mPa·sec) or glycerin ($\rho = 1{,}26$ g/cm^3, $\mu = 1490$ mPa·sec) with water ($\rho = 1{,}00$ g/cm^3, $\mu = 1$ mPa·sec) prolonged conservation of phase interface is observed in tank apparatus even under mechanical mixing. Significant increase of mixing effectiveness of two or more reagents differing in density and viscosity is reached at the expense of rise and stabilization on definite level D_t along reaction zone, in particular when local hydrodynamic resistances of divergent-convergent design are used [1, 21]. This determines the expediency of investigation of canal geometry influence on turbulent mixing efficiency in tubular apparatus.

One should know turbulence characteristics to estimate the characteristic time of reagents mixing. They proposed a lot of various methods for estimation of mixing time in turbulent flows particularly the review on this theme and mixing models classification are presented in [25]. Since in [21] liquid movement is described by average over Reynolds Navie-Stocks equations with the use of K-ε closing, so the characteristic time of turbulence mixing can be estimated as [1, 21]:

$$\tau_{turb} = l^2/D_t \tag{1}$$

here l is characteristic linear size of region where homogeneous reagents concentrations field should be created.

If one supposes that turbulence diffusion coefficient D_t is equal to kinematic coefficient of turbulence viscosity ν_t which in its turn can be expressed by specific kinetic turbulence energy K (m^2/sec^2) and rate of dissipation of last one is ε (m^2/sec^3) then (1) will be as following:

$$\tau_{turb} = 11{,}1\varepsilon\, l^2/\, K^2 \tag{2}$$

However, correlations (1) and (2) don't take into account the fact that in turbulent flow mass transfer processes are carried out at the expense of molecular diffusion and viscosity flows especially under polymer synthesis in a volume small enough. That is why if micromixing processes exactly are limitative as under polymerization then it is necessary to use other estimating expressions. In this case, as it was shown in [21] the engulfment model is used frequently enough [26], according to which characteristic time of micromixing is estimated as following:

$$\tau_{micro} = 17{,}3(\nu/\varepsilon)^{0{,}5} \tag{3}$$

here ν is kinematic viscosity.

In a number of cases homogenization of medium is limited by exchange processes between large turbulent flows and presenting in them smaller flows, i.e. mesomixing [26]:

$$\tau_{meso} = 1\div 2(l^2/\varepsilon)^{1/3} \tag{4}$$

Comparison of characteristic mixing times mentioned above allows revealing of limitative mechanism of reagents concentrations field equalization under fast processes carrying out in turbulent regime. For this aim out of values calculating from (1)-(4) the biggest should be chosen and then it should be compared with chemical reaction characteristic time τ_{ch}. If the last one is turned out to be significantly higher, so chemical transformation process occurs in kinetic region and diffusion limitations don't affect the resulting product structure. If we consider the mixer for medium homogenization without chemical transformation, so limitative mixing time should be compared with average reagents residence time in reaction zone τ_r.

The fact that in highly turbulent flows liquid viscosity doesn't influence on main volume medium movement is interesting and important enough [27]. In this case they say that flow is self-simila in relation to viscosity and the influence of the last one is displayed in a narrow enough wall layer. The value of Reynolds' criterion above which the self-simila field is observed in many respects is determined by flow geometry. For example, in [27] they showed that under sphere flow the self-simila field in which resistance coefficient doesn't depend on Re and consequently on viscosity comes at $Re_{cr} \approx 500$. It is very important to study the possibility and conditions of self-simila flow formation in relation to viscosity in reaction zone of cylindrical and divergent-convergent designs that will widen exploitation potential of novel technology under polymer synthesis.

The fundamental approaches to definition of turbulent flows macro-kinetics and macro-mixing processes are considered in [28]. Special attention was focused on micro-mixing models in the context of method based on equation for density of random variables probabilities distribution. Advantage of this method is that we can calculate average rate of chemical reaction if know the corresponding density of concentration and temperature possibility distribution.

Since intensive mixing of liquid flows is observed at developed turbulent regime, so according to [28] one can't directly apply ordinary equations of continuum movement (for example, Navie-Stocks' equation with molecular coefficient of viscosity) in this case. That is why it is generally accepted to use the so-called average equations of turbulent continuum movement, they are also called as average by Reinolds.

Numerical solution of equation of continuum turbulent movement in combination with expressions of K-ε turbulence model allows to obtain over the whole tubular apparatus volume the fields of axial and radial speeds, pressure, specific kinetic energy of turbulence, its dissipation and of some other characteristics that are expressed by listed values. This fact permits to calculate the optimal in respect to mixing effectiveness geometry of reaction zone under fast chemical processes including polymerizations in turbulent regime.

Development of Scientifically-Grounded Approach to the Selection of Optimal Reaction Zone Geometry under Fast Processes

Creation of high turbulence in reagents mixing zone without preliminary flows turbulization is necessary for the effective fast chemical reactions and mass-exchange physical processes proceeding in liquid phase. As a consequence, studying of fundamental regularities and revealing of quantitative dependences allowing creation of intensive turbulent mixing in reaction zone are very important stages of novel technologies development.

Mathematical Modeling

Theoretical description of reagents turbulent mixing in tubular canals is based on the following main model assumptions:

- the medium is Newtonian and incompressible;
- the flow is axisymmetric and nonswirling;
- turbulent flow can be described by standard model [29] with following parameters: kinetic energy density of turbulence K, dissipation rate of turbulence ε;

- coefficient of turbulent diffusion is equal to kinematic coefficient of turbulent viscosity $D_T = \nu_T = \mu_T / \rho$.

Then they choose numerical solution of continuum turbulent flow equations with effective viscosity coefficient $\mu = \mu_T + \mu_M$ (μ_M – coefficient of molecular viscosity) by the use of K-ε turbulence model with method of finite elements on irregular computational grid [30]. These equations in cylindrical co-ordinates are as following:

Equation of continuity

$$\frac{1}{r}\frac{\partial(ru)}{\partial r} + \frac{\partial v}{\partial z} = 0, \tag{5}$$

Nav'ye-Stocks' equation (equation of impulse transfer):

$$\frac{\rho}{r}\frac{\partial(ruu)}{\partial r} + \rho\frac{\partial(uv)}{\partial z} = -\frac{\partial p}{\partial r} - \left(\frac{1}{r}\frac{\partial(r\tau_{11})}{\partial r} - \frac{\tau_{33}}{r} + \frac{\partial \tau_{21}}{\partial z}\right), \tag{6}$$

$$\frac{\rho}{r}\frac{\partial(ruv)}{\partial r} + \rho\frac{\partial(vv)}{\partial z} = -\frac{\partial \rho}{\partial z} - \left(\frac{1}{r}\frac{\partial(r\tau_{12})}{\partial r} + \frac{\partial \tau_{22}}{\partial z}\right), \tag{7}$$

where stress tensor components are equal to:

$$\tau_{12} = -2\mu\frac{\partial u}{\partial r},\ \tau_{22} = -2\mu\frac{\partial v}{\partial z},\ \tau_{33} = -2\mu\frac{u}{r}, \tag{8}$$

$$\tau_{12} = \tau_{21} = -\mu\left(\frac{\partial v}{\partial r} + \frac{\partial u}{\partial z}\right), \tag{9}$$

Equations of transfer of kinetic energy density of turbulence and its dissipation:

$$\frac{\rho}{r}\frac{\partial(ruK)}{\partial r} + \rho\frac{\partial(vK)}{\partial z} = \frac{1}{r}\frac{\partial}{\partial r}\left(\frac{\mu}{\sigma_K}\frac{r\partial K}{\partial r}\right) + \frac{\partial}{\partial r}\left(\frac{\mu}{\sigma_K}\frac{\partial K}{\partial z}\right) + \mu_T G - \rho\varepsilon, \tag{10}$$

$$\frac{\rho}{r}\frac{\partial(ru\varepsilon)}{\partial r} + \rho\frac{\partial(v\varepsilon)}{\partial z} = \frac{1}{r}\frac{\partial}{\partial r}\left(\frac{\mu}{\sigma_E}\frac{r\partial \varepsilon}{\partial r}\right) + \frac{\partial}{\partial z}\left(\frac{\mu}{\sigma_E}\frac{\partial \varepsilon}{\partial z}\right) + \tag{11}$$

$$+ \mu_T C_1 G\varepsilon / K - C_2 \rho\varepsilon^2 / K,$$

$$G = \frac{1}{\mu^2}\left(\frac{1}{2}\left(\tau_{11}^2 + \tau_{22}^2 + \tau_{33}^2\right) + \tau_{12}^2\right), \tag{12}$$

$$\mu_T = \rho \frac{C_\mu K^2}{\varepsilon}, \tag{13}$$

where p – pressure; r, z – radial and longitudinal coordinates, accordingly; u, v – cross and longitudinal rate's components.

Standard parameters of K-ε turbulence model were used [30]: $C_1 = 1{,}44$, $C_2 = 1{,}92$, $C_\mu = 0{,}09$, $\sigma_K = 1{,}0$, $\sigma_E = 1{,}3$.

Equations (5)-(13) are true for the main liquid volume but cannot be applied for the region directly adjoining to reaction zone's wall. For the last case one should use wall's law according with which the flow speed profile close to solid wall obeys the logarithmic law:

$$\frac{V_{tan}}{\sqrt{\tau/\rho}} = \frac{1}{k} \ln \frac{E\delta}{\nu_M} \sqrt{\frac{\tau}{\rho}}, \tag{14}$$

where δ – the distance from the wall. In the course of iterative process at given rate of reaction mixture coaxial movement V_{tan} one calculates the tangential stress τ by (14) and then the effective viscosity:

$$\mu = \delta\tau/V_{tan}, \tag{15}$$

by this the turbulence kinetic energy K is calculated from K-ε turbulence model, and dissipation of kinetic energy density of turbulence ε as follows:

$$\varepsilon = \frac{C_\mu^{0,75} K_w^{1,5}}{k\delta} \tag{16}$$

For formulas (14)-(16) constants values are accepted k = 0,4, E = 9,0 and this is the standard boundary condition for all solid surfaces under turbulent flows [29].

Flow of liquid with viscosity coefficient $\mu_M = 1$ mPa·sec and density $\rho = 1000$ kg/m^3 was considered. Boundary conditions are the symmetry conditions along z axis and conditions of liquid adhesion to solid surfaces of reaction volume. They set pressure at apparatus output (on CD line) and linear flow speed V = 5 m/sec at input (on AB line) in the line of symmetry axis (Fig. 1). The lengths of input and output of reaction zone significantly exceed zone's diameter ($L >> d_d$) that allows exception of influence of input and output turbulence parameters on reagents mixing characteristics. The last ones are the subjects of inquiry.

They compared obtained theoretical results with available experimental data for reaction zone of cylindrical type to confirm adequateness of carried out calculations (Fig. 1,a)

($Re = 2 \cdot 10^5$) [48]. By this the received results are agree with calculations made in [23]. In particular, values of length L_{cir} of circulation zone appearing in peripheral regions of reaction zone directly after reagents introduction into extending canal are presented in Table 1. There is a good coincidence (error is not higher than 15%) of calculated and experimental values of circulation zone length.

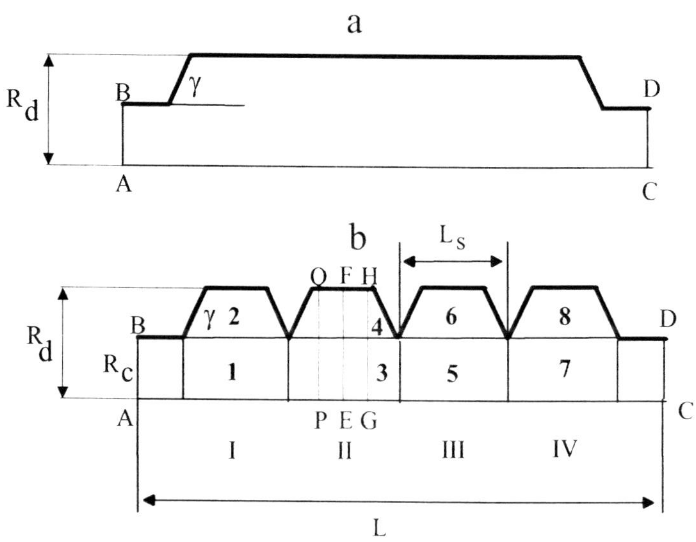

Figure 1. The schemes of cylindrical (a) and divergent-convergent (b) apparatus. γ – the angle of divergent opening; $R_d = d_d/2$ – radius of wide part (of divergent); $R_c = d_c/2$ – radius of narrow part (convergent); 1-8 – apparatus parts; I-IV – divergent-convergent sections.

Coincidence of results is also observed for axial rate profiles (Fig. 2) and for kinetic energy density of turbulence (Fig. 3). The obtained results allow predicting of reaction mixture turbulent mixing characteristics also for other conditions and canals of various geometry with confidence.

Thus, chosen mathematical model allows calculating of characteristics of turbulent mixing in tubular apparatus with various geometry of canal. Adequacy of obtained results (see Fig. 2 and 3) is well confirmed by correlation of experimental and calculating data.

Table 1. Calculated and experimental lengths of circulation zones L_{cir} / d_d

The angle of divergent opening **γ**, degrees	**L_{cir} / d_d**		
	Experimental data [31]	Calculation	
		Our results	[23]
30	4,1	3,4	3,5
90	4,6	4,7	4,7

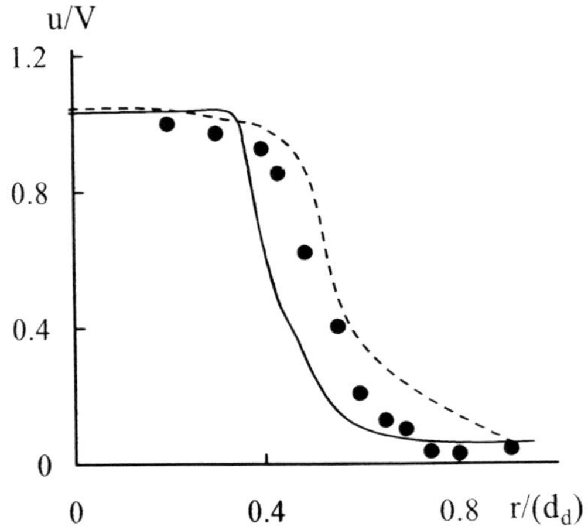

A.

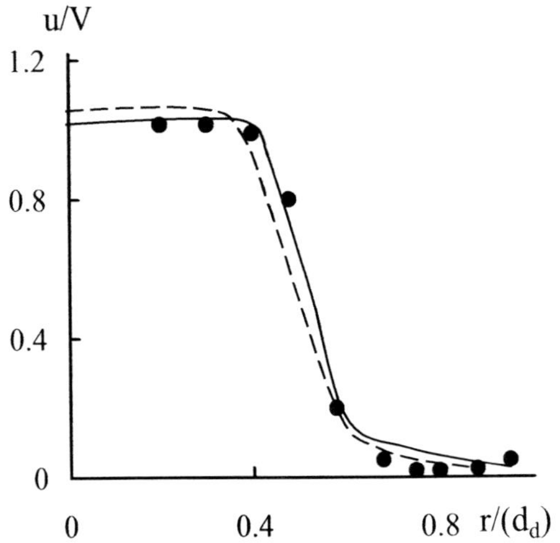

B.

Figure 2. The profile of axial rate in section $z = d_d$ of cylindrical apparatus at $\gamma = 30^0$ (a) and $\gamma = 90^0$ (b): • – experimental data [31]; dotted line – calculation data [23]; firm line – calculation data (our results).

Turbulent Mixing in Tubular Apparatus

Numerical calculations on the base of (5)-(14) equations allowed studying of regularities of turbulent diffusion coefficient D_t variation along the volume of tubular turbulent apparatus. Identification of characteristics of turbulent mixing in tubular turbulent apparatus with local hydrodynamic resistances of divergent-convergent design with optimization of their geometric parameters is of the main importance.

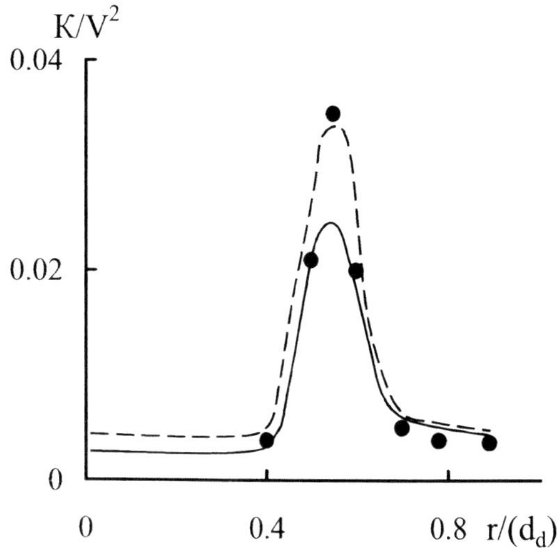

Figure 3.3. Profile of kinetic energy density of turbulence in the section $z = d_d$ of cylindrical apparatus at $\gamma = 90^0$: • - experimental data [31]; dotted line – calculation data [23]; firm line – calculation data (our results).

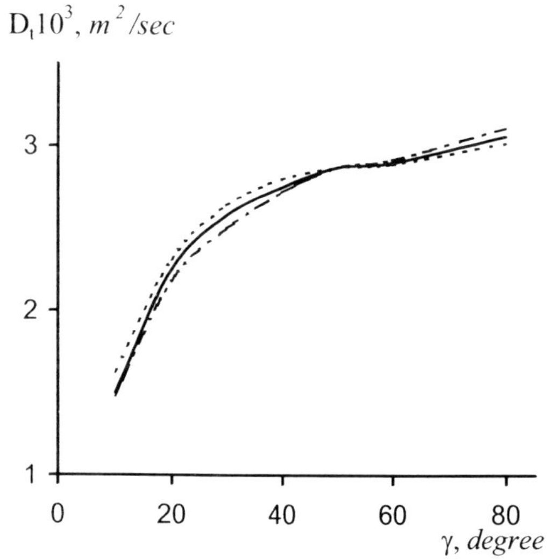

Figure 4. Coefficients of turbulent diffusion averaging by volume in central and peripheral parts of tubular apparatus of divergent-convergent design (Fig. 1,b) Peripheral – [-·-·-], central part – [- - - -], by volume – [———].

Calculations showed that when divergent angle of opening γ increases from 5 to 30^0C, i.e. at transition from cylindrical apparatus (Fig. 1,a) to divergent-convergent design (Fig. 1,b) the coefficient of turbulent diffusion rises in 3 times. But with further increase of angle the coefficient practically doesn't change (Fig. 4). The constancy of turbulent mixing level in apparatus peripheral and central regions is noticeable and it determines the equality of reagents turbulent mixing characteristics along the whole apparatus volume in wide interval of values of divergent angles of opening (Fig. 4). Firstly, this fact due to significantly lower convection rate of liquid flows in peripheral region ($R > d_c/2$) than in central part ($R < d_c/2$) of tubular turbulent apparatus of divergent-convergent design (Fig. 5). As a consequence the averaging of D_t along tubular apparatus volume at the expense of transfer processes predominantly occurs at turbulent exchange.

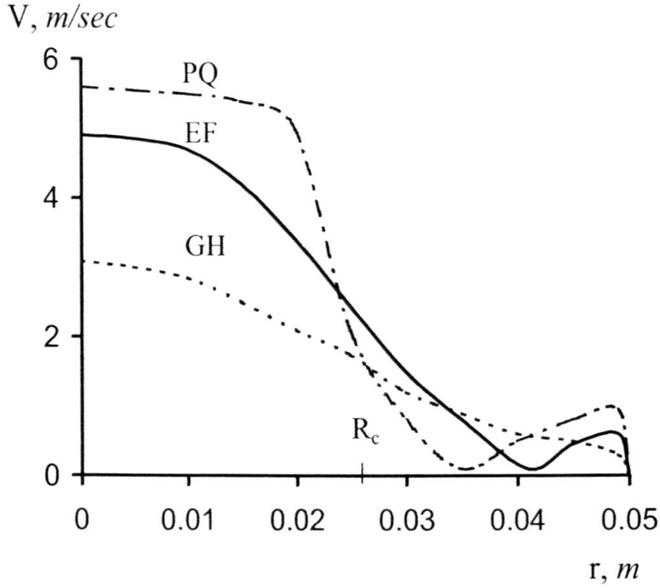

Figure 5. Profiles of absolute values of rate in reaction zone sections EF, GH and PQ at $\gamma = 45^0$ (see Fig. 1,b)

Comparison of turbulent diffusion coefficients D_t in various regions of tubular reactor showed (Table 2) that apparatus of divergent-convergent design provides in volume the field of D_t homogeneous enough (for comparison of characteristic times of diffusion τ_{mix} and chemical reaction τ_{ch} the order of D_t value is significant). Application of reactor of divergent-convergent design with divergent angle of opening γ in interval 20^0-45^0 is expedient under practical realization of fast chemical processes.

In apparatus of constant diameter (of cylindrical construction) initial parameters of turbulence at input, in particular flow geometry and the way of reagents introduction into apparatus significantly influence on reaction mixture turbulization degree. At that $\mathbf{D_t}$ decreases as moving off inlet part and reduces thereby the intensity of liquid medium mixing along apparatus length (Fig. 6, a). The usage of reactor of divergent-convergent design is advisable (Fig. 1, b) for increasing of flow turbulization degree and consequently reagents mixing efficiency (Fig. 6, b). Divergent-convergent canal allows maintaining high values of turbulence parameters along whole length of tubular apparatus made of several divergent-convergent sections of strictly limited extension (Fig. 6, b). In apparatus of such construction turbulence parameters are determined by turbulization appearing at the expense of canals' geometry and they are in order or higher than turbulence level creating as in tubular canals of constant diameter, so in stirred tank reactors even under application of very effective mechanical mixers.

Table 2. Turbulent diffusion coefficients $D_t \cdot 10^3$ m^2/sec averaging by volume in various parts and divergent-convergent sections (Fig. 1, b) of tubular turbulent apparatus at different angles γ. $Re = 2{,}5 \cdot 10^5$, $d_d = 0{,}05$ m, $V = 5$ m/sec, $\rho = 1000$ kg/m^3

γ / No.	5^0	10^0	17^0	30^0	45^0	60^0	75^0	85^0
Apparatus parts								
1	1,03	1,34	1,55	1,60	1,58	1,54	1,48	1,42
2	1,17	1,54	1,90	2,22	2,38	2,47	2,49	2,49
3	1,12	1,76	2,36	2,78	2,86	2,88	2,97	2,92
4	1,01	1,50	2,05	2,60	2,79	2,88	2,98	2,98
5	1,09	1,75	2,49	3,16	3,47	3,67	3,97	3,94
6	0,94	1,43	2,04	2,74	3,09	3,31	3,55	3,58
7	1,09	1,75	2,43	3,08	3,38	3,60	3,81	3,90
8	0,99	1,43	2,03	2,65	2,96	3,20	3,40	3,48
Divergent-convergent sections								
I	1,12	1,47	1,79	2,03	2,14	2,18	2,18	2,16
II	1,05	1,59	2,15	2,66	2,81	2,88	2,98	2,97
III	0,99	1,54	2,18	2,87	3,21	3,42	3,68	3,69
IV	1,02	1,53	2,16	2,78	3,09	3,32	3,52	3,61

(a)

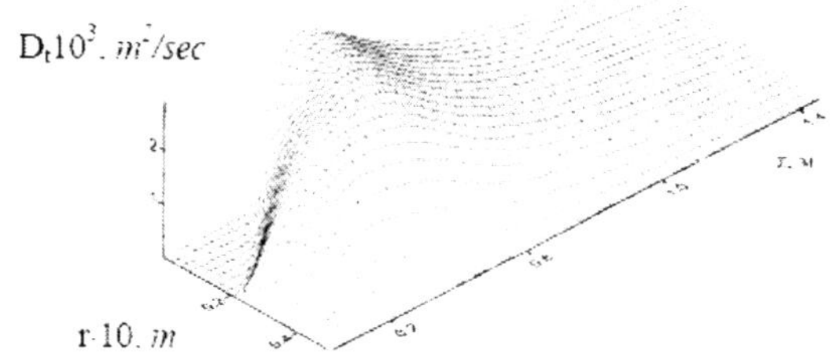

(b)

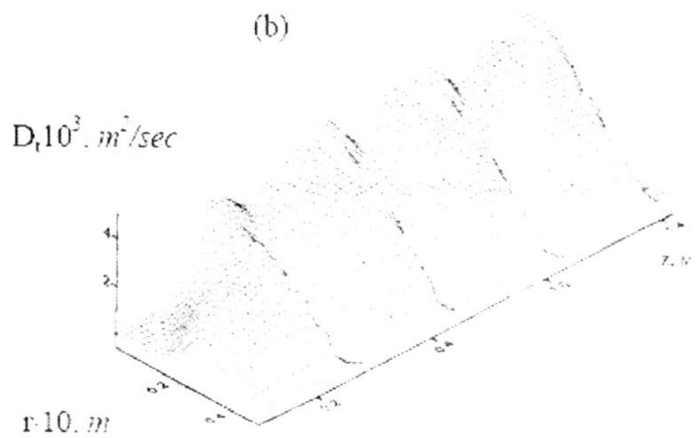

Figure 6. Distribution of turbulent diffusion coefficient (D_t) by reaction zone volume of cylindrical (a) and divergent-convergent (b) designs ($Re = 2 \cdot 10^5$, $d_d = 0{,}05$ m, $V = 4$ m/sec, $\rho = 1000$ kg/m^3).

In spite of divergent angle of opening γ the ratio of divergent diameter to convergent diameter d_d / d_c and section extension L_s/d_d are key parameters allowing optimization of effectiveness of turbulent mixing in apparatus of divergent-convergent design.

As a rule the time of micromixing is limiting time of mixing under polymer synthesis fast process due to high viscosity flows use. The maximum of turbulence kinetic energy density dissipation ε meets criterion of micromixing characteristic time minimum according with (3). That is why firstly it is necessary to study dependence of average value of turbulence kinetic energy density dissipation on ratio of reactor's geometrical sizes (d_d/d_c, L_s/d_d).

According with carried out calculations at fixed values of γ and d_d / d_c ratio section length L_s increase leads to the fact that turbulence kinetic energy density dissipation ε increases at first and then decreases. The analogous picture is observed at d_d / d_c ratio change. This testifies to the presence of maximum point of average turbulence kinetic energy density dissipation ε at some ratio of reaction zone geometrical sizes of divergent-convergent design. This ratio of sizes is optimal. Optimal ratio of geometrical sizes of tubular apparatus practically doesn't depend on angle γ that simplifies the problem.

The criterion for optimization of geometrical sizes ratio of tubular turbulent apparatus of divergent-convergent design is the maximum of average value of turbulence kinetic energy density dissipation ε, and parameters of optimization are the ratio of divergent-to-convergent diameters d_d/d_c and the ratio of section length-to-divergent diameter L_s/d_d. Figure 7 illustrates the dependence of average value of turbulence kinetic energy density dissipation ε on ratio of reaction zone geometrical sizes at $\gamma = 45^0$. The point of maximum M is indicated in Fig. 7 that corresponds to optimal parameters of reaction zone of divergent-convergent design: divergent-to-convergent diameters ratio $d_d/d_c = 1{,}6$ and the ratio of section length-to-divergent diameter $L_s/d_d = 1{,}7$. Optimal parameters are kept practically constant under angle γ changing from 30^0 to 85^0.

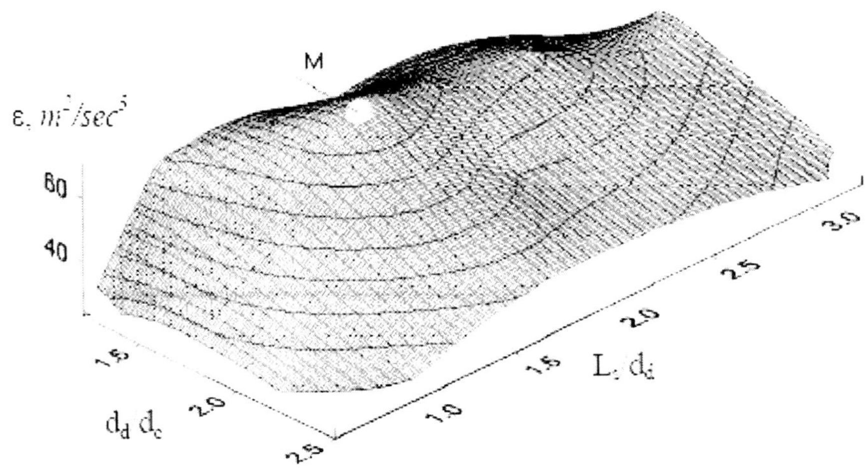

Figure 7. Dependence of turbulence kinetic energy density dissipation ε on reactors geometrical sizes ratio.

Thus, tubular turbulent apparatus of divergent-convergent design is able to provide in any chemical conditions and mass-transfer processes homogeneous conditions at high turbulent mixing level appearing only at the expense of canal geometry without application of mobile inside facilities. In the view of intensification of turbulent mixing in apparatus of divergent-convergent design the optimal ratios are $d_d/d_c = 1{,}6$, $L_s/d_d = 1{,}7$ and angle of divergent opening γ is in interval 20^0-45^0. Design simplicity and high reliability and also mass-exchange effectiveness make this type of apparatus very perspective for carrying out of fast chemical processes. In the case of the last ones it is very difficult to provide criterion Da < 1 ($\tau_{mix} < \tau_{ch}$) and to which very high safety requirements are made.

Low convective rate of liquid flows in peripheral parts of tubular turbulent apparatus of divergent-convergent design (Fig. 5) and conical extension in apparatus of cylindrical construction increase effectiveness of turbulent mixing and thereby reduce τ_{mix}. However the last fact would influence on distribution of reagents residence times in reaction zone and its shape determines fast processes character proceeding and quality of resulted polymer products.

Distribution of Reagents Residence Times in Apparatus of Cylindrical and Divergent-Convergent Types

The method of reception of curves of response to indicator introduction is useful for studying of reagents residence times distribution in reaction zone and estimation of hydrodynamic regime of tubular turbulent apparatus operation with different canal's geometry (cylindrical and divergent-convergent) and reagents introduction way (coaxial and radial).

For confirmation of adequacy of chosen technique for experimental determination of distributions of reagents residence times in tubular turbulent apparatus numerical calculation of three-dimensional turbulent liquid flow with the use of *CFD* soft *PHOENICS* was carried out.

Axially symmetric nonswirling turbulent flow of continuous incompressible Newton's fluid was considered. In this case the generalized equation of substance (mass, impulse, heat, turbulence kinetic energy) transfer is:

$$\partial(\rho \mathbf{G})/\partial\tau + \mathbf{div}(\rho \mathbf{u} \mathbf{G}) = \mathbf{div}(\mu \mathbf{grad} \mathbf{G}) + \mathbf{F} \qquad (17)$$

Here u – rate vector; F = f(G), – dependent variable indicating impulse of mass, enthalpy, turbulence kinetic energy units.

Moreover field of indicator movement speed satisfies the law of conservation of mass (continuity equation) of the following form:

$$\partial\rho/\partial\tau + \mathbf{div}(\rho \mathbf{u}) = \mathbf{0} \qquad (18)$$

Turbulent stresses are determined by standard and modified K-ε models of turbulence. For determination of flow field near the wall the method of parietal functions was used. Rates fields and pressures were corrected in the course of calculation according with *SIMPLE-C* algorithm. Diffusion of indicator was modeled as transmission of scalar introduced in less space of time in comparison with its average residence time in apparatus at fixed rate fields and turbulence parameters.

Experimentally received response curves are convenient to present by derived distribution curve by residence time in non-dimensional coordinates C-Θ that are calculated out of ratios [32] $C = C_i v_r / C_0$ and $\Theta = \tau_i / \bar{\tau}$, where C_0 – amount of introducing indicator, $\bar{\tau} = v_r / w$ – calculation residence time of indicator determining as apparatus volume v_r to volumetric speed of reaction mixture movement w ratio. Theoretical response curves were obtained, they characterized the flow structure and distribution of reagents residence times in tubular turbulent apparatus. Experimental and calculated functions of reagents residence times distribution were correlated with coefficient 0,95 (Fig. 8), that confirmed the obtained experimental data adequacy.

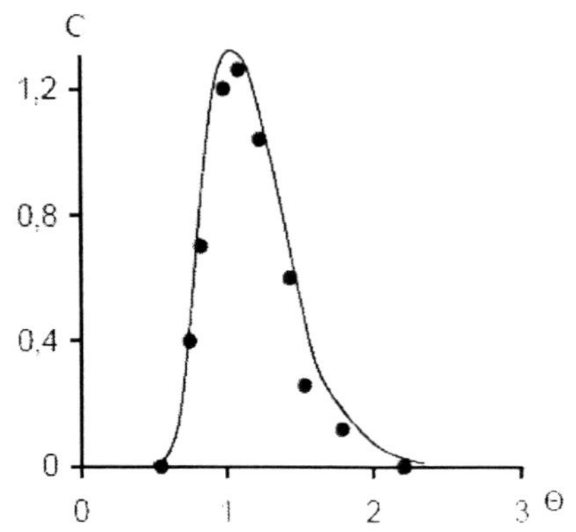

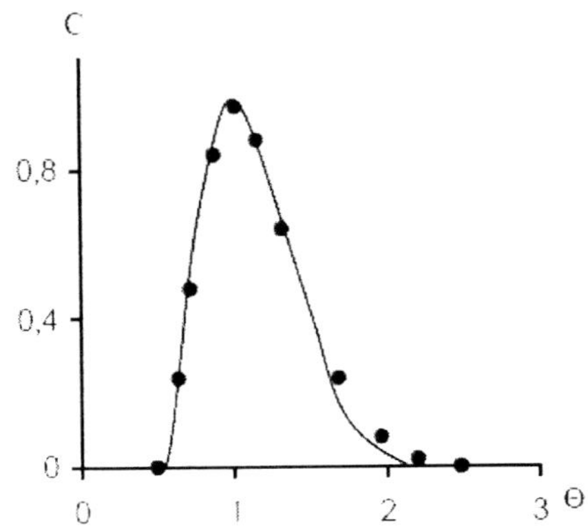

Figure 8. Distribution curves of reagents residence times in reaction zone. Apparatus V (a); VI (b), w = 130 cm^3/sec (Table 3). Line – calculation; points – experiment.

Table 3. Tubular turbulent apparatus design (Fig. 1)

Apparatus	$d_d=2R_d$, m	$d_c=2R_c$, m	L_s, m	L, m	w, cm^3/sec
Cylindrical design (Fig. 1, a)					
I	0,05	-	-	0,7	110-165
II	0,04	-	-	0,7	65-130
III	0,03	-	-	0,7	36-128
IV	0,023	-	-	1,1	37-140
Divergent-convergent design (Fig. 1, b)					
V	0,024	0,015	0,072	0,6	36-127
VI	0,024	0,015	0,048	0,5	36-130
VII	0,024	0,008	0,048	0,6	36-127
VIII	0,03	0,019	0,060	0,67	36-130

According with response curves (Fig. 8) tubular turbulent apparatus relate to apparatus of intermediate type, i.e. there is a deviation from plug-flow regime firstly at the expense of reverse current. The degree of the last one is determined by longitudinal mixing coefficient E.

Distribution curves of reagents residence times are converged with mixing τ_r to the low values region while volumetric speed of reagents w increases (Fig. 9) for all considered tubular turbulent apparatus constructions (Table 3).

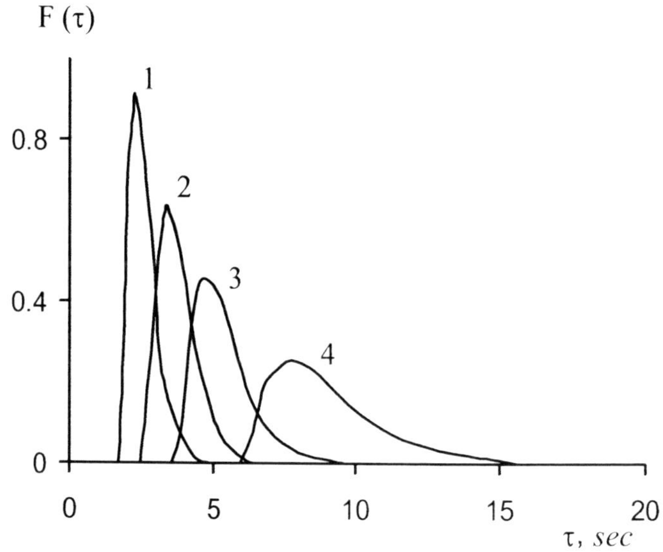

Figure 9. The influence of reaction mixture movement on distribution of reagents residence times in reactor of cylindrical type. Apparatus III (Table 3); w [cm^3/sec]: 130 (1); 91 (2); 62 (3); 36 (4).

Cellular and diffusion models are usually used for estimation of longitudinal mixing (turbulence) in reaction zone and consequently for evaluation of deviation degree of fluids hydrodynamic structure from ideal displacement and mixing regimes [17, 27].

Accordingly to cellular model fluids structure and response curve shape in apparatus are described by distribution differential function:

$$C(\Theta) = \frac{n^n \Theta^{n-1} e^{-n\Theta}}{(n-1)!} \tag{19}$$

Here n – the only parameter of cellular model equal to cells (reactors) number in cascade of ideal stirred reactors, ideal stirring regime is achieved at $n \to \infty$ [27]. It is accepted [33], that if cells number in reactor $n \geq 8$, then such apparatus can be calculated as plug-flow reactor with enough for industrial practice accuracy.

Accordingly to diffusion model any deviation in reagents residence times distribution from the distribution at ideal mixing independently of reasons is a consequence of longitudinal mixing and is determined by turbulence level [17]. Diffusion model means piston flow with superimposed effects conditioned by molecular diffusion, presence of small curls, stagnant zones and radial gradients of fluids speeds. In this case fictitious diffusion coefficient E (coefficient of longitudinal mixing) is used [34]. And mono-directional diffusion (along x axis of apparatus) is described by the correlation [27]:

$$\frac{dC}{d\tau} = -w\frac{dC}{dx} + E\frac{d^2C}{dx^2} \tag{20}$$

Solution of equation (20) at impact introducing of indicator leads to expression for function of residence time distribution [34]:

$$C(\Theta) = \sqrt{\frac{Bo}{4\pi\Theta}}\exp\left(-\frac{Bo}{4}\frac{(\Theta-1)^2}{\Theta}\right), \tag{21}$$

where $\mathbf{Bo} = \frac{L^2 w}{v_r E}$ - Bodenstain's criterion (or Pekle's criterion for longitudinal mixing Pe_L).

Flow structure is judged by numerical value of criterion Bo comparing its quantitative deviation from ideal displacement (at $Bo \to \infty$) and ideal mixing (at $Bo \to 0$) regimes.

Comparison of experimental derived curves of distribution by reagents residence times with curves calculated from (19) and (21) allows to receive numerical values of Bo и n and consequently to estimate degree of deviation of flows structures in reaction zone of various geometry from idealized models. Values $n \to 1$ (Fig. 10) and $Bo \to 0$ (Fig. 11) correspond to ideal mixing regime and when displacement conditions are reached – $n \to \infty$ (Fig. 10) and $Bo \to \infty$ (Fig. 11).

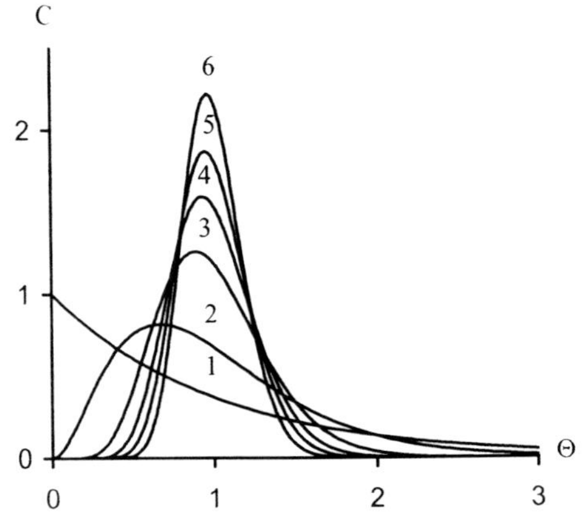

Figure 10. Differential curves of distribution of reagents residence times in reaction zone (cellular model), n = 1 (1); 3 (2); 9 (3); 15 (4); 21 (5); 30 (6).

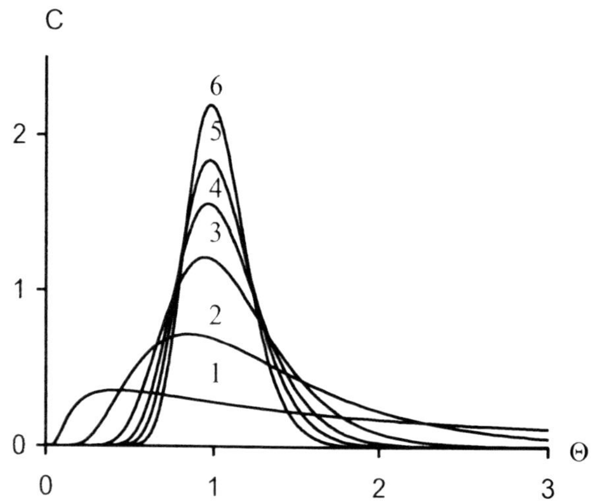

Figure 11. Differential curves of distribution of reagents residence times in reaction zone (diffusion model), Bo = 1 (1); 6 (2); 18 (3); 30 (4); 42 (5); 60 (6).

The inverse problem of response curves was solved for calculation of numerical values of Bodenstain's criterion Bo. For this purpose experimentally obtained differential response curves were approximated by dependences of cellular (19) and diffusion (21) models (Fig. 12). The biggest disarrangement between values calculated by (19) and (21) and corresponding experimental response curves didn't exceed 15% for all studied apparatus, and average disarrangement was 7%.

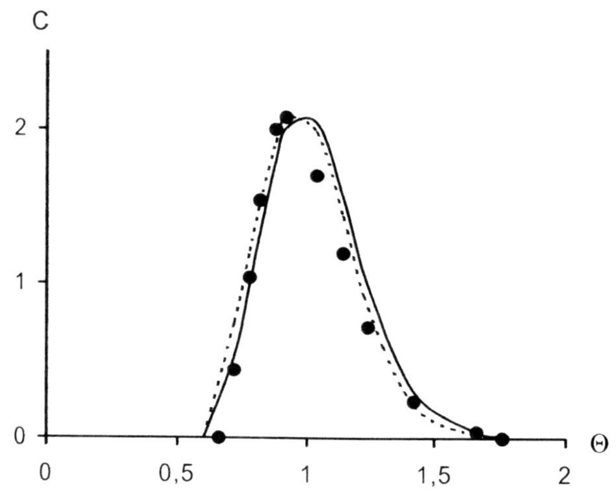

Figure 12. Experimental (points) and calculated (Bo = 57 (firm line), n = 28 (dotted line), w = 91 cm^3/sec) differential curves of reagents residence times distribution in reaction zone. Apparatus III (Table 3).

The influence of canal geometry on hydrodynamic regime of operation is characteristic for apparatus with coaxial reagents introduction (Fig 13, a,b). For apparatus of divergent-convergent design (Fig. 13, b) reduction of ratio of section length-to-divergent diameter L_s / d_d (apparatus V, VI), of diameter d_d (apparatus VI, VIII (Table 4)) and also the increase of canals profiling degree, i.e. ratio d_d/d_c (apparatus VI, VII) approach the liquid reagents structure to plug-flow regime that is determined by low values of criterion Bo (Table 4, Fig. 14). Thus, divergent-convergent design sections function as statistical turbulization devices increasing turbulent diffusion coefficient D_t (Fig. 6) and longitudinal mixing rate (Fig. 15).

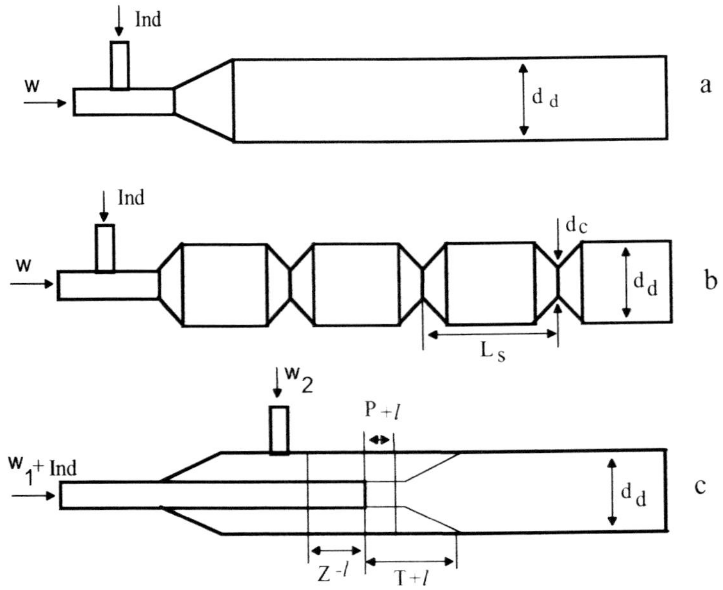

Figure 13. Tubular turbulent apparatus of cylindrical (a, c) and divergent-convergent (b) designs with coaxial (a, b) and radial (c) methods of reagents introduction. Ind – introduction of indicator. Reactors working regimes: P – plan front; T – torch; Z – drift regime.

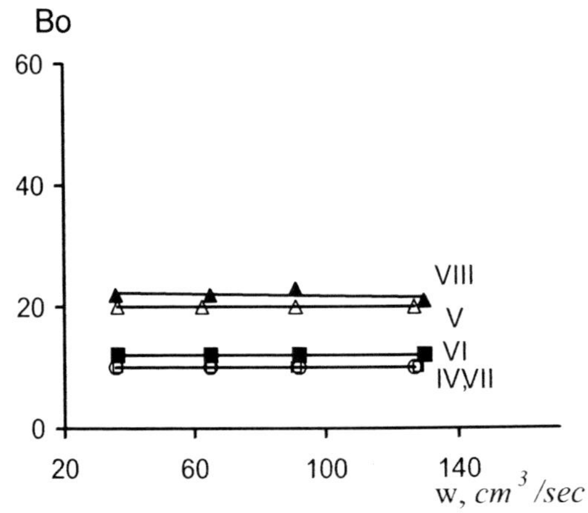

Figure 14. Dependence of Bodenstain's criterion on liquid flows' speed w in reactor of divergent-convergent design (V-VIII, see Table 3 and 4).

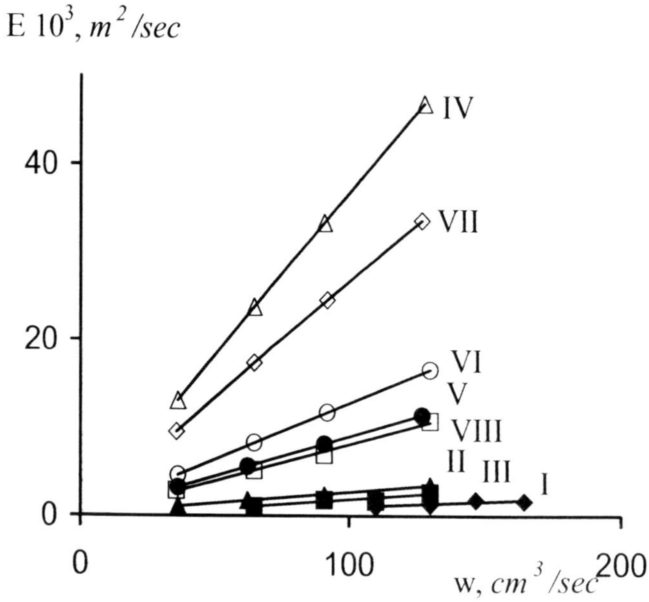

Figure 15. Dependence of liquid flows longitudinal mixing coefficient E on apparatus geometry (I-VIII, see Table 3 and 4) and reaction mixture volumetric rate w.

Table 4. Parameters of hydrodynamic structure of reaction mixture movement in dependence on reactors geometry (see Table 3)

Apparatus	n	Bodenstain's criterion, Bo
Cylindrical design (Fig. 13,a)		
I	25±1,75	50±3,5
II	26±1,82	52±3,64
III	26±1,82	52±3,64
IV	70±4,9	140±9,8*
Divergent-convergent design (Fig. 13,b)		
V	10±0,7	20±1,4
VI	6±0,42	12±0,84
VII	5±0,35	10±0,7
VIII	11±0,77	22±1,54

*w_1 = 24 cm³/sec; w_2 = 80 cm³/sec (w_1, w_2 – volumetric rate of central and axial flows correspondingly (Fig. 13,c).

Apparatus of cylindrical type with coaxial reagents introduction (Fig. 13, a) with $d_d \geq 0{,}03$m (apparatus I-III) is characterized by high values of criterion Bo (Table 4, Fig. 16) and consequently by higher in comparison with apparatus of divergent-convergent design approximation degree of reagents flow structure to plug-flow regime due to low longitudinal mixing rate (Fig. 15). In consequence there is narrow distribution of reagents residence times in reaction zone. As flows structures in apparatus of cylindrical design with $d_d \geq 0{,}03$m are practically equal (Bo ≈ 50) so there is no necessity in application of turbulent reactors of large diameters in industry for polymer synthesis that allows creation of compact highly productive technologies. It is characteristic that in apparatus of any structure with coaxial reagents introduction (Fig. 13, a, b) the volumetric rate of liquids flows (apparatus productivity) practically doesn't influence on criterion Bo (Fig. 14, 16). However, increase of longitudinal mixing rate occurs in this case.

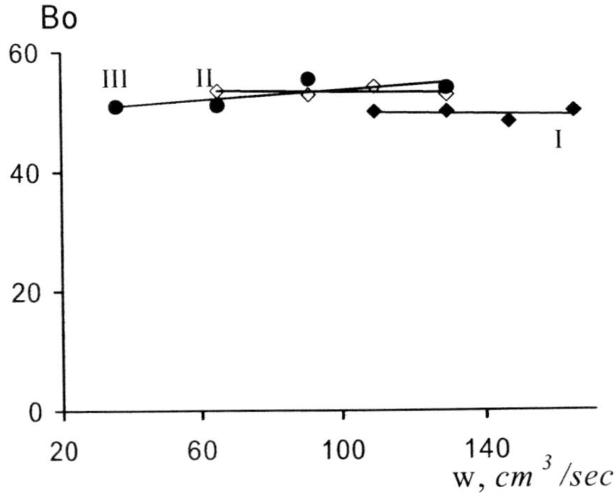

Figure 16. Dependence of Bodenstain's criterion Bo on reaction mixture movement rate w in apparatus of cylindrical design (I-III, Table 3 and 4).

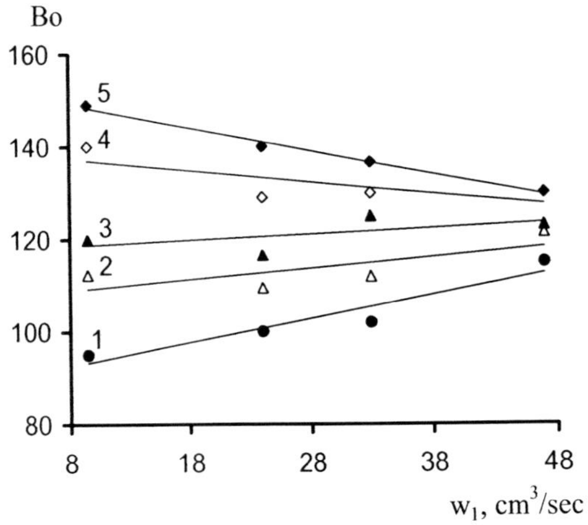

Figure 17. Dependence of Bodenstain's criterion Bo on the rate of central reagents flow w_1 at $w_2 = 41$ (1); 47 (2); 57 (3); 67 (4); 80 (5) cm^3/sec. Apparatus IV (see Table 3, Fig. 13, c).

For apparatus with redial flows introduction (Fig. 13, c) not only canal geometry but also the ratio of rates of initial reagents introduction w_1 and w_2 influence on hydrodynamic regime of their operation (Fig. 17). At fixed speed of central flow w_1 increase of w_2 leads to the rise of criterion Bo and approximate the operating regime of apparatus of this construction to plug-flow regime. At high rates of central flow w_1 the leveling of radial flow rate w_2 influence on hydrodynamic structure of reaction mixture movement occurs (Fig. 17).

The observed dependence of tubular turbulent apparatus work on the way of reagents introduction is explained by the fact that in this case the formation of various reaction fronts macrostructures in mixing zone is possible, in particular planar front (P), torch (T) and drift (Z) etc. (Fig. 13, c). At that the macrostructure in the form of planar reaction front corresponds to quasi-plug-flow regime in turbulent flows determining the optimal conditions of fast chemical processes realization under polymers synthesis at quasi-isothermal conditions, that is very favorable for production. The increase of radial flow rate w_2 leads to the transition between reaction fronts in following order – Z → П → T (Table 5). The rise of coaxial rate w_1 leads to the inversion of order of transitions between macrostructures (Table 5), criterion Bo approach to constant value about Bo ≈ 120 at that.

Table 5. Conditions of characteristic reaction fronts macrostructures formation in dependence on the ratio of reagents introduction rates. *l* – distance (cm) (Fig. 13, c)

w_1, cm^3/sec w_2, cm^3/sec	9,5	24	33	47
41	Z (l-1)	Z (l-1,5)	Z (l-2,5)	Z (l-2)
47	P (l+1)	Z (l-0,7)	Z (l-1)	Z (l-1,5)
57	T (l+1,5)	P (l+1)	P (l+0,5)	Z (l-0,5)
67	T (l+2,5)	P (l+1,5)	P (l+1)	Z (l-0,5)
80	T (l+3)	P (l+2)	P (l+1,5)	P (l+1,3)

Relative residence time Θ_r is a very important parameter describing the character of reagents movement in reaction zone. For the estimation of relative reagents residence time in reaction zone by experimental response curves medium-integral magnitude is τ_r calculated [33] it is a ratio of functions' integrals $\tau_i C_i = f(\tau_i)$ и $C_i = f(\tau_i)$ (Fig. 18).

$$\tau_r = \frac{\int_0^\infty \tau C_i(\tau) d\tau}{\int_0^\infty C_i(\tau) d\tau} \qquad (22)$$

In this case relative residence time of fluids in reaction zone characterizing stagnant zones and reagents slips (bypassing) is determined by ratio $\Theta_r = \tau_r / \bar{\tau}$. If $\Theta_п < 1$ then there is a slip of reagents in reaction zone that is undesirable under real processes of polymer production. When $\Theta_r = 1$ medium-integral magnitude of actual residence time τ_r corresponds to calculated $\bar{\tau}$ and hydrodynamic regime in reaction zone approximates to regime of ideal displacement.

Tubular turbulent apparatus of cylindrical design with diameter $d_d \geq 0{,}03$ m (apparatus I–III, Table 3) have $\Theta_r \leq 1$ (Table 6) that is characteristic for plug-flow regime. Obviously it relates to the fact that in apparatus of such construction turbulent mixing level (Fig. 6, a) and consequently the gradient of turbulent pulsations directed opposite to main flow reduce along apparatus axis x as moving off regents introduction zone. This determines narrow distribution of reagents residence times in reaction zone. At the same time, tubular turbulent apparatus of divergent-convergent design (apparatus V-VIII) are characterized by zones of product delay ($\Theta_r > 1$, Table 6) increasing reagents residence times in reaction zone.

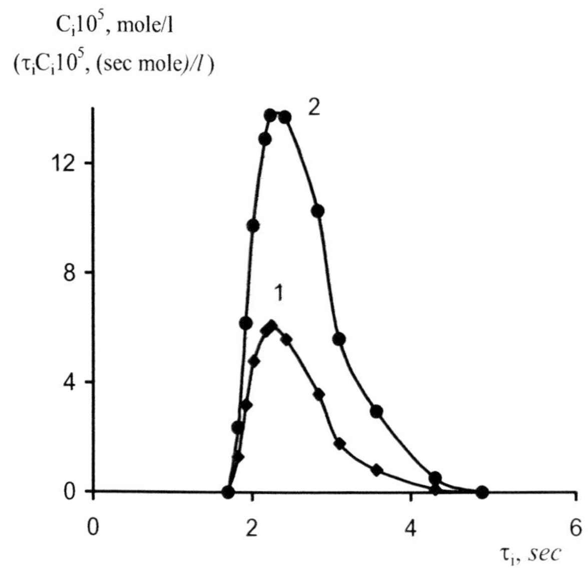

Figure 18. Dependence of $C_i(\tau_i C_i)$ on τ_i for determination of average-integral residence time τ_r. 1 – $C_i - \tau_i$; 2 – $\tau_i C_i - \tau_i$. Apparatus III, w = 130 cm^3/sec (Table 3).

Table 6. Relative reagents residence time Θ_r in reaction zone of various geometry

Apparatus (Table 3)	Relative reagents residence time Θ_r	Apparatus operation mode
I	0,97	Indicator slip
II	0,97	
III	1	Plug-flow regime
V	1,14	Indicator delay
VI	1,15	
VII	1,19	
VIII	1,05	

Thus, the influence of reaction zone geometry and reagents introduction way on hydrodynamic reaction mixture movement structure and reactors operating mode was revealed with the help of solution of response curves inverse problems. At coaxial reagents introduction the hydrodynamic regime of tubular turbulent apparatus operation is determined by reaction zone geometry. At radial reagents introduction in one and the same apparatus in dependence on the ratio of reagents introduction rates the formation of modes with various approximation degree both to idealized mixing and displacement models is possible. The last fact is impossible in the case of existing reactors of applied chemistry.

Noticeable differences between tubular turbulent apparatus of cylindrical and divergent-convergent design determine various spheres of their industrial application under fact processes realization in polymer synthesis. Tubular turbulent apparatus of cylindrical with $d_d < 0{,}03$m and divergent-convergent with $d_d \le 0{,}03$m; $L_s/d_d = 2\div3$, $d_d/d_c = 1{,}6\div3$ designs are characterized by intensive longitudinal mixing and presence of zones of reagents circulation that approach them to apparatus functioning in ideal mixing regime. In cylindrical apparatus with diameter $d_d < 0{,}03$m the rate of longitudinal mixing is comparatively not high ($E \le 4\cdot10^{-3}$ m^2/sec) and consequently there are practically no zones of reagents delay or slip ($\Theta_r \approx 1$), i.e. they work in quasi-plug-flow mode with narrow reagents residence times distribution. Reaction zone of cylindrical design is advisably to be used for realization of extra-fast chemical processes with characteristic reaction time $\tau_{ch} \le 0{,}01$ in quasi-plug-flow mode when the process to 100% proceeds at places of reagents introduction and where the maximum level of turbulent mixing is reached (Fig. 6,a). Divergent-convergent construction is effective under realization of fast exothermal reactions, at that intensive longitudinal mixing of liquid flows allows creation in reaction zone of quasi-isothermal (isothermal in any cross section of flow) regime. Intensive turbulent mixing allows recommendation to use tubular turbulent apparatus of divergent-convergent design as prereactors in processes where fast and slow processes proceed simultaneously to remove diffusion restrictions at fast stages of "gross" processes. High level of turbulent mixing and its constancy over the whole reaction zone volume (Fig. 6, b) and consequently high approximation degree to ideal mixing regime (Fig. 14) determine prospects of application of apparatus of divergent-convergent design for intensification of mass-exchange processes both in homogeneous and heterogeneous flows and also for intensification of convective heat-exchange at external thermostating of fast polymerization reactions.

SELF-SIMILAR REGIME OF REACTION MEDIUM FLOW

The main problem of polymer products production in solution, in particular ethylene propylene and chlorobutyl rubbers, is viscosity rise on one-three levels while polymer concentration in solution increases. High viscosities of polymers solutions as a rule do not provide intensive mixing of reaction mixture because values of Reynolds criterion (Re) and consequently turbulent diffusion significantly decrease. At that ineffective molecular diffusion is the most possible way of mixing. That is why, for example under polymerization, decomposition and washing out of catalyst, and also under polymer stabilization before its isolation they work with solutions diluted enough (not higher than 10-13 mass %) and it is a substantial disadvantage of acting productions. With monomer concentration decrease in reaction mixture polymerization rate and production efficiency reduce.

At the same time it is known that in high-turbulent flows viscosity doesn't influence on base medium volume flow characteristics because of self-similar liquid flow formation in relation to criterion Re and viscosity. The value of criterion Re over which self-similar region is observed is determined by reaction zone geometry. They may expect that self-similar regime will begin to form at significantly lower Reynolds number because in comparison with cylindrical canal in divergent-convergent design of turbulent apparatus at the same Reynolds values significantly higher turbulization degree of flow is achieved (Fig. 6).

Numerical solution of equation of liquid flows turbulent movement with the use of K-ε turbulence model (5)-(16) confirmed this suggestion. In divergent-convergent canal self-similar regime comes at $Re_{cr} = 800/f$. Parameter f is the function of angle of divergent opening γ and its values can be found by graphical dependence (Fig. 19) or by formula approximating this dependence:

$$f = 0{,}117 + 0{,}049\gamma - 0{,}0012\gamma^2 + 1{,}374 \cdot 10^{-5}\gamma^3 - 5{,}9 \cdot 10^{-8}\gamma^4 \quad (23)$$

In particular in interval of divergent opening angles γ 30^0-80^0 self-similar regime is observed at $Re \geq Re_{cr} = 950 \pm 50$ (Fig. 19). At the same time in apparatus of cylindrical design self-similar regime of reaction mixture flow is observed at $Re > 10^7$, i.e. is higher in four orders.

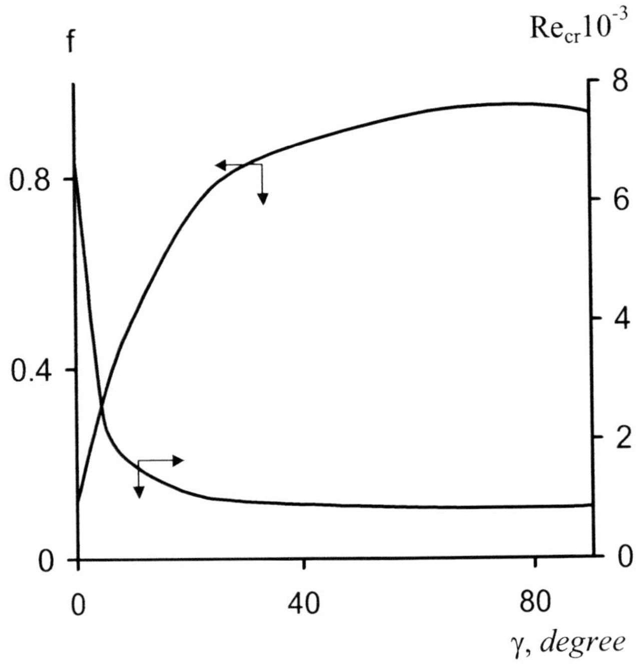

Figure 19. Dependence of critical value of Reynolds criterion (Re_{cr}) and parameter f on divergent opening angle (γ) in reactor of divergent-convergent type.

Thus, in self-similar regime all values determining reagents turbulent mixing when medium homogenization is limited by exchange processes between large turbulent flows don't depend on flows viscosities (self-similar flow in relation to Re). This fact constricts the circle of values determining properties of reagents turbulent mixing in tubular apparatus of jet type. Only three values characterizing large-scale movements remain: medium density ρ, apparatus diameter d and linear rate of flows movement V. The level of liquid flows turbulence depends on these three values at conditions of its independence on viscosity. With the help of these three values they may constitute the following single combinations with corresponding dimensions for average values of turbulence kinetic energy density K and its dissipation, turbulent diffusion coefficient D_t and hydraulic resistance Δp:

$$K_{av} \sim V^2;\ \varepsilon_{av} \sim V^3/d;\ D_{t\,av} \sim V \cdot d;\ \Delta p \sim \rho \cdot V^2 \tag{24}$$

In particular, the last fact can be illustrated by the example of pressure loss under liquid flows movement in cylindrical canals, where at laminar flow ($Re \leq 2300$) Δp depends on Re and doesn't depend on canal's wall roughness [27]:

$$\Delta p = \frac{32}{Re} \frac{\rho \cdot L \cdot V^2}{d}, \tag{25}$$

and at turbulent movement ($Re = (4\text{-}100) \cdot 10^3$) in self-similar region of flow in relation to Re, Δp stops to depend on liquid movement character and depends only on wall roughness [27]:

$$\Delta p = \frac{0{,}387 \cdot \rho \cdot L \cdot V^2}{d(\lg \delta^{-1})^2} \tag{26}$$

Here δ – relative roughness of wall equal to ratio of average height of roughness on inside surface of tubing (absolute roughness) to tubing diameter.

We succeeded in finding of numerical coefficients in (24) by data file handling received by solution of equations of continuum turbulent movement with the use of K-ε turbulence model (5)-(16) and by method of finite elements on irregular computational grid.

The average value of turbulence kinetic energy density:

$$K = f_c f^2 V_c^2 \tag{27}$$

The average rate of its dissipation:

$$\varepsilon = \frac{f_E f^3 V_c^3}{d_c} \tag{28}$$

The average value of turbulent diffusion coefficient:

$$D_{T} = \frac{0{,}09 f_c^2 f V_c d_c}{f_E}, \tag{29}$$

where coefficients f_c и f_E are determined by geometric parameters of reaction zone d_d / d_c and L_s / d_d:

$$f_c = -0{,}074 + 0{,}012\cdot\left(\frac{L_s}{d_d}\right) - 8{,}74\cdot10^{-3}\cdot\left(\frac{L_s}{d_d}\right)^2 + 8{,}64\cdot10^{-4}\cdot\left(\frac{L_s}{d_d}\right)^3 + 0{,}078\cdot\left(\frac{d_c}{d_c}\right) +$$

$$+0{,}021\cdot\left(\frac{d_d}{d_c}\right)\cdot\left(\frac{L_s}{d_d}\right) - 1{,}31\cdot10^{-3}\cdot\left(\frac{d_d}{d_c}\right)\cdot\left(\frac{L_s}{d_d}\right)^2 -$$

$$0{,}022\cdot\left(\frac{d_d}{d_c}\right)^2 - 3{,}22\cdot\left(\frac{d_d}{d_c}\right)^2\cdot\left(\frac{L_s}{d_d}\right) \tag{30}$$

$$f_E = -0{,}138 + 0{,}226\cdot\left(\frac{d_d}{d_c}\right) - 0{,}116\cdot\left(\frac{d_d}{d_c}\right)^2 + 0{,}019\cdot\left(\frac{d_d}{d_c}\right)^3 + 0{,}03\cdot\left(\frac{L_s}{d_d}\right) - 4{,}95\cdot10^{-3}\cdot$$

$$\cdot\left(\frac{d_d}{d_c}\right)\cdot\left(\frac{L_s}{d_d}\right) - 1{,}93\cdot10^{-3}\cdot\left(\frac{L_s}{d_d}\right)\cdot\left(\frac{d_d}{d_c}\right)^2 - 9{,}62\cdot10^{-3}\cdot\left(\frac{L_s}{d_d}\right)^2 + 3{,}22\cdot10^{-3}\cdot\left(\frac{d_d}{d_c}\right)\cdot\left(\frac{L_s}{d_d}\right)^2 \tag{31}$$

The possibility of self-similar regime formation in reactor of divergent-convergent design allows reception of acceptable for engineering calculations formulas of mixing characteristic times by substitution of (27)-(29) to (2)-(4).

Characteristic time of turbulent mixing:

$$\tau_{turb} = \frac{11{,}1 l^2 f_E}{f_c^2 f V_c d_c} \tag{32}$$

In this case characteristic time of micro-mixing (mixing at the expense of molecular diffusion) can be calculated by ratio:

$$\tau_{micro} = 17{,}3\sqrt{\frac{\nu d_c}{f_E f^3 V_c^3}} \tag{33}$$

Characteristic time of meso-mixing (mixing at the expense of exchange between large turbulent flows and being inside of them little flows) is calculated by ratio:

$$\tau_{meso} = 3\sqrt{\frac{l^2 d_c}{f_E f^3 V_c^3}} \tag{34}$$

Formulas (32)-(34) are suitable for calculation of turbulent mixing characteristics in following ratios intervals: $d_d / d_c = 1{,}2\div2{,}5$; $L_s / d_d = 0{,}5\div3{,}5$; $L_s / d_d > (1 - d_d / d_c)ctg\gamma$.

Comparison of mixing characteristic times calculated by (32)-(34) with chemical reaction characteristic time τ_{ch} or liquid flows residence time in apparatus τ_r allows calculation of optimal construction of tubular turbulent apparatus for both fast chemical reactions realization and flows mixing with the aim of their homogenization.

Formation of optimal hydrodynamic regime in reactor of divergent-convergent design causes possibility of polymer products concentration increase in solution under rubbers and thermoplastics synthesis and also under operation with their high-viscosity solutions up to the stage of resulted products isolation including fast chemical reactions realization. There is an exigency of transition of a number of polymer productions in solutions to the resources- and energy-saving highly productive technologies of heightened environmental safety with wide use of flowing compact tubular turbulent apparatus of divergent-convergent design.

Thus, the possibility of realization of self-similar flow regime in tubular turbulent apparatus of divergent-convergent design at comparatively low reagents movement linear rates enlarges the spheres of their industrial usage for the work with high-viscosity mediums and also allows reception of equations for calculation of average values of turbulent diffusion coefficient D_t, turbulence kinetic energy density K, its dissipation ε and characteristic times of flows mixing at various scales.

Thus, when changing the geometry (design) of tubular turbulent apparatus of divergent-convergent construction, dynamics of its operation and also physical parameters of reagents liquid flows one may optimize the values of turbulent mixing characteristics in accordance with proceeding process specificity limited by mass-exchenge. There are intervals of values of diameter of tubular turbulent apparatus of divergent-convergent design and of liquid flows movement linear rate at which conditions for diffusion limitations taking off for fast chemical reaction proceeding are created. In accordance with process character (kinetic parameters, physical characteristics of liquid flows, etc.) regularities obtained in the work allow scientifically-grounded selection of optimal conditions for its carrying out (reaction zone geometry, dynamic regimes, etc.).

REFERENCES

[1] Al. Al. Berlin, K. S. Minsker, K. M. Dyumaev *New Unified Energy- and Material-Saving, High-Performance, Ecological-Friendly Technologies based on Tubular Turbulent Reactors,* Moscow (1996) (in Russian)

[2] K. S. Minsker, Al. Al. Berlin, V. P. Zakharov *Vysokomol. Soedin.,* 44, No. 9, 1606-1627 (2002).

[3] Yu. A. Sangalov, K. S. Minsker *Polymers and Copolymers of Isobutylene: Fundamental Problems and Applied Aspects,* Gilem, Ufa (2001) (in Russian).

[4] K. S. Minsker, Yu. A. Sangalov *Isobutylene and its polymers,* Khimiya, Moscow (1986) (in Russian).

[5] Al. Al. Berlin, K. S. Minsker, Yu. A. Prochukhan, M. M. Karpasas, N. S. Enikolopyan *Vysokomol. Soedin.,* 28, No. 6, 461-465 (1986).

[6] Al. Al. Berlin, K. S. Minsker, Yu. A. Prochukhan, M. M. Karpasas, N. S. *Enikolopyan Dokl. Akad. Nauk,* 287, No. 1, 145-148 (1986).

[7] Ya. B. Zel'dovich *Chemical Physics and Hydrodynamics,* Nauka, Moscow (1984) (in Russian).

[8] V. Z. Kompaniets, A. A. Ovsyannikov, A. S. Polak *Chemical Reactions in Turbulent Flows of Gases and Plasma,* Nauka, Moscow (1979) (in Russian).

[9] Al. Al. Berlin, K. S. Minsker *Technology of the XXI century. Nauka proizvodstvu,* 53, No. 3, 7–12 (2002).

[10] Al. Al. Berlin, K. S. Minsker, Yu. A. Sangalov, V. G. Oshmyan, A. G. Svinukhov, A. P. Kirillov, N. S. Enikolopyan *Vysokomol. Soedin.,* 22A, No. 3, 566-574 (1980).

[11] Al. Al. Berlin, K. S. Minsker *Dokl. Akad.* Nauk, 355, No. 3, 346-348 (1997).

[12] Al. Al. Berlin, K. S. Minsker, K. M. Dyumaev, S. V. Kolesov, S. P. Gantseva *Khimicheskaya Promyshlennost',* No. 5, 27-30 (1997).

[13] D. A. Frank-Kamenetskii *Diffusion and Heat-Transfer in Chemical Kinetics,* Nauka, Moscow (1987) (in Russian).

[14] Al. Al. Berlin, S. A. Vol'fson *Vysokomol. Soedin.*, 36, No. 4, 616-628 (1994).

[15] V. M. Barabash, N. N. Smirnov *Zh. Prikl. Khimii,* 67, No. 2, 196-203 (1994).

[16] J. Baldyga, J. R. Bourne, R. V. Gholap *Chemical Engineering Science*, 50, No. 12, 1877-1880 (1995).

[17] D. A. Baizenberger, D. Kh. Sebastian *Principles of Polymerization Engineering,* Khimiya, Moscow (1988) (in Russian).

[18] L. N. Braginskii, V. I. Begachev, V. M. Barabash *Mixing in Liquid Mediums: Physical Bases and engineering calculation methods*, Khimiya, Leningrad (1984) (in Russian).

[19] V. M. Barabash *Teoreticheskie Osnovy Khimicheskoi Technologii*, 28, No. 2, 110-117 (1994).

[20] A.N. Blaznov, V. A. Kunichan, D. V. Chashilov *Zh. Prikl. Khimii,* 74, No. 4, 621-624 (2001).

[21] R. G. Takhavutdinov, G. S. D'yakonov, R. Ya. Deberdeev, K. S. Minsker *Khimicheskaya Promyshlennost',* No. 5, 41-49 (2000).

[22] V. P. Budtov, V. V. Konsetov *Heat- and Mass-Transmission in Polymerization Processes Khimiya,* Leningrad (1988) (in Russian).

[23] E. Turgeon, D. Pelletier, L. Ignat *Paper of the 36 th Aerospace Sciences Meeting and Exhibit. Proceeding of the American Institute of Aeronautics and Astronautics,* 1-19 (1998).

[24] Al. Al. Berlin, V. Z. Kompaniets, A. A. Konoplev, K. S. Minsker, S. K. Minsker, Yu. A. Prochukhan, E. A. Ryabenko, N. S. Enikolopyan *Dokl. Akad. Nauk SSSR,* 305, No. 5, 1143-1146 (1989).

[25] J. Villermaux, L. Falk *Chemical Engineering Science*, 49, 5127-5132 (1994).

[26] J. Baldyga, J. R. Bourne, S. J. Hearn *Chemical Engineering Science*, 52, No. 24, 457-501 (1998).

[27] A.G. Kasatkin *Basic Processes and Apparatuses in Chemical Technology,* Khimiya, Moscow (1971) (in Russian).

[28] V. A. Kaminskii, A. B. Rabinovich, A. Ya. Fedorov, V. A. Frost, A. A. Nur *Zh. Fizicheskoi Khimii,* 69, No. 8, 1456-1461 (1995).

[29] B. E. Launder, D. B. Spalding *Mathematical models of turbulence*, Acad. Press 6 th, London, 16-35 (1972).

[30] O. Zenkevich, K. Morgan *Terminal Elements and Approximation*, Mir, Moscow (1986) (in Russian).

[31] M. C. Chaturvedi *Journal of the hydraulics division. Proceedings of the American Society of civil Engineers,* 89, 61-92 (1963).

[32] V. M. Ramm, Gases Absorption, Khimiya, Moscow (1976) (in Russian).

[33] A.M. Zhurba, S. V. Kurilov, L. L. Gerasimova, I. B. Vil'chinskaya *Theoretical basis of applied chemistry,* 29, No. 1, 22-30 (1995).

[34] P. Torres, F. A. R. Oliveira, S. P. *Fortuna Journal of Food Engineering,* 35, No. 2, 147-163 (1998).

In: Synthesis and Properties of Low- and High-Molecular Compounds ISBN 1-59454-716-5
Editor: Gennady E. Zaikov et al., pp. 321-327

Chapter 18

SWELLING OF THE FILLED POLYMER COMPOSITIONS

O. A. Legonkova, A. A. Bokarev and V. S. Ivolgin*
Moscow State University of Applied Biotechnology,
Russia, Moscow, 109316, Talalikhina str., 33.
*Nursery "Sady Podmoskowya"
140055, Russia, Moscow Region, Lubertsy town, Smirnovskaya str, 2B
Tel\fax: +7(095) 276 22 48
E-mail: ol@te-ka.ru

ABSTRACT

Behavior of different compositions based on synthetic polymers and copolymers and different fillers were investigated. The choice of polymer matrix and fillers was stipulated by the requirements to the final compounded mix.

Key words: organic and inorganic fillers, compounded materials, controlled mass transportation.

INTRODUCTION

Lately a great attention is paid to technology of controlled excretion of nutritious substances from polymer biodegradable materials [1]. These biodegradable materials are widely used in various fields of life: agriculture, medicine, etc. These materials consist of a tremendous variety of nutritious matters depending on the final purposes. Nevertheless the interest to exploration of properties of such materials is still growing.

That's why the aim of the present article is to study of behavior of the filled with organic and inorganic polymer compounded mixes after being put into distilled water.

Materials and Methods

The following polymers were chosen as polymer matrix: copolymer of ethylene and vinyl acetate (CEVA) with different content of vinyl acetate groups; co-polyamide (Co-PA), received by polycondensation of adipinic and sebacic acids and hexamethylendiamine, trade mark – H-005 (Tg = 115-120^{0}C, melting index – 15 g/10min). The criterion, governing the chose of the said above polymer materials, was the presence of functional groups in all these polymers, and as sequence, capable to biodegrability [2]. Another determining factor was the low temperature of their processing (130-150^{0}C), this is very important taking into the account the fact of preservation of properties of fillers during processing of compounded mix.

Organic and inorganic compounds were taken as fillers. Waste of grain thrashing were chosen as an organic filler. It has particles of 63-240 mkm in dimension, piled density – 350 kg/m^3, moisture – 4%. Water soluble mineral complex fertilizer of type "Rastvorin-A" was used as an inorganic filler which consists of the necessary microelements as well as the main trace elements, such as: Mg, Cu, Zn, B, Mo, in the form of their water-soluble salts, needed for growth and evolution of plants.

Investigation of mass changes of the samples was carried out through gravimetric analysis, titration, pH-measurement. Mechanical properties of samples were measured through "Instron" machine.

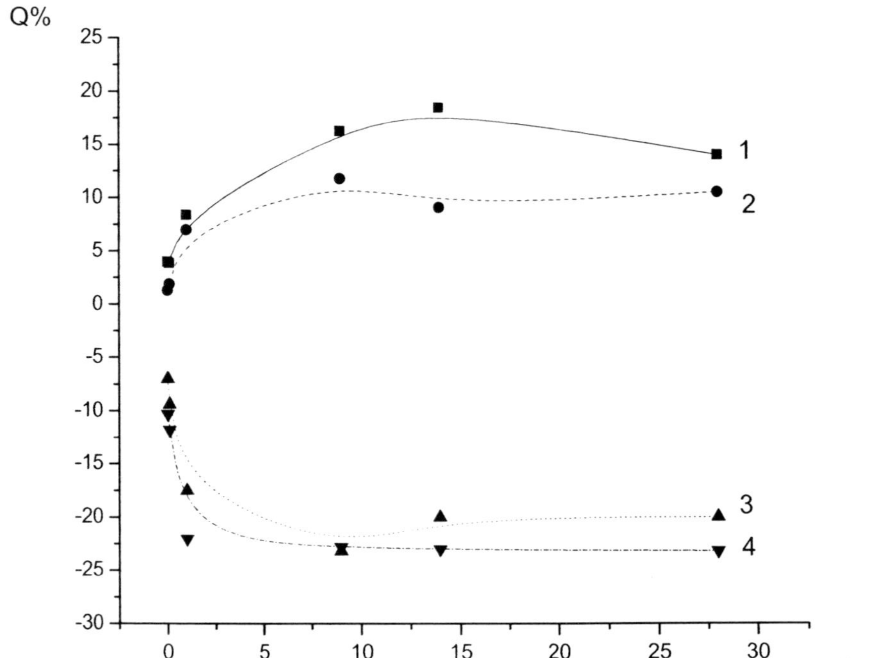

Figure 1. Mass change of the samples made of Co-PA and inorganic filler with different content of inorganic component: 1- 10% of inorganic filler, 2- 25% of inorganic filler, 3- 40% of inorganic filler, 4- 50% of inorganic filler.

EXPERIMENTAL DATA

Time changes in mass (Q) of the samples based on Co-PA polymer and different content of inorganic filler are represented on the fig.1. As it is shown, when the small content of the inorganic filler is (up to 25%) in the compounded mix, the mass of the sample grows. Then, with the increasing filling the mass of the sample diminishes. It's obvious to suppose that this "negative swelling"[3] connected with washing the water-soluble components of the inorganic filler up.

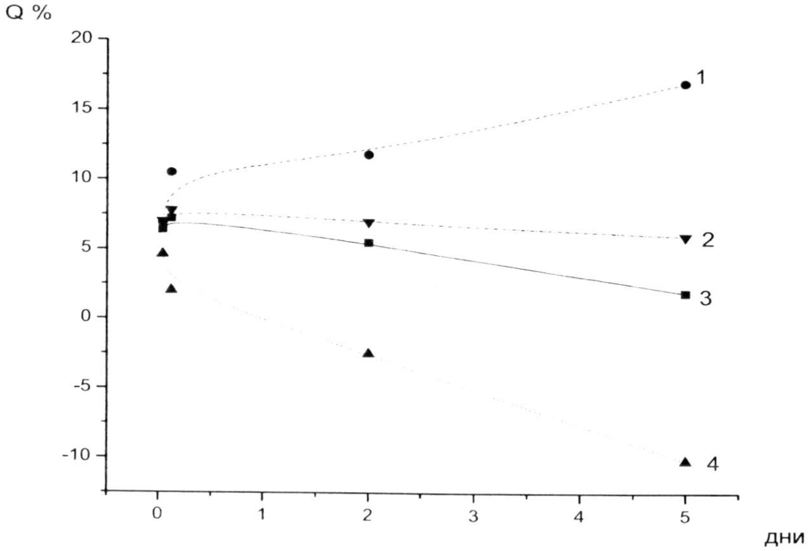

Figure 2. Mass changing of the samples, Co-PA-organic fillers-inorganic fillers: 1 - 50%-40%-10%; 2 – 50%-25%-25%; 3 – 50%-20%-30%; 4 – 50%-10%-40%.

The addition of organic fillers into the two-component system Co-PA-organic filler leads to deceleration of mass exchange processes, fig.2.

In case of changing polymer matrix, the same behavior of the filled samples was noticed, table 1.

In spite of the fact that two-component systems (polymer-inorganic filler) with the increasing amount of inorganic matter diminish their mass, fig.1, the amount of Mg^{2+} ions in water extraction decreases, fig.3,a. It could be explained by saponification of vinyl acetate groups of CEVA and interaction of OH^- groups with Mg^{2+}. Presence of organic filler slow down the process of swelling of the samples, fig.2, and as sequence, the excretion of Mg^{2+} ions into the water. In case of Co-PA matrix the effect of decreasing of extraction of Mg^{2+} with the increasing of inorganic content in samples and with the increasing of the content of organic filler was also revealed. So, changes of ingredient content in composed mix give us the chance to directed regulating of transportation of mineral substances out of filled polymer into the water and finally into the environment.

Table 1. Mass change of the filled systems

Composition, mass %			Mass changing, %,		
polymer	Organic filler	Inorganic filler	During 24 hours	During 120 hours	During 720 hours
1	2	3	4	5	6
CEVA					
80	20	-	6,1	8,2	11,3
60	40	-	20,7	21,2	22,5
50	50	-	25,8	27,5	30,0
40	60	-	29,6	29,8	34
80	-	20	0,13	9,1	28,9
60	-	40	-18,0	-10,5	-4,9
50	-	50	-7,5	3,5	14,9
40	-	60	-27,8	-24,3	-14,9
20	60	20	19	21,9	9,2
25	50	25	5,5	7,5	3,0
30	40	30	2,3	-2,4	-2,4
35	30	35	-5,1	-4,9	-7,6
40	20	40	-9,9	-8,0	-12,6
Co-PA					
90	10	-	4,7	9,7	11,2
75	25	-	8,0	30,3	20,4
60	40	-	14,4	22,4	27,8
50	50	-	16	24,0	28,0
40	60	-	27,6	28,4	30,0
80	-	20	8,4	16,3	18,5
75	-	25	7,0	11,8	10,5
60	-	40	-17,5	-23,2	-20,0
50	-	50	-22,0	-22,8	-23,2
10	40	10	10,5	17,0	-
25	25	25	7,8	6,0	-
30	20	30	7,2	1,9	-
40	10	40	2,0	-10,2	-

If saponification of vinyl acetate groups of CEVA and further chemical reactions take place, then we are to have changes in pH of water extraction: pH of water extraction should decrease. On the fig.4 pH changes are represented. And as we can see, pH decreases. The only thing that has to be explained is the enlarging of pH at 20% content of inorganic filler.

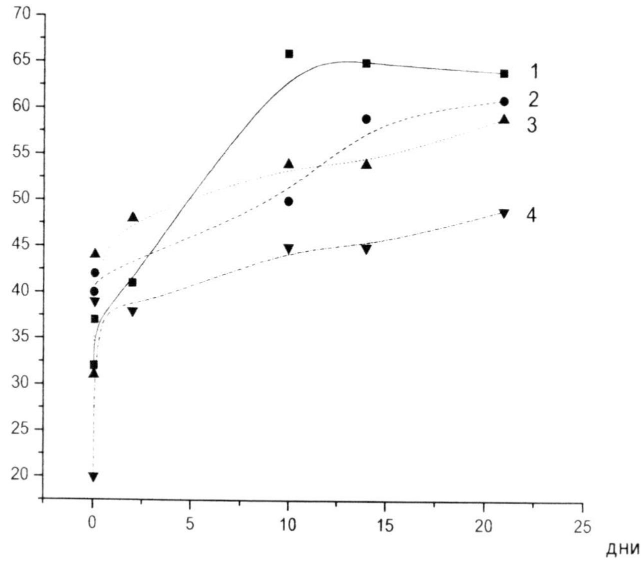

A.

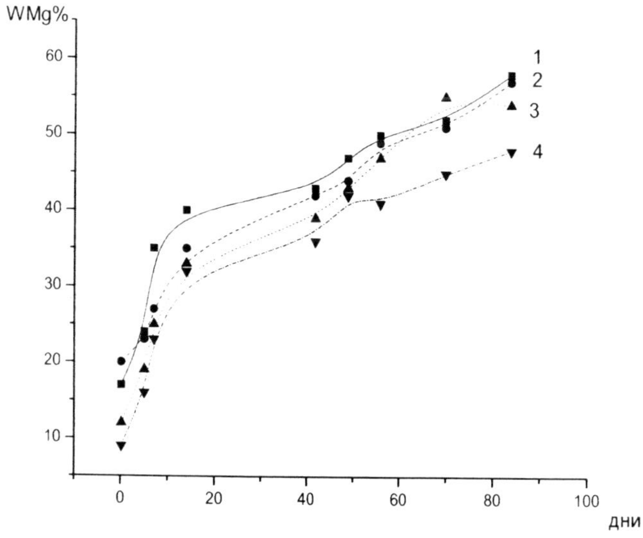

B.

Figure 3. Excretion of Mg^{2+} ions out of the samples into the water: a) CEVA-inorganic filler, mass %: 1–80-20; 2–60-40; 3–50-50; 4–40-60. b) CEVA-organic filler-inorganic filler, mass %: 1– 20-60-20; 2– 25-50-25; 3– 30-40-30; 4 – 40-20-40.

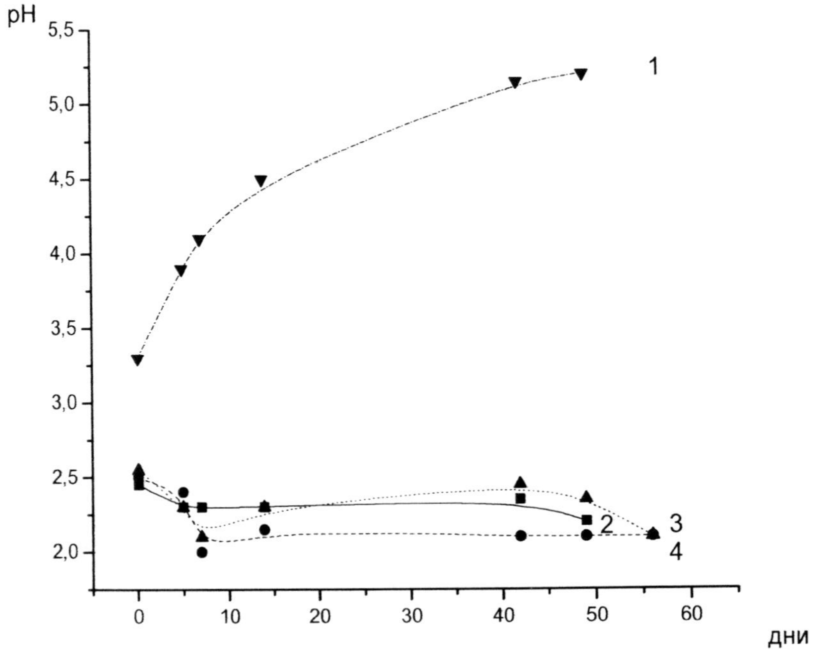

Figure 4. Changes of pH of water extraction of the two-component samples CEVA-inorganic filler, mass. %: 1– CEVA-inorganic filler : 80-20; 2 – CEVA-inorganic filler : 50-50; 3 – CEVA-inorganic filler : 60-40; 4 – CEVA-inorganic filler : 40-60.

During the processes of swelling in time the strength of the filled samples decreases: for four weeks the durability fell in 6 times, deformation reduced in 3 times, module diminished in 7 times. This can be easily explained through the effect opened by Rebinder [5].

Conclusions

The processes of swelling in the samples filled with organic filler prevail. While bringing into composed mixes inorganic filler the washing up of mineral substances predominates. Thus through variation of ingredient composition we can regulate migration of components of inorganic filler into the environment.

References

[1] Grigorjantz I.C., Trihanova G.A. *Technology of controlled isolation*, Moscow: MGIU, 2001, 344 p.

[2] Aminabhavi T.M., Balundgi R.H., Cassidy P.E. *//Polym.-plast.technol.eng*. 1990. V.29 , N 3, P. 235-262.

[3] Lipatov U.S. *Physical and chemical basis of filling of polymers*. Moscow, Chemistry, 1991. 260 c.

[4] Fillers for polymer composed mix.

[5] Zimon A.D., Leshenko N.F. *Colloidal chemistry*. Moscow, 1999. 320 p.

In: Synthesis and Properties of Low- and High-Molecular Compounds ISBN 1-59454-716-5
Editor: Gennady E. Zaikov et al., pp. 329-337

Chapter 19

STRUCTURE AND PROPERTIES OF COMBINED SYSTEMS BASED ON BUTADIENE—NITRILE AND TERNARY ETHYLENE—PROPYLENE ELASTOMERS

Irina M. Zhiltsova**[*1]**, Yury V. Evreinov**[2]**, Yury I. Lyakin**[2]**,
***Vladimir A. Shershnev**[2]** and Anatoly A. Popov**[1]*
[1]Emanuel Institute of Biochemical Physics, Russian Academy of Sciences, Moscow, Russia
[2]Lomonosov State Academy of Hyperfine Chemical Technology, Moscow, Russia

ABSTRACT

Ozone-resistant polymer compositions based on butadiene—nitrile rubbers (NBR) of variable polarity and ethylene—propylene—diene elastomers (EPDM) were studied by the methods of optic microscopy, hydrostatic weight, thermomechanical analysis, and equilibrium swelling. It was shown that the distribution of the EPDM dispersed phase is so much the better, the lower the polarity of NBR. It was determined that the deformation properties of the mixtures and the degree of swelling of vulcanizates are so much the higher, the higher the EPDM content.

INTRODUCTION

At present, butadiene—nitrile rubbers (BNR) are extensively used as general-purpose ones due to their high operating properties. Rubber products made of BNR are characterized by high oil and gas resistance, high strength of pure-gum rubbers, and high resistance to wear;

* Correspondence to: Irina M. Zhiltsova, Emanuel Institute of Biochemical Physics, Russian Academy of Sciences, 119991, Moscow, Kosygina Str., 4, Russia; E-mail: Irina752001@mail.ru

these properties are so much the higher, the higher the content of acrylonitrile (AN) in the initial rubber [1].

A serious drawback of NBR-based rubber products is their low weather- and ozone-resistance.

Doping the formula of NBR-based rubber mixtures by combinations of waxes with amine and phenol antioxidants, e.g., Ionol, makes it possible to enhance the ozone-resistance of commercial rubber products; the strongest effect is achieved by using, instead of pure NBR, its combinations with ozone-resistant polymers (PVC, EPDM, butyl rubber, etc.) [2—4].

The properties of the above compositions depend strongly on the interaction of the matrix and dispersed phase, the character of distribution of particles, and amount of the ozone-resistant component used.

EXPERIMENTAL

In this work, we studied the relation between the phase structure of mixtures of elastomers and important properties of combined systems (physicomechanical properties and ozone-, oil-, and gas-resistance).

We selected three types of NBR with variable AN content: BNKS-18, BNKS-28, and BNKS-40 (the numbers denote the amount of AN bound, wt %). An ozone-resistant component used was a ternary ethylene—propylene—diene copolymer (EPDM) SKEPT-60 (the viscosity after Mooney 59; the ratio of ethylene and propylene chains 71/25, according to the data of IR—Fourier spectroscopy).

In combining nonpolar EPDM with polar NBR, one should take into account the difference in the distribution of the dispersed phase in the matrix in going from lower-polarity to higher-polarity NBR. This difference can affect considerably the properties of the system combined.

Phase Structure

To investigate the distribution of EPDM in NBR, we prepared the mixtures on a laboratory roll mill for 10 min. The samples obtained with the EPDM content from 5 to 40 wt % were placed between the slide and cover glasses and pressed at 100°C with subsequent cooling to room temperature without removing the loading.

The structure of the preparations was studied and photographed with the aid of an MBI-6 research optic microscope in the transmitted light using the phase contrast. With this method, it is possible to obtain a contrast image of a soft-contrast object, e.g., a mixture of polymers, by recording a change in the phase of the transmitted light waves due to the difference in the optical density of the mixture components.

As seen from Fig.1, the most uniform distribution of EPDM particles is noted for the BNKS-18-based compositions. At a low EPDM content, particles of the dispersed phase are small and the spread in the sizes is insignificant. With an increase in the EPDM content to ~ 20 wt %, continuous structures are formed. In case of the BNKS-40 matrix, the mixture structure is coarse-dispersed; a continuous EPDM phase is formed at its content of 35—40%.

The structure of BNKS-28-based mixtures is intermediate (25—30%); this status may be accounted for by a high interfacial tension.

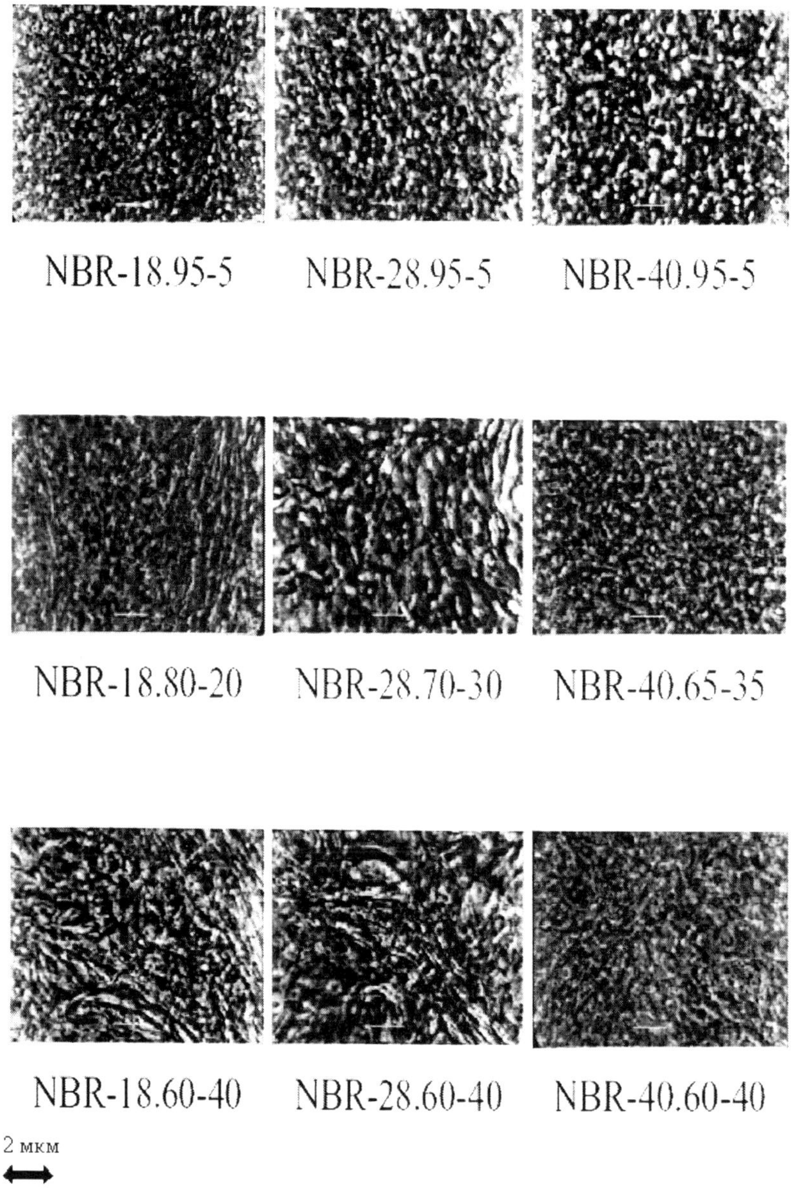

Figure 1. Distribution of the dispersed phase in the NBR— EPDM mixtures.

Thermomechanical Analysis

The presence of a soft and nonpolar polymer in a polar one manifests itself in a change in the composition behavior during deformation and a thermal process. We studied these effects by invoking a method of thermomechanical analysis. The samples of rubbers under study

(1.75 mm) were pressed at 100°C for 10 min. From the plates obtained (1.55—1.65 mm thick), pellets with diameter 6 mm were cut.

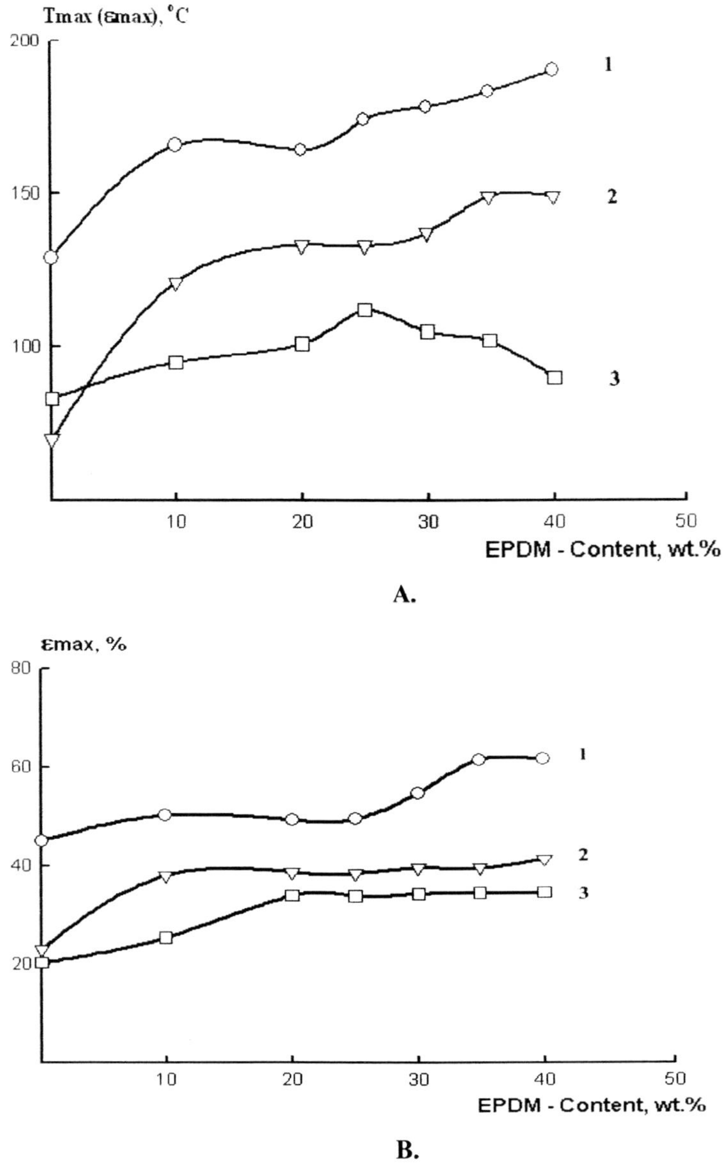

Figure 2. (a) Dependence of the maximum reversible deformation on the EPDM content: (1) BNKS-18, (2) BNKS-28, and (3) BNKS-40. (b) Dependence of the temperature of the maximum reversible deformation on the EPDM content: (1) BNRS-18, (2) BNRS-28, and (3) BNRS-40;

The study was performed by the penetration method (a version of the method of uniaxial compression) using a UIP-70 setup operating in a pulse mode in the temperature range -77—220°C. The method makes it possible to assess a reversible and irreversible stages of deformation of samples at any temperature [5].

Results of the study showed (Fig. 2a) that the maximum reversible deformation of the samples increases with an increase in the EPDM content. The maximum is shifted to the range of higher temperatures as compared with pure rubbers (Fig. 2b). The character of dependence of the curve of deformation does not depend on the matrix polarity, which is evidence for the general thermostabilization effect of EPDM additives to NBR. Note that the addition of EPDM does not affect the temperature of vitrification of the mixtures, which points to the incompatibility of the components.

For the BNKS-18 compositions, a sudden change in the course of deformation is observed at a EPDM content of ~20%, which, according to the microscopy data, corresponds the moment of formation of the developed EPDM structure. With an increase in the NBR polarity, the properties of the compositions vary increasingly monotonically, without sudden changes, due to a non-uniform distribution of the dispersed phase already at its low concentrations.

Interphase Interactions

The interaction between the matrix and dispersed phase in the rubber mixtures was studied by applying for the first time the method of hydrostatic weight; the method makes it possible to record changes in the specific volume of vulcanizates in tension. Previously, the method was used to study the behavior of elastomer extender in the rubber matrix [6].

The rubbers were combined on a roll mill for 10 min; then, ingredients were added (for 10 min). The mixtures were allowed to relax for 24 h and then were vulcanized at 150°C for 30 min. The composition of the mixtures is cited in Table 1.

As shown in Fig. 3a, on extension of the vulcanizates, the specific volume of the system increases already at low degrees of deformation, which is evidence for the absence of a chemical interaction between the matrix and second component of the mixture. The process of separation of the matrix from the dispersed phase lasts up to the moment of formation of the EPDM own continuous grid, i.e., the structure of interpenetrating grids.

For the composition with a maximum increase in the specific volume (EPDM content 25 wt %), a step-by-step substitution of part of BNKS-28 for the lower-polarity BNKS-18, with the EPDM concentration remaining unchanged, (Fig. 3b) inhibits significantly the process of separation of the dispersed phase due to an increase in the degree of dispersion of the components or promotion of the formation of the structure of interpenetrating grids. Thus, in going from a binary BNKS-28— EPDM system to a ternary BNKS-28—BNKS-18— EPDM one, it is possible to achieve a more uniform distribution of the dispersed phase particles for a medium-polarity BNR. In this case, the EPDM own grid is formed at a concentration characteristic of the BNKS-18-based compositions.

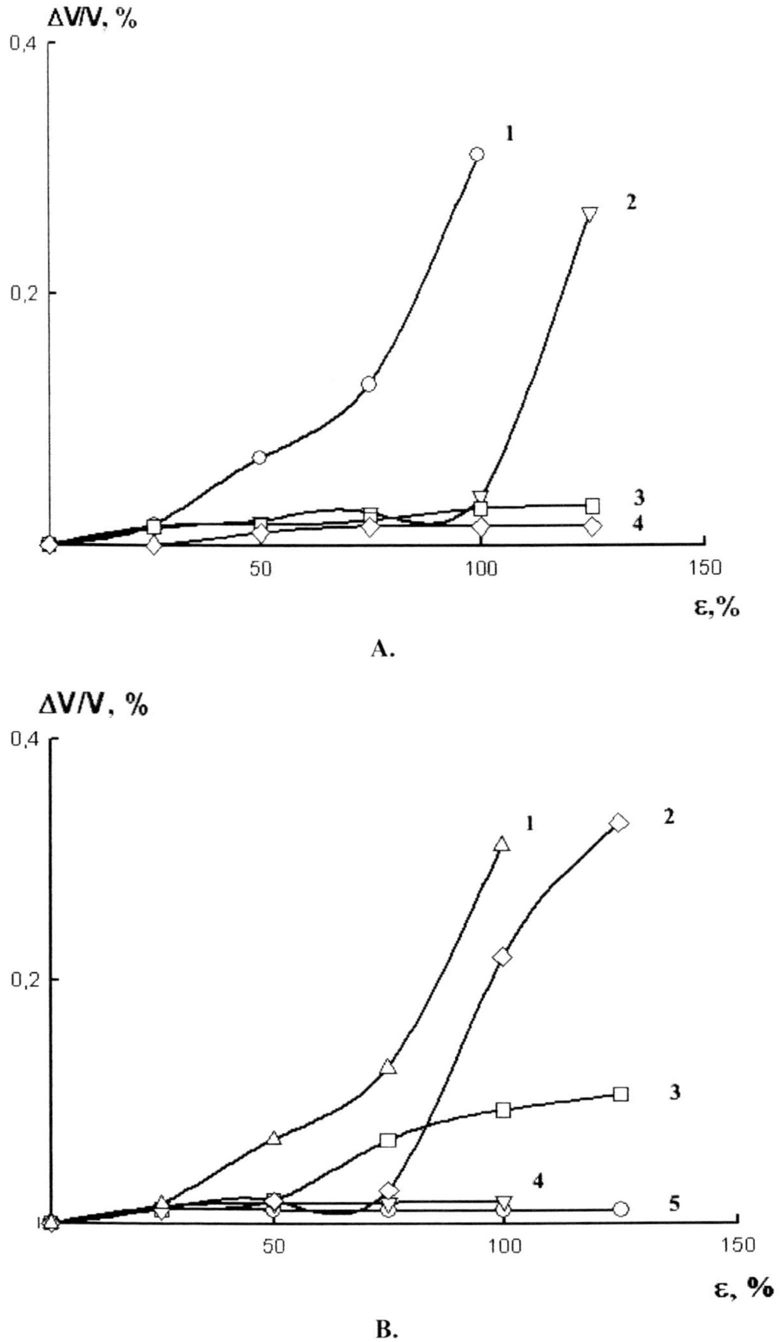

Figure 3. (a) Variation in the specific volume of vulcanizates of the BNKS-28— EPDM mixtures: (1) 75/25, (2) 80/20, (3) 85/15, (4) 50/50, and (5) BNKS-28. (b) Variation in the specific volume of vulcanizates of the BNKS-28— EPDM mixtures in the presence of the third component (BNKS-18): (1) 75/25/0, (2) 70/25/5, (3) 68/25/7, and (4) 65/25/10.

`Gas Resistance

To assess the effect of EPDM additives on gas resistance of the compositions, we carried out a study on vulcanizates swelling in isooctane. The composition formula is shown in Table 2. The samples of average mass of 9 - 12 mg were weighed and placed in isooctane (a standard solvent used in studies on gas resistance) for 24 h. Then the samples were weighed again. The degree of swelling was calculated by the formula $[(m_1 - m_0)*100]/m_0$, %, where m_0 and m_1 are the sample masses before and after swelling, respectively.

We showed (Fig. 4) that even a small amount of EPDM in the composition increases the degree of its swelling in isooctane, i.e., the gas resistance of vulcanizates decreases.

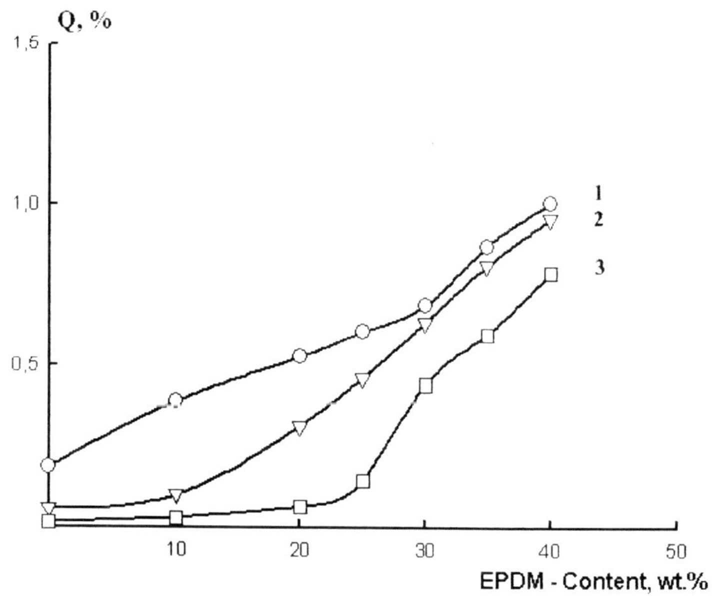

Figure 4. Dependence of the degree of swelling of vulcanizates in isooctane on the EPDM content: (1) BNKS-18, (2) BNKS-28, and (3) BNKS-40.

RESULTS AND DISCUSSION

On addition of EPDM to NBR of variable polarity, we observed the difference in the distribution of the dispersed phase as a result of the difference in the affinity of the components to each other. The most uniform dispersion of EPDM was observed in a low-polarity NBR, because the affinity of the components in this case is maximal. Previously [7], it was shown that a sudden change in the ozone-resistance of the compositions occurs at the moment of formation of the own spatial structure of the ozone-resistant polymer. With an increase in the NBR polarity, the size of particles of the dispersed phase increases and the formation of the developed spatial structure of EPDM is shifted to the region of high concentrations. Simultaneously with an increase in the EPDM content, the basic property of NBR vulcanizates – gas resistance – decreases.

To retain the valuable properties of the compositions, it is expedient to add EPDM in amounts lower than those needed for the spatial structure to form.

A change in the specific volume of vulcanizates in tension points to the absence of chemical interaction between the phases, i.e., no covulcanization of rubbers occurs. EPDM behaves as an elastomer extender, which separates from the matrix in the course of deformation. The affinity of the components of these compositions makes it possible to achieve a high degree of dispersion of EPDM.

We showed a feasibility of adding a small amount of a third component to binary systems to achieve a high degree of dispersion of EPDM in NBR. The additive should have a high affinity to both components of the composition. In the given composition, this third component may be represented by an elastomer of intermediate polarity. In this case, no covulcanization between the phases occurs; a high degree of dispersion is achieved due to a decrease in the interfacial tension.

The addition of EPDM improves the thermomechanical properties of the compositions: the thermal stability of the system increases due to the presence of particles of a soft and thermally stable component. Particles of the dispersed phase loosen the rigid matrix and enhance the elasticity of the composition.

CONCLUSION

We studied the dependence of the structure of non-vulcanized mixtures of elastomers on the matrix polarity and the effect of EPDM additives on physicochemical properties of the compositions. It was shown that the degree of dispersion of EPDM in NBR can be enhanced by adding a small amount of an elastomer of intermediate polarity. Thus, the optimum properties of the system can be achieved by adding a smaller amount of EPDM, as compared with the case of a binary system.

REFERENCES

[1] Hofmann, W.: Elastomere Werkstoffe fuer oel- und waermebestaendige Dichtungen – Eine Trendanalyse. *Gummi Asbest Kunstst.* 39 (1986) S. 511 – 526

[2] Livanova, N.M., Popov, A.A., Karpova, S.G., Bogaevskaya, T.A., Farmakovskaya, M.P.: Ozone resistance of vulcanized NBR/PVC blends. *Polym. Sci.* 42 (2000) № 6 pp. 661 - 666

[3] Layer, R.W., Lattimer, R.P.: Protection of Rubber against Ozone. *Rubber Chem. Technol.* 63 (1990) pp. 426 - 450

[4] Hofmann, W.: Elastomere fuer technische Anwendungen. *Kunststoffe* 74 (1984) № 10, S. 610 – 617

[5] Sokolova L.V., Evreinov Yu.V.: Vliyanie vysokotemperaturnykh perekhodov na deformiruemost' ryada gibkotsepnykh polimerov. *Vysokomolek. soed.,* 35 (1993) № 5, S. 244 – 249

[6] Kulesnyov V.N., Dogadkin B.A., Lyakin Yu.I.: Izmenenie udel'nogo ob'ema pri rastyazhenii vulkanizatov, soderzhatshikh mikrogel. *Kolloidn. Zh.*. 32 (1970) № 6, S. 869

[7] Khanin S.E., Angert L.G., Kulesnyov V.N., Shashkov A.S.: Vliyanie phazovogo sostava smesej polimerov na ozonostojkost' rezin na ikh osnove. *Kauchuk i rezina.* № 1 (1974) S. 30 - 32

INDEX

A

B

C

F

G

H

M

N

Q

R

S

W

X

Z